THE
DAMMED

by the same author

WATERSHED: THE WATER CRISIS IN BRITAIN
ACID RAIN
TURNING UP THE HEAT
GREEN WARRIORS
IAN AND FRED'S BIG GREEN BOOK

THE
DAMMED

*Rivers, dams, and the coming
world water crisis*

Fred Pearce

THE BODLEY HEAD
LONDON

First published 1992
© Fred Pearce 1992
The Bodley Head, 20 Vauxhall Bridge Road, London SW1V 2SA

Fred Pearce has asserted his right under the Copyright,
Designs and Patents Act 1988 to be identified as the author
of this work

A CIP catalogue record for this book is available from the
British Library

ISBN 0-370-31609-6

Phototypeset by Computape (Pickering) Ltd, North Yorkshire
Printed in Great Britain by
Mackays of Chatham PLC, Chatham, Kent

We cannot command nature except by obeying her.

Francis Bacon

CONTENTS

Maps

INTRODUCTION

The Great Man-made River

It is one of the largest tracts of true desert in the world. The thousand kilometres from the coast of eastern Libya inland to the oasis at Kufra are so bereft of water-holes or vegetation that even the camel trains didn't cross it until the nineteenth century. But now the desert has a river, Libya's first, flowing all the way to the coast. The river is almost as long as the Rhine, carries as much water as the Mersey or the Rio Grande – and is enclosed inside a metal pipe big enough to drive a truck through. They call it the Great Man-made River. It is the first of two such rivers being built by Colonel Gadaffi to tap ancient water buried beneath his vast and empty country.

Gadaffi opened the first pipeline one hot desert night in the summer of 1991. It was Libya's National Day, 22 years after the young Colonel had seized power. As fireworks shot into the sky, fellow leaders from Africa and the Middle East gathered to celebrate an endeavour that had drained Libya's coffers for almost a decade, and seemed set to carry on doing so well into the next century. They heard the Colonel compare his great work to the pyramids of Ancient Egypt, and watched him unleash into a reservoir the first water from a pipeline that stretched out into the desert. A thousand Libyans rushed forward as one, to take ecstatic sips of the precious liquid which had lain untapped beneath the desert for tens of thousands of years.

Gadaffi boasted that his new river was a revolutionary triumph against the tyrants of the US and Britain. He forgot to mention that the project was masterminded from an office on the fourth floor of a tower block near the railway station at Hampton Wick outside London. There, through the bombings and kidnappings and murders that characterised British–Libyan relations of the 1980s, the European office of the American consulting engineers Brown & Root had continued collaboration with Gadaffi's staff to make the Colonel's pipe-dream come true.

Gadaffi has had his pipe painted emerald green. This is the colour of Islam, of Gadaffi's 'green book', of his national flag and of his revolution, and it symbolises his desire to green the Libyan desert, to turn his huge land, almost the size of the European Community, into a granary for the Middle East, producing a million tonnes of wheat a year.

The engineering is vast. When completed, the two Great Man-made Rivers will pump half as much water from the desert each day as gushes from all the world's oil wells. 'In future, water will be a commodity as important as oil,' says the Colonel's man in Hampton Wick.

In the first phase, Gadaffi drilled hundreds of wells in the desert at Tazirbu and Sarir. Between 1985 and 1991, his South Korean pipe-makers linked the wells to the reservoir outside Benghazi. They did it by assembling a quarter of a million sections of pipe, each weighing 80 tonnes and driven into the desert from their factory aboard daily convoys of a hundred or more huge transporters. The pipe contract, at $3.3 billion, was the largest civil engineering contract ever signed, and there are four phases to come in the entire project to plumb the desert.

The second Man-made River, to be built to the west during the 1990s, will be more difficult. It crosses some 700 kilometres of rocky plateaux, wadis and steep slopes, requiring pumps and tunnels and syphons along the way. Then, in phases three to five, Gadaffi intends to link up the two rivers and extend them yet deeper into the desert, almost to the border with Chad.

Throughout history, mankind has settled where there is water. But in Libya in the 1990s the water is being pumped – out of a 450-metre well and over wadi and mountain – on a nine-day journey to where the people are. It may be a sign of the way the world is going. As the climate zones shift in the global greenhouse, and new deserts shrivel the world's rivers, perhaps many more of us will drink from great man-made rivers in the future. Or perhaps the sound of water down Gadaffi's pipe is the death rattle for the kind of engineering hubris that insists on remaking the world in iron and concrete.

These rivers are the monuments by which Gadaffi wishes to be remembered, and no nation has ever mortgaged so much of its future on a single project. Phase one, the first river, cost $5 billion. All five phases will cost at least $20 billion – more than twice Libya's annual gross domestic product. And for what? In total, the rivers will irrigate fields that could be comfortably fitted into Hertfordshire, or half of Delaware. It works out at $130,000 per hectare, making them the most expensively watered fields in the world.

In any case, the Sahara's water will not flow for ever. While the Colonel talks of 'several hundred years of potential pro-duction' from the wells, his engineers give it fifty years before the level of water in the underground reservoir is lowered so much that pumping must cease. By then, Gadaffi hopes that his country will have been transformed by water. But, boom or bust, the one certainty is that, sometime before the twenty-first century is out, the pumps will run dry and sand will replace water in the pipes. The Great Man-made Rivers will have to be abandoned.

There is something about giant water projects that both inspires and unhinges leaders of men. Marshall Goldman, the Soviet analyst, identified 'an almost Freudian fixation. Nothing seems to satisfy the Soviets as much as building a dam or draining a swamp.' In the last generation, newly independent nations all over Africa and Asia have staked their futures on giant structures to control rivers, such as Nasser's High Aswan Dam on the Nile and Nkruma's Akosombo Dam on the Volta, which all but bankrupted Ghana. Jawaharlal Nehru in India called his dams 'the new temples of India, where I worship'.

It was the same urge that turned the US, after constructing the Hoover Dam, the first superdam in the heart of the Great American Desert, into the most prolific dam-building nation

on earth. And right-wing military regimes in Brazil and Paraguay more recently have built the world's largest hydroelectric
project in the heart of South America on the wild Parana
River.

As Gadaffi opened the tap on his first Great Man-made
River, others round the world were making similar grand
gestures to tame the world's water. That month in India, the
first villages were flooded behind the first dam of the
Narmada valley project, a 50-year enterprise to harness one of
India's largest and most holy rivers, while Chinese leaders
pushed ahead with their plan to build the world's most
powerful hydroelectric dam at Three Gorges on the River
Yangtze.

In Canada, the Quebec government was about to begin
building a road into the Arctic wilderness for the next phase
of the $70-billion James Bay hydroelectric project. In Bangla-
desh, they dug the first embankments for a billion-dollar
Flood Action Plan that will make the rich safe from floods and
leave millions of poor farmers more exposed than ever. And in
the fractured remains of the Soviet Union, engineers finished
building a dam taller than the Eiffel Tower that will complete
the desiccation of the Aral Sea.

Man's determination to control and dominate nature is not
new. The biblical command to subdue nature was first written
in ancient Mesopotamia, where the earliest man-made rivers
were huge irrigation canals that fed Ur of the Chaldees,
Nineveh and Babylon.

What is new today is the technology that can indeed tame
nature. Modern engineers have transformed the desert of
southern California into one of the most productive farming
systems in the world. They have irrigated the 'green revolution' and generate a fifth of the world's electricity. The
world's artificial reservoirs today hold as much water, and
cover as much land, as the North Sea.

But in the process they have created hydrological chaos.
They have all but drained the Aral Sea, once the world's
fourth largest lake. They have flooded tens of millions of
people from their homes and farms, while ending the natural
floods on which tens of millions more once depended for

irrigation. They have brought billions of tonnes of poisonous salt to the world's fields, dissolved in irrigation water. They have destroyed fisheries and rainforests, Arctic tundra and wetlands that teemed with free food for hungry countries.

The Dammed is the story of the rise of human control over rivers, from the early 'hydraulic civilisations', through the colonial era when the Nile and the Ganges were harnessed to imperial will, to the modern superdams and a possible future world criss-crossed by great man-made rivers. But it also explores a parallel tradition in which rivers and their natural wealth are conserved, not confronted. This is a world that encompasses village wells and *qanats*, tunnels dug for tens of kilometres into Iranian hillsides. It includes walls across deserts that harvest rainfall, the huge water-tanks that cover India and Sri Lanka, the banks across the wet South American pampas that could feed millions, and the river diversions that once made Bangladesh safe from floods. It is a world now attracting the attention of hydrologists as well as archaeologists.

If we are to survive and prosper in an increasingly crowded world, where resources as basic as water become scarce, we shall need to re-learn some of the old skills and old attitudes to rivers and water.

As Gadaffi's engineers spend the 1990s sweating in the desert of western Libya, attempting to hoist their leader's second great river across the wadis, they may notice strange lines of stones in the deserted wadi bottoms. They are what is left of water-gathering structures that made it possible 2,000 years ago to farm the desert. The land that the great river will by-pass on its way to Gadaffi's reservoirs was once harvested for its rain. There was enough, properly used, to grow figs, olives, vines and barley for export to Ancient Rome. No agriculturalist could accomplish that today, and no hydraulic engineer could lay out the walls to catch the rain. The knowledge of how to do it has been lost. Instead, Libya has the Great Man-made River.

PART I

Traditions

I

HYDRAULIC CIVILISATIONS

Ur is, they say, where Western civilisation began – one of
mankind's first towns. It looked more like the place where
civilisation ended.

Richard Dowden, *The Independent*, 1991

Five millennia ago, Ur of the Chaldees was the greatest city in
the world. It ruled over a wide plain where humans first
gained mastery of rivers. The plain between the rivers Tigris
and Euphrates, which the Greeks named Mesopotamia, was
transformed by hydraulic works into the granary of the
Middle East and the most heavily populated area on the
planet at that time. Now it is desert once more.

When Richard Dowden clambered to the top of the ancient
ziggurat at Ur at the end of the Gulf War in 1991 to deliver
the despatch quoted above, this unique ruin occupied the
cordoned-off backyard of an Iraqi air base. A week before, it
had escaped complete destruction by seconds, when an
American colonel aboard a bomber realised the true identity
of what was marked on his target map as an enemy bunker.

Around 7,500 years ago, early Sumerians constructed the
first known irrigation works 200 kilometres from Ur. In the
fields they planted the forerunners of modern wheat and
barley, developed from natural grasses in the nearby Zagros
mountains. These early irrigators diverted water from tributaries of the great rivers, usually by digging a hole in the river
bank and channelling water to plots close by. Over the
centuries, the Sumerians moved from the shadow of the hills
and spread across the plain. They began digging longer canals
to far-off fields, and in the lower parts of the plain they

erected defences against the floods that poured down the Tigris and Euphrates from the mountains of Turkey and Iran each spring. As the German hydrologist Gunther Garbrecht puts it: 'The hydrological chaos of the valleys was transformed into flourishing gardens, fields and meadows that in mythology was named the Garden of Eden.'

Soon, the simple farming communities turned into far larger and more complex social organisations. These, the world's first cities, were ruled by an all-powerful priesthood, and later by kings and military leaders. The Sumerians built eight cities including Ur, Kish and Uruk, the largest, which alone eventually had a population of around 50,000 inhabitants. Out of the adversity of a near-desert, they had invented what we now call civilisation.

The Mesopotamians were not alone. In time, other civilisations sprang up along the fertile valleys of the Nile in Egypt, the Indus in Pakistan and the Yellow River in northern China. In each case, they were made possible by great public works that irrigated crops and protected farmland from floods. Karl Wittfogel, an American history professor writing in the 1950s, called them 'hydraulic civilisations', and proposed that they had developed specifically in order to organise the large labour forces necessary to create and maintain the canals and embankments. The whole edifice of modern society, he argued, arose out of mankind's desire to control rivers, to separate the water from the land.

The Sumerian city-states of southern Mesopotamia went on to create the first examples of writing, in cuneiform script scratched on to clay tablets. Most of the inscriptions are detailed records of the management of the hydraulic projects that were essential to the cities' survival.

The citizens of this first civilisation fought the first water wars over their irrigated fields, orchards and palm groves. Around 4,500 years ago on the River Euphrates, the King of Umma sent soldiers to raid the fields of his downstream neighbours at Girsu, cutting the banks of canals and spilling water across the plain. The King of Girsu saved his kingdom by digging a new canal to the Tigris. Soon, his control of the Tigris gave him a large empire that eclipsed Umma. Tablets dating from this period record that most of Sumer 'was watering its fields in joy under him'.

But the warring Sumerian city-states overreached themselves. Sumer was taken over by the Amorites from Syria. The Amorites maintained the canals and adopted the ancient Sumerian water law, in which the river is a vengeful deity, deciding the fate of men. A man charged with a crime was forced to throw himself into the Euphrates. If the river overpowered him, then his accuser took over his estate; if he survived, the accuser was killed.

By the time of the Amorites, the fields of southern Mesopotamia faced a new threat unimagined in water law. Something was destroying their fertility. Crop yields had been as high on the Mesopotamian plain as any that would later be achieved in medieval Europe. But first the wheat refused to grow and then its replacement, barley, also began to fail. The hidden menace was salt.

The salt came not from the sea, but from the mountains. Water dissolves salt as it passes over rocks, especially in the upper reaches of river catchments. In an untamed river, the salt usually passes harmlessly to the sea. But, when rivers are diverted into irrigation canals and on to fields, the salt can end up in the soil, poisoning crops and eventually caking the surface with white salt. By 3,800 years ago, Mesopotamian tablets were recording 'black fields becoming white' and 'plains choked with salt'.

Archaeologists who have painstakingly counted grains found in the remains of Girsu found that 5,500 years ago, farmers grew as much wheat as barley. But wheat is far more vulnerable to salt than barley and by 4,500 years ago, barley fields outnumbered wheat fields five-to-one in southern Mesopotamia. After another 500 years the ratio was ten-to-one. Then barley began to fail.

When Sir Leonard Woolley excavated Ur in the 1930s, he wondered at the barren land around the great ziggurat. 'Only to those who have seen the Mesopotamian desert will the evocation of the ancient world seem well-nigh incredible, so complete is the contrast between past and present. Why, if Ur was an empire's capital, if Sumer was once a vast granary, has the population dwindled to nothing, the very soil lost its virtue?' Today, few doubt that what another British archaeologist, Sir John Marshall, once called this 'satanic mockery of snow' was a prime cause of both the ecological and political downfall of Sumer.

Salt chased civilisation north through Mesopotamia as mercilessly as any barbarian horde. Its second great invasion occurred around 3,000 years ago in central Iraq, south of Baghdad. But a thousand after that, these northern lands flourished again under the influence of the Persians, then the world leaders in water engineering.

Around AD 500, the Persians constructed at Nahrwan their most remarkable project: two canals that carried water from the Tigris to irrigate fields on either bank for a distance of 300 kilometres on either side of the river. These canals were on a scale little different from the largest built today. 'We are dealing', say American investigators Thorkild Jacobsen and Robert Adams, 'with a whole new conception of irrigation which undertook bodily to reshape the physical environment.' The project 'criss-crossed formerly unused desert and depression areas with a complex – and entirely artificial – system of branch canals'. In places, the canals were 100 metres wide, and, according to Sir William Willcocks, Britain's foremost Victorian water engineer, 'must have been capable of quite crippling the Tigris when it was carrying its full supply'.

According to Jacobsen and Adams, the Persians had kept salt at bay by avoiding over-irrigation and planting weeds to lower the water-table, thus keeping salty water away from the roots of crops. The main Nahrwan canal suffered less from salt than from a second scourge of irrigation canals. Silt, washed down from the Turkish and Iranian hills, settled in rivers and canals as it reached the flat plain. Thousands of slaves constantly dredged and cleaned the waterways. But when Islamic rulers took over from the Persians, the work was left undone, and sometime in the twelfth century, disaster struck. The pride of Persian engineers, a region of irrigated fields measuring 400 kilometres by 30 kilometres, was destroyed.

Views differ about exactly what happened. Willcocks, who

spent the early years of this century dreaming of reconstructing the Nahrwan Canal, wrote of a 'terrible catastrophe [which] in a few months turned one of the most populous regions of the Earth into a desert'. Jacobsen and Adams, however, concluded that the build-up of silt was much more gradual, and long before the end there was 'only a trickle of water passing down the upper section of the main canal to supply a few dying towns in the hostile desert'. Whichever theory is correct, the subsequent victory for Mongol horsemen, who stormed through Baghdad in 1258, had been prepared for them by the eclipse of the Persian mastery of the Tigris.

Modern urban societies, according to Wittfogel's argument, arose out of the need to organise the collection and distribution of water, the only essential ingredient for agriculture that could best be developed on a large scale. To control rivers required hiring farmers and coercing slaves into digging and maintaining dykes and canals and watching for floods. So dominant was water in such societies that the people put in charge of the dykes and canals were able to make themselves the sole masters. 'It is this combination of hydraulic agriculture, a hydraulic government and a single-centred society that constitutes the institutional essence of hydraulic civilisation.'

In these civilisations, Wittfogel saw the adoption of 'a more rational approach to nature'. The citizens of hydraulic civilisations began to look at the world in a more scientific way. They became astronomers and mathematicians and accountants, as well as hydraulic engineers. 'Until the industrial revolution, the majority of human beings lived within the orbit of hydraulic civilisations.'

It is remarkable, indeed, that the adversity of the desert should nurture the greatest strides towards civilisation and sustain such large communities. In Ancient Egypt, population densities rose as high as 180 people per square kilometre in the Nile valley, a figure almost double that of modern France. In the Americas at one time, 75 per cent of the population lived in a few small 'hydraulic regions' in Mexico and Peru, where water was intensively managed. Later, Cordoba, the capital of Moorish Spain, where irrigation water was essential to survival, may have been the first city to exceed one million inhabitants – this at a time when the largest city north of the Alps was London with a mere 35,000 people.

While modern water engineers often claim descent from these early architects of the modern world, not everybody takes a sanguine view of their civilisations. The anthropologist and environmental campaigner Teddy Goldsmith sees a parasitic menace to both humans and the environment. Traditional farming systems based on small-scale irrigation were thrust aside by the city-dwellers, he says. 'The massive increase in irrigation works in the Euphrates valley does not seem to have been designed to improve the irrigation system of the local tribesmen, but rather to satisfy the requirements of a burgeoning urban society.'

The debate may sound abstruse. But for the people of the Third World today it raises issues that go to the centre of debates about economic development. Can Africa, for instance, best feed itself by investing in great hydraulic projects such as the Great Man-made River? If so, must its citizens put up with the kind of autocratic government necessary to run them?

One place to pursue the argument is the Nile valley. People have lived here for at least the past 15,000 years. For much of that time, the Nile valley was a permanent swamp, peopled by hunters and gatherers. Out in the Sahara, which was then still wet, farmers were herding sheep and goats and cultivating emmer wheat.

But, as the climate became drier around 7,000 years ago, more and more people came into the valley to find water. (The word 'desert' is derived from an Egyptian hieroglyph meaning a place abandoned or left behind.) By the time of the ancient dynasties, Egypt and the Nile valley were rainless and its people entirely dependent on the waters of the Nile rushing out of the heart of Africa. The Greek historian Herodotus called Egypt 'the gift of the Nile', because without the river there would be no country, only desert. Both the Egyptians and the Mesopotamians had myths about a great flood. In

Mesopotamia the flood indicated disaster, but in Egypt it was a saviour.

The Nile's floodwaters came cascading down from the faraway and mysterious 'mountains of the moon' in East and Central Africa during July and August. Farmers began 7,000 years ago to plant seeds along the river banks, where the water flooded out of the main channel and deposited fertile silt. Then they started to make small breaches in the banks to channel water and silt into primitive fields in the lowland behind. The first record of Egyptian irrigation, dated at 5,100 years ago, is in the decoration on a ceremonial mace head in the Ashmolean Museum in Oxford. It depicts a leader known as the Scorpion King digging a trench that supplies a field containing a palm tree.

The Nile water covered the fields to a depth of a metre for six to eight weeks before departing as the flood abated, leaving behind enough moisture for the crops to grow in the coming months. The water also brought each year roughly a millimetre of fertile silt, much of it eroded from the highlands of northern Ethiopia, where the Blue Nile rises.

Irrigation along the Nile was very like the first attempts to water the Mesopotamian plain. But in the narrow Nile valley there was less possibility for farmers to dig long canals to water faraway fields. The simple system, known as flood irrigation, meant that there was no risk of the silt clogging up irrigation networks. And as the floodwaters retreated, they flushed out salts, which might otherwise have accumulated and poisoned crops. Flood irrigation had its disadvantages, of course. The amount of land that could be farmed each year depended critically on the height of the flood.

The gradual drying of the region over thousands of years eventually created a hydrological crisis in the valley that brought famine and warfare about 4,100 years ago. Historians mark this point as the end of the Old Kingdom. The start of the New Kingdom, 3,500 years ago, coincided with the first appearance of a mechanical water-lifting device known as the *shaduf*. It was little more than a bucket on a pole, suspended on an axle, and counterbalanced at the other end. But it must have been more important for the Egyptians than the invention of the wheel. It allowed one farmer to raise water up to three metres into fields during the increasingly frequent years when the floods did not rise high enough to inundate them. It was later complemented by a labour-saving invention known as the Archimedean screw. With the turn of a handle, the screw allowed two farmers working together to raise enough water for a hectare through a tube dipped into the river. And later still the Egyptians adopted the Persian wheel, a system of clay pots on a chain that could be powered by an animal on a treadmill.

What is interesting about all this in terms of Wittfogel's idea is that none of the features of the hydraulic civilisation of the Nile required central organisation. Each farm or village dug its own water channels. No all-powerful priesthood or rulers were necessary to operate the *shaduf* or Archimedean screw.

According to Karl Butzer, in a study of *Early Hydraulic Civilisation in Egypt*, almost none of the voluminous written records that have survived from Ancient Egypt refer to either the law or the administration of irrigation. This, he says, 'suggests that water legislation was not overly complex and was administered locally' according to an ancient tradition which pre-dated literacy. The system survived, essentially unchanged, into the nineteenth century, and perhaps a sixth of Egyptian farmland remains to this day watered with traditional flood irrigation. *Shadufs*, screws and Persian wheels can still be seen in daily operation beside the river.

On a cliff near Zhengzhou, 700 kilometres southwest of Beijing in northern China, stands a giant statue of the mythical Chinese emperor Yu. He towers above the floodplain of the Yellow River, the great waterway of northern China, with one beneficent hand outstretched, as befits a man who was said to have brought prosperity to his people. But the other hand carries the tool with which the Chinese people first erected dykes and dug out irrigation canals in the valley 4,000 years ago. His face looks defiantly towards the river: taming it had been a grim, remorseless task.

The Yellow River is, as the Chinese put it, the joy and

sorrow of the nation. It is the most silty river on Earth, carrying to the sea 2 billion tonnes of soil from the steppes of western China each year. Its water and silt have allowed the Chinese to create rich farmlands for a thousand miles from Zhengzhou to the sea. But its floods have killed more people than any other single feature on the Earth's surface.

The valley of the Yellow River was the cradle for a Chinese civilisation that became a supreme example of a hydraulic society. Controlling the river has always been a symbol of good government. Indeed, in many ways it is the reason for the creation of a single government covering such a vast area and containing at different times between a third and a fifth of the world's population.

From the time of their arrival on the floodplain of the Yellow River around 8,000 years ago, farmers have built dykes to protect themselves from the river, which once meandered freely across its plain, regularly changing course and spreading the entire area with a bed of silt. But the task of holding back the river, once begun, is never completed. After farmers began to contain it behind dykes, the river deposited the silt on its new permanent riverbed, which began to rise above the floodplain around it. It is still rising. Today most of the main channel is between 4 and 8 metres above the surrounding land, and the river finally reaches the sea on a 25-metre-thick bed of its own silt.

Untold endeavour has been required throughout China's history constantly to raise the dykes and dredge channels. Right up until today, farmers along the Yellow River are required by law to give their labour during the winter to maintain and improve waterworks, in anticipation of the summer floods. News pictures of a million Chinese shoring up dykes during the floods of 1991 reaffirmed that the power of the hydraulic civilisation lingers on here. The Chinese have a word for it: *schin*, which means both 'to regulate water' and 'to rule'.

The tragedy is that when the ever-higher dykes break, the resulting floods can be ever more disastrous, with death tolls measured in hundreds of thousands. Unable to change its course naturally, the river moves occasionally but catastrophically whenever it is freed by a dyke breach. Between 600 BC and 1949, the river's main course shifted 26 times. Floods killed 900,000 people in 1887 and again in 1931. A similar number drowned in 1938, when Chinese generals deliberately breached dykes along the Yellow River to beat off Japanese advance during the Sino-Japanese war.

Millet was China's first principal crop. Rice remained a luxury food until the introduction into southern China of rice paddies, a new invention from Vietnam, around 500 BC. The paddy system grew rice in small flooded fields and required yet more back-breaking labour from Chinese peasants, especially in managing the water. But it brought great rewards, especially after the arrival of new quick-growing varieties from India, and could support a large population.

East Asian farming became far more productive than anything seen in Europe, and by the end of the eleventh century, China supported more than 100 million people. It was the largest, most literate and most technically advanced country in the world. Such inventions as gunpowder and paper took place on the back of hydraulic and agricultural innovation, of rice and its paddies.

Two hundred years later, China completed one of the great waterworks of the pre-industrial era, the Grand Canal. The canal, which is being renovated today, ran from north to south for 1,800 kilometres – the distance from London to Helsinki. It linked the Yangtze and Yellow rivers. While past canals had been little more than straightened river channels, the Grand Canal required reservoirs to feed its higher stretches. It boasted the first lock-gates anywhere in the world. The gates allowed boats to enter the canal from the Huai River without first being hauled on to a slipway.

The Chinese dug the canal to distribute grain from the paddies of the south, which had become the nation's food basket, to the drier, cooler north. By the thirteenth century, when the canal reached the new capital of Beijing, it carried 400,000 tonnes of grain each year, helping to feed an army of more than a million soldiers, camped in the north to repel barbarians. Thus, it neatly encapsulated the twin roles of

Chinese government then and ever since: the military and the hydraulic.

The fecundity of the soils of eastern and southern Asia, coupled with the technology of water management through canals and paddies, spawned several other advanced hydraulic civilisations that were at their height around a thousand years ago. The empire of Angkor in the flooded jungles of Cambodia was among the most remarkable. Here in the ninth and tenth centuries, the Angkor kings used large forces of slave labour to construct canals, dykes and reservoirs, known as *barays*, to control the waters of local rivers and the giant Mekong, whose monsoon floods spread across the forest floor each summer. The waterworks encouraged trade and allowed the production of three or four crops of rice each year. So richly endowed, the kings began to build ever grander temples, culminating in the great city of Angkor Wat, built in the twelfth century by Suryavarman II.

As the slaves of Cambodia constructed Angkor Wat, the subjects of King Parakramabahu in Sri Lanka were creating another great jungle city, Polonnaruwa. This, too, was the crowning achievement of a hydraulic civilisation. Today the proud stone face of the king still looks out over the sea of Parakrama, a man-made reservoir covering 24 square kilometres on the edge of the city, one of many great reservoirs constructed during the civilisation that once flourished here.

A cursory look at any modern map of Sri Lanka shows a collection of large lakes dotted across the countryside. One or two of the smaller ones are modern reservoirs, part of the billion-dollar Mahaweli irrigation scheme built during the 1980s. But the larger ones are ancient. King Parakramabahu built more than 1,400 reservoirs and 500 canals, including the Ellahara, an extraordinary waterway that straddles much of the centre of the country, linking several large reservoirs.

Polonnaruwa was capital only for a brief period, after the long ascendancy of nearby Anuradhapura, which boasts three great reservoirs of its own, dating back to the fourth century BC. They receive their water from a system of canals stretching more than 80 kilometres into the hills and from the huge

Kalawewa reservoir at their head.

Sir James Emerson Tennent, a nineteenth-century British traveller and historian, called these hydraulic remains 'the proudest monuments of what remains of the former greatness of the country ... no similar constructions formed by any race, whether ancient or modern, exceed in colossal magnitude the stupendous tanks [reservoirs] in Ceylon.' The great kings, said Edmund Leach, former professor of anthropology at the University of Cambridge, 'had reputations as irrigation engineers rather than conquerors'. And yet, he argued, many of their grandest works may simply have been monuments – they supplied water for temples, public parks and to create splendid vistas for statues of their creators to look out over. The villages were served by their own small reservoirs in nearby hills. Every village had its rice paddy and every paddy had its reservoir. Leach commented: 'When the central government was disrupted and the major works fell into disrepair, village life could carry on quite adequately.'

Hydraulic civilisations took many forms. The Sri Lankans and the peasants along the Nile could get along very well without kings or canals, high priests or hydraulic engineers, but in China it is hard to imagine life continuing on the floodplain of the Yellow River without central government management of the construction and maintenance of dykes. In Mesopotamia, village cultivation must have prospered on the plain for many centuries before cities developed and took control. As great civilisations rose and fell, exhausting themselves and the environment on which they depended, they left many achievements behind, both physical and intellectual. Less commented upon, but equally remarkable, is the continuity and ecological sustainability of peasant agriculture, as first learnt almost 10,000 years ago, and as practised round the world even to this day.

2

FIGS, VINES AND OLIVES

The hand of the Lord came upon him. And Elisha said: make
this valley full of ditches. Ye shall not see wind; neither shall
ye see rain, yet that valley shall be filled with water.

Kings II, 3:15–17

The world's first town was not in Mesopotamia or China or
Egypt, but on the west bank of the River Jordan. Jericho,
9,000 years ago, was modest enough, nothing like the great
cities of Mesopotamia four millennia later. It covered around
four hectares and had a thick defensive wall. Inside were a few
hundred people and a tower, now the world's oldest surviving
man-made structure.

Close by was a spring, known in the Bible as Elisha's
Spring, that irrigated crops of wheat and barley. Today, the
spring still gushes forth 76 litres a second into ancient irrigation furrows and ditches that distribute its water to the
fields and orchards of this desert oasis.

The ancient town was destroyed by floods around 8,000
years ago. But the agricultural heritage lived on. Without the
ostentation of Mesopotamia's great cities and canals, the
people living in the lands of present-day Syria, Lebanon and
Israel, the Levant, founded within a few thousand years of the
close of the Ice Age one of the earliest, most stable and
longest-lasting of all the farming systems on Earth. It was a
system that endured as the great Mediterranean urban civilisations of Greece, Rome and the rest came and went. In
essence, much of it survived into the present century.

The Levantines were the first to cultivate wild grains, such
as barley, as well as einkorn and emmer, the predecessors of

wheat. Emmer grew naturally only in the upper Jordan valley around Jericho. By the time that the first walls of Jericho were built, they also grew peas and beans. By 6,000 years ago, orchards of olives, vines and figs grew on the hillsides. Soon their ideas were being adopted to the east in Asia, to the west in North Africa and Spain, and later, via Greece, in the colder, heavily forested lands of central and northern Europe.

The Roman authors Pliny and Virgil both wrote about the irrigation of vineyards, gardens and fields of cereal crops in Italy. But these irrigated farms began in places to destroy the soils and springs on which they depended. Four hundred years earlier, the Greek philosopher Plato in the *Critias* had described the decay of the environment around Athens thus:

> The soil was once deep, and therein it received the water, storing it up in the retentive loamy soil and providing all the various districts with abundant supplies of spring waters and streams, whereof the shrines still remain even now, at the spots where the fountains formerly existed ... In comparison to those old times, like a body of whom because of a wasting disease only the bones are left, the fertile and soft soil is everywhere eroded and only the sterile skeleton is left.

There is dispute about how common such destruction was, but where there was erosion, the people of the Mediterranean frequently found a solution. One of the earliest and greatest inventions of the Levantines were hill terraces. They cut the hillsides into dozens of steps, like a series of tiny dams. The purpose was to conserve both water and soil on the hillsides by preventing heavy rains from washing down the steep slopes, taking fertile soil with it.

The idea spread. Homer in his *Odyssey* describes the irrigation of terraced hillsides. Around the Mediterranean, they are found today from Palestine, where more than half of the Judaean hills are still terraced, to the olive groves of Tuscany, Algeria and Spain, where some may have been in use for almost 5,000 years. Now, in the moment of their final capitulation to the modern world, these systems are themselves being 'rediscovered' by archaeologists and geographers.

Spain has over the millennia developed irrigation systems both large and small to boost agricultural productivity in the arid but fertile valleys, known as *huertas*, in the east and south of the country. Until a new round of building this century, most of the large irrigation systems of Spain had been in place since the Roman era. The canals link the great east-flowing rivers to farmland from Andalusia to Valencia and Zaragoza.

Ancient water law has often survived, too, little changed since Islamic and perhaps Roman times. At noon every Thursday, in the *Puerta de los Apostales* outside the cathedral in old Valencia, the *Tribunal de las Aquas*, the water tribunal, still holds its sessions. The tribunal was founded by the Moors in 960, in the reign of Caliph Abderraman III of Cordoba, in the days when the cathedral site was occupied by a great mosque. Eight men in black shirts, elected by representatives of local farming communities, sit in judgment on all water disputes brought to them from across the irrigated land around the city. Nothing is ever written down, the fines are imposed in the medieval local currency, *lliures valencianes*, and the entire proceedings are conducted in the ancient Valencian language.

Out on the plains, between the large canal systems, there are dozens of smaller-scale village irrigation networks, mostly of Moorish origin, tapping springs and wells. The rules attached to operating the irrigation systems survived the expulsion of the Moors in the seventeenth century, and only in the past 30 years has the system crumbled. At Ahin (which is Arabic for 'spring'), for instance, three large cisterns collected spring water through each winter for a thousand years. Each June for a few weeks, more than a hundred farmers opened the cisterns and water flowed along a kilometre-long canal to irrigate crops of wheat, maize, beans, cherries and almonds.

But since the 1960s, many farmers have left the village, the cisterns and canals have silted up, taps have gone unopened and, since about 1970, no records of the irrigation system have been kept. Dotted across the ancient fields are an abandoned storage dam, much larger than the present construction, two abandoned Persian wheels, once operated by a donkey, and even an old *shaduf*.

The Moors brought water to the fields of many valleys and

coastal plains across Spain. Their mastery of water became folklore after the Reconquest of the thirteenth century by Christians, largely because of the failure of the Spanish king-doms to match their irrigation works or, in many cases, even to keep them repaired.

The indifference of the conquerors to water is illustrated in the story of Queen Isabella during the Reconquest. During the campaign against Granada she stayed at the Alcazar of Cordoba, where a magnificent Moorish water-wheel scooped up water from the River Guadalquivir to irrigate the city's gardens and fill its fountains. The noise of the wheel kept Isabella awake so, apparently unaware of its purpose, she had it dismantled.

Seven centuries later, on the opposite side of the Mediter-ranean, the 'reconquest' of Palestine by Jewish settlers brought a similarly abrupt halt to a traditional water tech-nology. The half-million Palestinians who fled the country in 1948 left behind them a sophisticated farming and water collecting system, much of which had been in use for 2,000 years. It was, says Israeli geographer Zvi Ron from the Uni-versity of Tel Aviv, an agricultural and hydrological tragedy. Their irrigated hill terraces have been left untouched by the Jewish kibbutzim, whose tractors cannot scale them. And while the Israelis have introduced irrigation to their farms on a scale unimagined by their Palestinian predecessors, they have ignored the remarkable ancient system of hundreds of tunnels dug into the dolomite hills to enlarge the flows of springs.

Typical is the spring tunnel of Ein Khandaq, close to the main road from Tel Aviv to Jerusalem, which was left behind in 1948, perhaps by farmers who expected to return in a few weeks, after the civil war was over. Fifty years on, the spring waters collect in a cavern, before flowing through a tunnel to a reservoir at the surface. The reservoir still overflows into a series of channels, small waterfalls and by-passes which cascade down a terraced flight of stone-walled fields, ensuring that each field automatically receives as much water as it needs and passes on the remainder.

No computer-controlled Israeli irrigation system could

have worked better. 'This shows real hydrological knowledge,' says Ron. The reservoir fills from the bottom but spills
out at a point two metres higher, thus raising the water
enough to irrigate the topmost terrace, without reducing the
flow from the spring. 'We hydrologists know this relationship
between flow and water height as Darcy's Law,' says Ron,
'but whoever built this had obviously figured out the law long
before Darcy. They didn't make this up as they went along.
They had to design the whole thing before they could begin
digging.'

Ron has surveyed more than 250 spring tunnels in the hills
of Palestine. The longest tunnel, Ein Jeweizeh, winds for more
than 200 metres through hard rock. The tunnels turned hill
springs, many little more than intermittent trickles of water
from the rock, into reliable water sources. When Ron began
investigating, the tunnels were completely unknown to outsiders. 'The majority are hidden, with only small dark open-
ings. Perhaps researchers didn't mention them because they
were afraid to enter them,' he says.

Some Palestinians claim that the tunnels are an indigenous
Arab technology. But archaeological evidence points to their
excavation 2,000 years ago, when Jews fought Romans in
these hills. One tunnel lies beneath a monastery at Abu
Ghosh, a small, picturesque Arab village outside Jerusalem.
The monastery was a Crusader church in the twelfth century
and before that the crypt was a Roman reservoir. The reservoir itself was built on top of a spring tunnel big enough for a
man to walk through. French surveyors renovating the monastery a century ago assumed that the tunnel had been an
escape route to the surrounding fields for Crusaders in case of
a siege; but the monastery today takes water from its crypt
reservoir.

As in Spain, ancient water customs have survived along
with the spring tunnels. At Battir, near Bethlehem, eight Arab
clans continued until the 1980s to take water from a spring
tunnel, to irrigate vegetables in their fields and to fill pitchers
for their houses. The clans tapped the reservoir at the mouth
of the tunnel once every eight days. An elder of the village
measured the daily ration by putting a notched stick into the

reservoir and then opening a sluice-gate to divert water until
the water-level had fallen by one notch on the stick. This
ritual may have been carried on for 1,700 years, by Jew and
Arab alike. Battir was the site of a famous Jewish fortress –
the last to fall to the Romans during battles in the second
century AD – and beside the entrance to the tunnel is a Roman
inscription.

While these ancient peasant irrigation systems, quite remarkable pieces of engineering in their way, have been ignored by
Europeans from the modern urban world, the aqueducts of
the Roman imperial engineers – the great man-made rivers of
their day – have inspired adulation. They are in many ways
the key to the modern engineer's view of water.

In its early days, Rome took its water from the River Tiber.
But the risk of disease from sewage dumped into the river
encouraged the city's elite to establish for themselves in 312 BC
a clean water supply, which they brought from springs outside
the city along an open water conduit, the Aqua Appia. Forty
years later, they built another and these watered the houses of
the rich and well-connected for almost 300 years.

Then, with the city's population nudging a million, mostly
living in tenements with no access to clean water, Agrippa
built the first public baths. He also added the first stages of a
sewer system to clear the stench of a city full of cesspits. The
baths required large amounts of water, and the sewers needed
flushing, so over the next few generations, the city built 11
conduits with a total length of over 500 kilometres, tapping
ever more remote springs and mountain streams. Aqua
Claudia, a 70-kilometre aqueduct, carried others on its back
near the city, and ran for several kilometres on colonnades
above the valley, like a raised urban motorway. In one place,
five aqueducts intersect in an aquatic version of Spaghetti
Junction as they approach the city from the east.

Aqueducts became enduring monuments to Roman water
engineers. Carthage in North Africa took its water from
springs at the foot of mountains 50 kilometres away. The
three-tiered Pont du Gard in southern France was part of a
system to deliver water 50 kilometres to Nimes. Most of these

aqueducts took their water from springs – the Romans, for all their engineering prowess, built few dams. There was nothing to compare with the Egyptians' dam at Wadi el Garawi, built 4,900 years ago outside the ancient city of Memphis; or the Marib Dam, 15 metres high and 700 metres long, which was built in Yemen some time before 750 BC and operated for 1,300 years. But while the technical prowess of Roman hydraulic engineers was far from unique, they did leave behind structures to inspire the Europeans of the renaissance.

Says the British geographer Denis Cosgrove: 'The crumbling evidence of Roman hydro-engineering became for renaissance observers signs of the power and the glory of Empire.' The aqueducts also became a symbol of a particular kind of attitude to water. 'The geometric precision of an aqueduct signifies the engineer's vision of water flow, a bounded channel form that has become the common conception of how even a natural river should appear.' The Romans imparted from the ancient to the modern world a vision of nature tamed, remade in the image of engineering, of the land separated from the water. It was a world in which water flowing to the sea was wasted, in which marshes were for draining and floods for controlling.

3

RENAISSANCE AND REASON

For they do mean all fens to drain
And water overmaster,
All will be dry and we must die,
'cause Essex calves want pasture . . .

Fenlanders' seventeenth-century chant

The story of the creation of modern Europe over the past 500 years is frequently that of a campaign to tame the forces of nature and gather its wealth under human control. The process was fuelled by notions about private property that went far beyond any seen in previous civilisations in the Middle East or the Mediterranean. As the oak forests that once covered northern Europe were cut down, so they were frequently privatised. Often, the act of destroying a forest conferred a right of ownership over the bare land left behind. Likewise the great drainage projects in marsh, bog and fen conferred property rights on those who 'improved' what had once been commonly owned resources, available to all.

The tensions between ancient common rights over natural resources and private property rights were a running sore through the period. They stoked the fires of the English Civil War, and exacerbated conflict during the spread of European ideas and technologies round the world. Of all the natural resources, water was the least amenable to private ownership. Yet its control through engineering schemes frequently became a proxy for ownership both of the water itself and the land it served.

In northern Europe, few farmers shared the interest of the Mediterraneans in irrigation. Drainage was far more important here. In England, which like most of the rest of the north was sparsely populated during the Middle Ages, most lowland towns and villages were surrounded by large forests and seasonally flooded river valleys. The gradual clearing, draining and cultivation of these valleys gathered pace after the introduction in the eleventh century of the heavy plough, pulled by teams of oxen or horses. This agricultural revolution provided new rich land to farm, improved yields on existing farms, and greatly increased the length of navigable waterways, allowing an expansion in river trade that eventually helped trigger the Industrial Revolution.

The Dutch were the pioneers of drainage in Europe – with reason. The Low Countries were indeed low, exposed to the storms of the North Sea and floods coming down the Rhine and Meuse. Early efforts to hold back the sea by building dykes on the Zuider Zee had failed in the storms on St Elizabeth's Day 1421, when the sea reclaimed 500 square kilometres. Perhaps 10,000 Dutch farmers died in their beds that night, after a hard day tilling the former seabed. Twenty villages disappeared permanently beneath the waves.

In his study of the Dutch 'golden age', *Embarrassment of Riches*, Simon Schama shows how drainage became both a symbol of national aspiration and an engine of economic growth. The period started badly. In 1570, a series of storms culminated in floods that once again breached all defences and killed tens of thousands. And four years after that, William of Orange had to breach the dykes himself in order to repulse the Spanish army which was laying siege to the towns of Rotterdam, Gouda and Leiden.

The foundation of a new, independent nation appeared to depend upon harnessing the natural force of water. When engineers switched their attentions from reclaiming the seabed, which had proved little short of catastrophic, to draining marshes, the Calvinist clergy deemed the task sacred. 'The making of new land belongs to God alone, for He gives to some people the wit and strength to do it,' wrote Andries Vierlingh, a sixteenth-century Dutch water engineer.

As important as God or the Dutch people were the windmill, which gave the engineers power to pump water, and the new companies set up to finance the task. Altogether, the Dutch reclaimed some 300 square kilometres of bog in the early decades of the seventeenth century. In one scheme, the Beemster drainage north of Amsterdam, 43 windmills drove wheels strung with buckets that lifted water from trenches dug in the mire and tipped it into canals. They created 70 square kilometres of new land, making it possible to feed Amsterdam whose population grew fivefold to 150,000 between 1580 and 1650. The Beemster project was a great financial endeavour, too, largely financed by syndicates of urban capitalists. The country's chief minister, Johan Olden-barneveld, joined the investors. Capital, God and national identity came together in a way typical of the era, as they did across the North Sea in England.

Take a train across the English fenlands today, from Cambridge to King's Lynn, past the great cathedral of Ely; or travel the length of the Netherlands, and you see an entirely man-made landscape. Where once there were forests of reed and willow, rivers and pools full of eels and all kinds of fish, skies festooned with geese and storks, an atmosphere thick with mists, marsh gas and malaria, now there is a symmetry of rectangular prairie fields, canalised rivers and sluice-gates.

A few hints of the old landscape are visible from the air. At Cambridge University, among a vast assembly of aerial photographs, there is a shot of the modern fenland landscape, of roads and drainage canals, a study in straight lines. But meandering ghost-like across the land for many miles, are the whitish silt remains of a long-vanished riverbed. It stands out against the black peat of the remaining soil, entirely oblivious of the new order.

Roman engineers were the first to venture into the Fens with the aim of changing their hydrology. They dug several canals, short cuts through the quagmire of sodden peaty soils and shallow lakes that make up the southern half of the Fens. The purpose was to speed the transport by boat of grain from the fields of East Anglia to garrisons in northern England. Closer to the sea, the Fens were drier, with silty soils on which cattle grazed. Here the Romans practised skills in land drainage learned in the Po valley of northern Italy, though after their departure the drainage channels silted up.

Through the Middle Ages, locals appear to have been happy enough to live off the marsh, which they visited by flat-bottomed boat from their homes on higher land, such as the Isle of Ely. The bogs and winding channels held none of the fears for them that outsiders felt. Chroniclers in the twelfth century wrote of salmon and sturgeon in the fenland waters in quantities 'as to cause astonishment in strangers, while the natives laugh at their surprise'. Fast coaches took live fish and wildfowl to London.

The Domesday Book's records of the Fens show a wealthy economy based on eels, which were caught in their hundreds in wicker traps or nets. Ely gained its name as the 'eel district', because of the quantity of eels in the waters around it. Eels became a local currency, and Wisbech rendered to the authorities in 1086 a sum amounting to 33,260 eels. Fenlanders paid their rents in eels, and local tithes were accounted for in 'sticks', being about 25 eels, the number that could be spiked through the gills on to one stick.

The urge to drain England's wetlands grew as the population recovered from the Black Death. Market towns grew – London especially so – bringing an increasing demand for food, and offering the prospect of rich pickings for landowners. The age-old cry of water engineers was heard as they asked for public funds to pay for private drainage projects. They promised private wealth and national prosperity.

When the drainage engineers arrived in earnest in the seventeenth century they claimed that, as Jeremy Purseglove puts it in his essential history of drainage, *Taming the Flood*, 'a fat ox was better than a well-grown eel, and a tame sheep more use than a wild duck'. But the fenlanders were not so sure, especially as the eel and duck were free, while the ox and sheep were not. They knew what was coming, however. The chronicler Thomas Fuller wrote in 1655: 'As now the great fishes therein prey on the less, so the wealthy men would devour the poorer sort of people . . . and the rich men, to make room for themselves, would jostle the poor people out of their commons.'

Dutch engineers crossed the North Sea to make their grand proposals in the drawing-rooms of the English gentry and the corridors of the Treasury. In 1600 Queen Elizabeth signed an Act of Parliament 'for the recovering of many hundred thousand acres of marshes'. And before long the newly patented Dutch windmills sprouted all over the marshes.

Out on the fens, a series of disastrous floods presented the engineers with their chance. Under the first major scheme, approved in 1630, the Earl of Bedford, who owned 8,000 hectares of the Isle of Ely, and other 'adventurers', agreed to drain a large area of the southern Fen. In return, they and the Crown would divide between them almost 40,000 hectares of former common land. It was an ill-disguised carve-up at the expense of the fenlanders, who received no compensation for the loss of their commons.

The celebrated Dutch engineer Cornelius Vermuyden was appointed to construct the Duke of Bedford's dykes and dig the canals. It is hard to tell whence Vermuyden's celebrity came. He had arrived in Britain nine years before and rebuilt the Thames flood defences. According to an inquiry he left the capital's protection 'in a worse condition than it was before'. From there he moved to the River Trent, which he proposed to drain as a dry run for the Fens. Here, Dutch workers caused uproar on Hatfield Chase. They apparently deliberately released drainage water to flood out truculent commoners, and killed at least one local during angry confrontations. Vermuyden's main drainage channel on the Chase, the Dutch River, proved unable to carry the amount of water discharged by his pumps and the great engineer landed in gaol for failing to pay the cost of repairs.

The fenlanders, warned of his reputation, met the arrival of the newly knighted Vermuyden with stones, shovels and axes, and chanting:

> For they do mean all fens to drain
> And water overmaster,
> All will be dry and we must die,
> 'cause Essex calves want pasture ...
> The feather'd fowls have wings

To fly to other nations,
But we have no such things
To help our transportations.
We must give place (oh grievous case)
To horned beast and cattle,
Except that we can all agree
To drive them out by battle.

Vermuyden dug six great 'cuts', straight artificial rivers that would carry the water until then taken by meandering rivers such as the Ouse, Nene and Welland. The slow-flowing Great Ouse was for 50 kilometres replaced by a 35-kilometre drainage channel called the Bedford River. On paper it sounded fine, but in practice it was the same old story. Seven years on, with the Bedford River completed, there was outcry on the Fens when the 'adventurers' declared the job done and petitioned for their profits, while flooding appeared as great a danger as ever.

The King intervened to assuage the rioters. But then he inflamed them by re-engaging Vermuyden to try again. The Dutchman, as slippery as the eels he wished to banish from the wetlands of England, had flattered Charles I with promises to build a new city in the reclaimed fen, to be called Charlemont. Resentment towards the drainage grew and eventually became fused with resentment of the King himself on the eve of the Civil War, and nothing more was ever heard of Charlemont.

From the 1620s, Oliver Cromwell, who inherited a fenland estate at St Ives from his radical uncle, was fighting on behalf of the commoners to prevent drainage in the Fens. The man who was later to lead the English Revolution first tasted armed rebellion here as fenlanders responded to his encouragement when 'armed with scythes and pitchforks, [they] uttered threatening words against anyone who should drive off their cattle' from common pastures.

Yet, a decade later in 1649, Cromwell's world had changed, and with it his attitude to the fenlanders. That year, he executed the King and joined the Earl of Bedford as a commissioner to oversee the new efforts to drain the Fens. Three days after he dissolved the Rump Parliament in 1653, Cromwell sent the army to suppress commoners opposing the New Bedford River, a project from which he himself gained 80 hectares of drained land. In it, no doubt, he saw both private wealth and national advance.

By the end of the century, the draining of the English Fens was far from complete, but it had contributed substantially to a seventeenth-century green revolution that had increased the country's arable farmland by 10 per cent, and helped to turn England from a country of intermittent famine into one that exported corn. However, there were great losses: in fish and fowl, eels and thatch, not to mention the lives of the fenland commoners. They were unappeased when some land was belatedly set aside for 'poor commoners' – before the drainage, they might have said, the commoners had not been poor.

There was also a large and continuing bill to be paid in maintaining the system and renovating it to cope with the shrinkage of peat as it dried out. At times, flooding became worse. Rainwater no longer stayed on the fens, but rushed off quickly into drainage channels and the new rivers. As it flowed towards the sea, it met tidal waters coming the other way. The Denver sluice, the lynchpin of the entire system, where the Bedford rivers met up with the Great Ouse, frequently could not release river floodwater at high tide. In 1713, a tidal surge whipped up by North Sea storms washed the Denver sluice out to sea, causing widespread damage throughout the drainage system.

In 1777, one fenland engineer, John Golborne, noted: 'Look which way you will, you will see nothing but misery and desolation; go but half a mile from Ely, and you come to Middle-Fen, a tract of sixteen thousand acres, given up and abandoned; there you see the ruins of windmills ... houses without inhabitants, and lands incapable of either pasturage or tillage.' It is arguable that, if the steam engine had not come along to enhance the pumping power of the old windmills in the nineteenth century, the entire system might have fallen into day.

What they had attempted in the Fens and the Low Countries,

European engineers also tried for most of the continent's river valleys. To a remarkable extent, what most of us today regard as a river – a single flow of water in a well-defined channel making steady if not geometrically straight progress to the sea – is a product not of nature but of the activities of water engineers in the past 300 years or so. From piecemeal dredging, dyking and construction of weirs, engineers graduated to large projects taking in hand long tracts of major rivers such as the Loire, Rhine or Trent.

The organisation and investment involved were considerable, and only governments could underwrite the costs. There was, too, a new view of the world, based on scientific observation and determined on subjugation of nature. Industrialists had been among the first people to 'improve' Europe's rivers. They built weirs to divert water to their mills and they began to dredge riverbeds and cut off meanders to improve navigation. From the end of the seventeenth century, northern industrialists began to make greater demands that in time created largely artificial waterways.

The Mersey, Irwell and Weaver navigations allowed ships to penetrate up the Mersey estuary as far as Manchester and the Cheshire salt fields. Then on the other side of the Pennines, the Aire, Calder and Don navigations opened up cities such as Leeds and Sheffield. From the mid-eighteenth century, engineers dissatisfied with the arrangement of the nation's rivers began a complex network of canals. They linked inconveniently situated industrial towns such as Birmingham and the Potteries to the rivers of the northwest and the south. Even the Pennines were crossed by stairways of locks.

To provide headwaters for their canals, the British began to build dams to hold reservoirs of water on the moors. Later, by impounding the short volatile Pennine streams, they provided water to the factories and slums of the growing industrial towns of the north of England.

At first, progress was fitful, punctuated by a series of flooding disasters. In 1852, undermined by leaks, the Bilberry Dam on the moors above Huddersfield in West Yorkshire collapsed and killed 81 people. In 1864, the Dale Dyke Dam on a stream above Sheffield collapsed soon after being filled.

In all, 250 people died in their beds as a million cubic metres of water and earth destroyed their stone cottages.

None the less, the idea of building grand structures in the hills to supply cities had taken hold. Where there were no nearby hills, the water would be impounded far away and brought to the cities. So, in the 1880s, when Liverpool needed more water, it built a masonry dam in the hills of North Wales, creating the largest artificial lake in Europe. In 1894, neighbouring Manchester completed a dam on Thirlmere in the Lake District, also connected to the city by a long aqueduct. And in 1904 Birmingham completed its series of giant masonry dams in the Elan valley in central Wales. These structures remain central features of Britain's water supply system to this day.

The canals and dams were a powerful indication both of growing human frustration with the impositions of nature on economic progress, and of the increasing ability of engineers to recreate the landscape according to their own requirements.

During the eighteenth and especially the nineteenth centuries, major drainage and channelling works were completed on virtually all the main rivers of Europe, both to improve navigation and to increase the amount of flood-free farmland. Perhaps the most dramatic of these was the reconstruction of the Rhine. It began in the Low Countries early in the eighteenth century, when Dutch water engineers, tired of allowing the Rhine to meander freely across its floodplain before entering the North Sea, began to train it into three separate but permanent channels. They dug the Pannerdens Canal in 1707 and the Bijlands Canal in 1780.

The Dutch appear to have concluded that, once canalised, the river was theirs to do with as they liked. Four years after the completion of the Bijlands Canal, the Emperor Joseph II presented an angry note to the Dutch government demanding that the outlets of the Rhine be kept open for navigation. Eight years later, the new French Republic decreed that 'the stream of a river is the common undeniable property of all the countries which it bounds or traverses ... nature does not recognise privileged nations'. This statement became a principle of international law and was enshrined in European law by the Congress of Vienna in 1815. It was invoked when, in the Americas, President Jefferson demanded that Spain allow US ships to use the Mississippi and that the British allow them use of the St Lawrence in Canada.

The most spectacular nineteenth-century river engineering project in Europe was the Upper Rhine 'rectification' programme undertaken by Johann Tulla between 1817 and 1876. The very name 'rectification' indicates the extent to which human notions of reason by then took precedence over nature. The river, which had remained largely undisturbed in its upper reaches even at the start of the nineteenth century, was to be 'rectified' from its natural state towards a human vision of what it ought to be like. Just as British landscape gardeners such as Capability Brown wanted to remake nature in a more ordered form, replacing the diversity of nature with manicured lawns and trees sited with architectural precision, so Tulla sought a harmonious, rational river.

At the start of the nineteenth century, the Rhine for most of its length still took a tortuous path across a wide floodplain of woods and water meadows. In Alsace was the 'furcation zone', where the river split into myriad branches, each periodically forming, disappearing and moving its bed. North of Karlsruhe, all the way to Mainz, the stream became one. But it meandered drunkenly, doubling back on itself and leaving behind ox-bow lakes. The silty Rhine water still slipped over dykes, through forests, across meadows and on to fields during each summer flood.

The split channels and wide meanders were inconvenient for navigators – whose journeys were slow, tortuous and impossible aboard all but the smallest boats – and for flood-threatened towns built on shifting river banks. They also threatened farmers who wanted to convert the meadows to arable fields. So Tulla's plan was to force the furcation zone of the Upper Rhine into a single channel, which would take the shortest convenient path towards the sea. His statement of intent for the Rhine, that 'as a rule, no stream or river needs more than one bed', has become an unquestioned maxim for water engineers ever since.

The scheme achieved its initial objectives admirably. It conveniently prepared the Rhine, the only Alpine river to drain into the North Sea, for its role as the great fluvial highway of the new empire of Germany, which was created in 1871. Along the Rhine's newly stabilised banks grew the great industrial cities of the new Germany. And the river, which drained a third of the country, was connected to others by canals, which it increasingly resembled.

But the rectification also began one of the earliest lessons in the hidden dangers of meddling with rivers on a large scale, a lesson still being learned on the Rhine today. The canalisation of the Upper Rhine reduced the river's length by around 100 kilometres. In so doing, it increased the speed of its flow by 30 per cent in places. The faster river sped boats to the sea but also scoured its bed and banks. At Basel, the bed of Tulla's rectified river fell by seven metres, the height of a two-storey house. Three hundred kilometres beyond the end of the works, at the great Ruhr port of Duisburg, it fell by almost four metres, and the port had to be rebuilt. As the riverbed dropped, so did the water-table in the alluvium along the river's floodplain. For several kilometres on either side of the river, fields and ancient forests of oak and elm and willow dried out. Wells ran dry. Meanwhile, the scouring brought downstream large amounts of gravel, which impeded river flow in places – a case of nature trying to undo the damage caused by man. The engineers responded by excavating new channels, causing yet more erosion. They were engaging in a battle with nature that could never cease.

The irony is that today, with 90 per cent of the natural floodplain of the Rhine cut off from the river behind dykes, the river is more prone to flooding than it has ever been. The same amount of water still flows down the Rhine – and by being concentrated into a single channel and sent at express speed to the sea, it becomes that much harder to contain.

In the past 60 years, the river has been virtually remade for a second time between Basel and Strasbourg. A scheme known as the Modern Upper Rhine Development has largely abandoned Tulla's version of the Rhine (now known as the Rest Rhine) in favour of an entirely engineered channel, on which stand giant locks and a series of hydroelectric plants. This has halved once more the time taken by the winter flood peak to pass out of the Alps as far as Karlsruhe. It now takes just 30 hours, and coincides with peak flows in several tributaries, such as the Kinzig and Murg, as they meet the main river – creating a flood surge that rushes downstream towards Bonn and Cologne. Cities such as Mannheim and Ludwigshafen that in the 1950s had protection from floods expected once in 200 years are now no longer safe from 50-year floods.

The dykes are also making the river dirtier. While sewers and factories disgorge wastes into the Rhine, the river has been cut off from its natural cleansing mechanisms. The vegetation of the floodplain can no longer provide its biological purifying services; the gravel beds beneath the river can no longer filter the waters. The dykes prevent fish from taking refuge from pollution disasters, such as the release of chemicals from a big fire at a chemical works in Switzerland in 1986.

Some engineers want to admit defeat. They are losing the battle with the river. To meet the latest threat to the old dream of a perfectly managed river, they want to go back to natural solutions. Starting in 1994, engineers in Baden-Wurtemberg hope to create a dozen 'flood retention basins' beside the Rhine. These will not be concrete-lined pits sitting empty for year on year, ready to scoop up excess water in a major flood. Instead, the idea is to cut the dykes permanently and let the water back on to its original floodplain, through the old silted-up channels to backwaters filled with reeds and fish. Eels will swim once more between the roots of flooded forests.

Helping to draw up the billion-Deutschmark scheme for the state government are scientists such as Georg Rast, a former engineer who now works at the World Wide Fund for Nature's institute for floodplain ecology on the Rhine at Rastatt. Here he surveys the two faces of the great river. Outside the town, the other side of high dykes, sits a giant river lock, where barges laden with containers travel up and down a concrete-lined river, fuelling the German economic miracle. But down the road is the Rastatter Rheinaue, a riverside nature reserve that Rast boasts is the best surviving floodplain forest in the whole of the Upper Rhine. It too is currently protected behind dykes, though Rast wants to hand the forest, and many other less well preserved areas of forest and pasture, back to the river.

Amid the roe deer and wild boar and the whiff of wild garlic, Rast says: 'The aim of the Baden-Wurtemberg scheme is to combine conservation with flood protection by giving back to the remnants of the floodplain their former role as flood retention reservoirs. In the old furcation zone, from here past Strasbourg to Mulhouse, wherever it will not endanger people, we want to lower the dykes and let the floodplain ecosystems re-assert themselves.'

The eventual plan is to turn 75 square kilometres of land back into near-natural landscape. As the floods return at the height of the winter and summer flood seasons, so water-tables will rise, silt will be deposited and the natural forests that once filled the wide valley of the Upper Rhine will return.

4

THE LOUISIANA PURCHASE

Ol' man river, he just keeps rollin'.

Negro spiritual

The Spaniards who arrived there in the sixteenth century thought better of building on the floodplain of the Lower Mississippi. They left its great expanse of marshes and lakes, recipient of the entire flow from the second largest river catchment in the world, to the Indians. The French settlers who followed them felt no such constraints. They founded a city in the delta, New Orleans, then another, Baton Rouge, and called their marsh colony Louisiana. The French government kept it for a hundred years before selling to the US in the Louisiana Purchase at the start of the nineteenth century.

Orleans on the Loire, back in France, had always been a periodical victim to terrible floods, so perhaps the French knew they courted disaster when in 1718 Jean Baptiste le Moyne, the governor of Louisiana, began to build New Orleans. Certainly as water filled the foundations of their new city in its first months, they knew they were in for a fight. It is a fight that continues to this day – and still nobody is sure who is winning.

The first houses of New Orleans were on the river's levees, the natural banks that rise above the surrounding countryside. But these levees, created as the floodwaters poured out of the riverbed and dropped their load of silt, were a sign of flooding, not a protection against it. So the French built the levees higher – and higher. The city flooded in 1735. The governor built 70 kilometres of earthworks, but it still flooded. After each flood, the defences were raised and the city declared flood-proof, but it never was.

After the Louisiana Purchase in 1803, slaves on dozens of cotton plantations, equipped with shovels and wheelbarrows, raised hundreds of kilometres of banks to carry 'ol' man river' down to the sea without taking his usual detours across the floodplain.

In mid-century, the US Congress stepped in with the Swamp Land Acts. These handed ownership of the 260,000 square kilometres of unclaimed swamplands across the whole of the US to state governments, who could then sell them to raise money for levee building. Rising prices for farm products and the growing world market combined to make land drainage increasingly attractive in the US, as it was in Europe. As levees rose, the land behind was progressively drained, using new technologies such as tile-pipes and steam-powered machines for digging ditches.

These Swamp Land Acts changed the face of the US, destroying vast natural wealth on the marshes in the hope of creating new private wealth with drain and plough. Land outside Chicago, along the Minnesota, described a few years before as 'a low, flat and swampy prairie, very thickly covered with high grass, aquatic plants and wild rice ... [which] overflowed in the spring, and canoes pass in every direction', joined the grain belt of the Midwest.

Whatever was lost, in the Midwest drainage was successfully accomplished. Not so down south. As fast as the Louisiana state government sold off its 30,000 square kilometres of swamp (more than a quarter of the entire state), farmers drained them to create plantations. In doing so, they undermined the flood protection work of the raised levees. The swamps, looked at in hydrological terms, were giant holding reservoirs for the river's natural flooding. They spread the river's flow through the year, holding on to the floodwater during high flow and letting it seep back during low river flow.

Now, barricaded off from the river by levees and drained altogether in many places, the swamps could no longer perform this role. So the river floods got higher and the

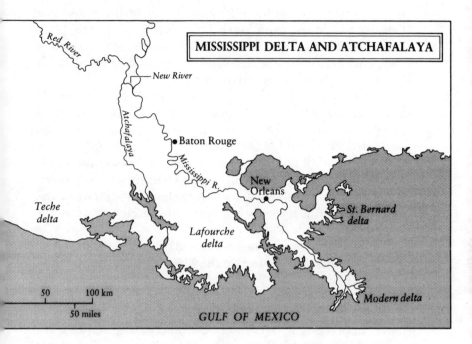

MISSISSIPPI DELTA AND ATCHAFALAYA

Red River

New River

Atchafalaya

Baton Rouge

Mississippi R.

New Orleans

Teche delta

St. Bernard delta

Lafourche delta

50   100 km

50 miles

Modern delta

GULF OF MEXICO

inevitable breaks in the levees became more and more devastating, as the great floods in 1862, 1866 and again in 1867 showed. Congress, upping the stakes in what the US Army's Corps of Engineers described as a 'war' against the river, created the Mississippi River Commission, and handed control of the commission to the Corps with the task of 'preventing destructive floods'.

The corps announced that it would fight its war with science. James Eads, its foremost engineer, declared:

Every atom that moves onward in the river, from the moment it leaves its home among the crystal springs or mountain snows, throughout the 1,500 leagues of its devious pathway, until it is finally lost in the vast pathways of the Gulf, is controlled by laws as fixed and certain as those which direct the majestic march of the heavenly spheres ... The engineer need only to be insured that he does not ignore the existence of any of these laws, to feel positively certain of the results he aims at.

It was a far cry, as John McPhee notes in his book *The Control of Nature*, from Mark Twain's observation that 'ten thousand River Commissions, with the mines of the world at their back, cannot tame that lawless stream, cannot say to it Go here or Go there and make it obey'.

The river gave its reply to the formation of the Commission by breaking the levees in 280 places in 1882. Floods continued every three or four years until 1927, when a vast inundation destroyed every bridge for 1,500 kilometres downstream of Cairo, a small Illinois town with a name as presumptuous as the Corps of Engineers' science. New Orleans was only saved when, in an admission of defeat for the high levee strategy, the corps blew up a levee downstream of the city to draw off some of the river's flood.

The following year Congress passed the Flood Control Act. The Act launched a project on the Mississippi that more than 60 years later has cost $7 billion and is still only 80 per cent completed. It amounts to a final attempt to engineer the river from mountain to sea. Levees were raised once, then twice more. In places, the river in flood would be allowed to leave the main river and follow engineered floodways.

Dams were raised in the river's tributaries, themselves great rivers such as the Tennessee, partly to hold back floodwaters. But as the Mississippi's engineers built these artificial flood-water stores, they continued to cut meanders and drain swamps. Upstream, too, human artifice was creating natural catastrophe. As McPhee put it:

> Every shopping centre, every drainage improvement, every square foot of new pavement in nearly half of the United States was accelerating runoff towards Louisiana ... The precipitation that produced the great flood of 1973 was only about 20 per cent above normal. Yet the crest at St Louis was the highest ever recorded there.

After engineering for a century to prevent floods, in the late 1980s, the Corps found itself with a new crisis: drought. Thousands of barges were laid up when the river ran low for much of its length as the Midwest dried out. Yet this too was partly a response to the new engineered river, which has no natural water storage to fill rivers in dry years any more than to empty it in wet years. In July 1988, at the height of the drought, more than two-thirds of the Mississippi flow came from water released from man-made reservoirs.

Great rivers such as the Mississippi have long and complex histories. While the engineering projects of man may, with a bit of luck, be able to make the Mississippi valley fit for cities for a few decades, the longer term may be different. The Mississippi drains 41 per cent of the land area of the 'contiguous' United States. The river has created a delta of alluvium 5 kilometres thick at the river's mouth and extended the coastline 800 kilometres south from Cairo, Illinois, to its present line. Such forces cannot easily be halted, nor the consequences of so doing be predicted.

Engineers have so effectively channelled the river that most of the silt that once settled along the floodplain and on to the delta is now either trapped behind dams upstream or shot far out into the Gulf of Mexico. A delta that was extending itself until about 1900 is now retreating at a rate of 7 centimetres a day in places.

Since the end of the last Ice Age, the river has created ten separate deltas across the coastline of Louisiana. Five thousand years ago, it flowed into the Teche delta, 200 kilometres west of its present outlet. Then it created the St Bernard delta in the east, before swinging south to the Lafourche delta and, in the past thousand years, to the modern delta, which extends like a bird's foot into the ocean.

This process occurs because as the river reaches the ocean it lays down large amounts of silt, forever extending the delta. This in turn gives it a longer, more sluggish route to the sea. In time, some more vigorous stream cutting back from the ocean nearby will reach the main river and begin to take its flow. If not, then the river will itself take a leap to by-pass its own deposits. Once a new route is established, offering a quicker route to the sea, it will capture ever more of the flow, carving for itself an ever more efficient path until it takes the majority of the river's discharge.

Right now, there is a young pretender: the Atchafalaya River. A little under 150 years ago, it was a lazy backwater clogged with logs. Then it was cleared by an energetic employee of the Corps of Engineers. Henry Shreve was anxious to please his bosses by cutting all impediments to navigation in the rivers of the Mississippi delta and began not just clearing out logs, but removing meanders too. One day he cut off a meander of the Mississippi where it nudges the Atchafalaya.

At that time, the two rivers' waters met, but barely mingled. However, in cutting the meander, which in theory should have severed the connection, Shreve had made a terrible mistake. A small amount of water continued round the meander after his new cut, but now it joined the Atchafalaya. The Atchafalaya became greedy and day by day it took more water from the Mississippi's meander. Within a month, the abandoned meander had become a river in its own right, now called the New River, draining water from the Mississippi into a suddenly rejuvenated Atchafalaya. With every year that passed, the upstart took more and more water on its short cut to the sea – a journey 100 kilometres less than the old, slow Mississippi. In 1945, it captured the waters of the Red River, a tributary of the Mississippi that until then entered the main river nearby. After that, a third of the flow of 'ol' man river' was being syphoned off into the younger river.

The Mississippi downstream of the attempted capture is today one of the great industrial heartlands of the union, with petrochemical plants by the score. The old Cajun communities that once fed themselves from the wetlands on alligator stew and clams, now thrive on the pay cheques of DuPont, Dow Chemicals and Monsanto. Their wealth is dependent not on the water in the marshes, but on the water trapped by the levees. It forms a waterway for navigation by large vessels coming up from the ocean to Baton Rouge and New Orleans. The bulk of the US's vast grain exports from the Midwest also leave through New Orleans. If the river moves, these cities lose their livelihoods. So, in 1963, the Corps of Engineers built a giant plug, 30 metres high and weighing 5 million tonnes, in the New River to keep the Atchafalaya and Mississippi separate. So far it has held. A lock allows 30 per cent of the river to flow into the Atchafalaya in normal times (a figure imperiously determined by Congress) and up to 70 per cent in floods, when it makes a convenient overflow channel. But nobody knows if one day the Atchafalaya will refuse to give back the 70 per cent after a flood. It nearly happened in 1973, when the flood, in its endeavour to find its way into the Atchafalaya, carved a hole larger than a football stadium under the barrier. It held, but only just.

What's it all for, this war with the Mississippi? The answer may be in a small typewritten report, *Energy Systems Overview of the Mississippi River Basin*, from Howard Odum and his colleagues at the Center for Wetlands at the University of Florida. 'Much of the economic value of the Mississippi River basin is based on nature's work,' the report begins. 'Often, the work of the economy inadvertently eliminates some of this value.'

Nature made the fish; nature brought down the silt that fertilises fields; it is nature's water that the ships float on. But 'in the past, calculations of economic values of a single function such as navigation, flood control or short-term yields of farm products have led to the work of humans being directed in opposition to that of nature'. In other words, because the fish in the bayou or the silt in the river have no quoted economic value because nobody owns them, they get ignored in the kind of cost-benefit analyses that engineers and economists love.

Odum attempts to answer the questions that have lurked behind opposition to big drainage and dyking projects, at least since the fenlanders raised their pitchforks and eel-sticks against Cornelius Vermuyden in the 1620s. Is the eel in the fen worth more than the cow in the field? More pertinently for the Mississippi, does the nation get its money's worth for the expenditure of dredging 200 million tonnes of sediment from the river and its harbours each year? If the dredging helps shipping, does it also degrade the Louisiana coastal fisheries, still the most productive in North America?

Odum attempts to put dollar values on such natural 'services' as those provided by the wetlands, and to line those up on the same menu as conventional services such as barge hire or farm yields. In the process, his basic statistics undergo an extraordinary metamorphosis. Jules of energy (for rainfall and river flow; oil yield and fuel for opening and shutting locks) and grams (of sediment and coastal land loss) and energy flows (of coal in barges, water in rivers and biomass that feeds fish) are poured in at one end and emerge as billions of dollars at the other.

The conclusion is striking. Floods may have looked bad to the French when they were digging foundations for New Orleans, and when plantation dykes gave way. But there was another side. Floods put fertile silt on to the land and sustained fisheries. But 'by dyking, channelising and making economic developments that were not adapted to the flood cycle, a benefit was often turned into a stress'. The 'flood resource' was squandered. Through 150 years of engineering 'very large values in wetland service, in sediment deposition, and in water control were diverted into the sea by dyking and channelising'.

In Ancient Egypt, in Alexandria and Memphis, silt was the great resource brought by the sea. But for their namesake cities in Louisiana and Tennessee, silt was something that clogged up shipping lanes. Odum says that the Ancient Egyptians had it right. The economic value of river transportation in the Mississippi is only $5 billion a year, compared to the loss of floodplain value from dyking of $22 billion. If anything, flood-protection dams in the Mississippi tributaries are even worse. They both hold up shipping and accumulate silt uselessly in their reservoirs.

Odum does not say that the Mississippi floodplain should have been left for the birds and fish. 'General economic development produced higher macrovalues,' he says – meaning Americans came out of it better than they went in. The oil and gas industries made a lot of mess in the marshes, but made even more money, however you look at it. But the gains 'were much lower than those possible with a better use of the river'.

The findings, he says, 'justify measures for restoring wetlands'. The Mississippi must now be re-managed for the benefit less of barges and Baton Rouge and more for fisheries, forests and flood absorption. Odum believes that the overall economic output of the lower Mississippi could be made more than three times higher by 'refitting the pattern of humanity to use the river flooding resource instead of shunting it to sea'. For the future, the report concludes with a strong echo of what ecologists have in mind for the Rhine. The policy should be to 'dyke people in rather than dyking the river out'.

5

THE ALTERNATIVE
TRADITION

It's fantastic. There's a whole system, abandoned before any
Europeans came, now being restored by the local community.

William Denevan, University of Wisconsin, on the raised
fields around Lake Titicaca

'The entire region is hopeless desert,' wrote an American
surveyor who visited the Sonoran Desert on the Arizona
border with Mexico in 1894. 'It is unadapted for agriculture.
Yet, when the July rains commence, the Papago Indians
forsake their *rancherias* and hasten to their *temporales* where
they plant corn, pumpkins, melons etc.'

The surveyor was unusually observant. Many other travellers had dismissed the Papago as nomads. Explorers in the
Great American Desert beyond the Mississippi saw what they
wanted to see – and they wanted to see a wild untamed
landscape where only the most rude and primitive existence
was possible. They wanted an empty canvas for their own
heroic exploits. They certainly did not want to discover
people with a markedly superior ability to live in the hostile
environment to their own.

By the 1890s, the invaders had penned the Papago within
the San Xavier reservation, west of Tucson, where they
farmed about 4,000 hectares. The first written record of the
Papagos' basic method of irrigation does not appear until
1917, when a man called Clotts wrote that 'they have a very
ingenious plan of throwing out long dykes or wings, which
converge on a few acres like the sides of a funnel. Thus the
rainfall from hundreds of acres is diverted into a pocket of a

few acres where the soil is suitable for cultivation.' The Papago were practising one of the oldest arts of water management – the harvesting of rainfall. They left mile upon mile of low walls across the desert. Yet the new Americans rode back and forth across the land without noticing, let alone understanding, the purpose of the structures in front of them.

By 1954, the botanist Edgar Anderson was in no doubt that the desert agriculture of the Papago Indians was 'one of the most remarkable agricultural systems in the world', but by then it was largely history. The walls were derelict and the former fields dotted with houses and schools and chapels and cotton fields irrigated by deep wells sunk into the aquifer beneath the desert.

All is not lost for the Papago farmers. They have been allocated large amounts of water from the Central Arizona Project. The $4 billion aqueduct brings water to Phoenix and Tucson from the River Colorado on the other side of the state. It extends several tens of kilometres beyond Tucson to the Papago reservation, thanks to a series of legal judgments in favour of the claims to water of the Indian nations of the American West. But it is hardly a triumph of the modern world to first force the Papago to give up harvesting rainwater on their own land, and then to spend billions of dollars bringing them water that fell as snow a thousand kilometres away on the mountains of Colorado and Wyoming.

All across the arid American West there are the remains of once-flourishing agricultural civilisations. The sprawling metropolis of Phoenix is built on the remains of the Hohokam Indian nation, which diverted the waters of the Salt River to irrigate its fields. In the far north of Arizona – over the ridge from the Navajo Generating Station, the hydroelectric power-house of the Glen Canyon Dam in the Colorado canyons – the Hopi Indians still cultivate fertile valley soils. They created the soil for themselves by building low walls that capture the water and silt rushing out of gullies in the surrounding hills. Before the arrival of the Spaniards in the sixteenth century, the Navajo ruled across much of the southwest. The name, given to them by the invaders, means 'great planted fields'. And from before them, on the Colorado Plateau, the Amasazi people have left behind dams and terraces where they once captured water to grow crops that fed a substantial civilisation.

The more that archaeologists become attuned to the possibilities of water management in the world's arid landscapes, the more examples they find. The greatest dam of the ancient world was the Marib Dam on the Wadi Dhana in Yemen, built around 800 BC. Seven hundred metres long and as high as a four-storey house, it captured water from flash floods in an area the size of Yorkshire, and operated for 1,300 years until washed away in a flood. After a good flood, 100 square kilometres of fields could be covered with water to a height of 60 centimetres, leaving behind a layer of silt a centimetre thick. The dam sustained the Sabean civilisation. Once, when the dam collapsed, the Sabeans assembled 20,000 people and 14,000 camels from all over Arabia to rebuild it. The ultimate failure of the dam meant the end of their civilisation.

Such spectacular projects win the plaudits of modern engineers. But in reality it is thousands of smaller structures that predominate in the desert. Some of the most remarkable discoveries about the ancient cultivation of deserts come from the Negev Desert, which stretches from Sinai in Egypt, across southern Israel to Jordan.

Today, the state of Israel makes part of the desert bloom by bringing water south from the Sea of Galilee. On the once-barren hillsides around the desert boom town of Beersheva, there are citrus groves and long lines of avocado and pomegranate trees. But if you drive on into the desert, past the desert research institute at Sede Boker and the tomb of David Ben Gurion, the founder of the nation whose dream it was to make the deserts bloom, you discover that ancient desert dwellers, the Nabateans, first made the desert here green around 2,000 years ago.

The Nabatean kings may have been the three kings of the Nativity story. Establishing their kingdom in the Negev Desert in the first century BC, they controlled the caravan trade routes from Arabia to the Mediterranean ports, trafficking in frankincense and myrrh. The kingdom's six imposing desert cities –

including Petra, Shivta and Avdat – were models of how to live in the desert without the benefit of a water pipeline.

The ruins of each of these cities has a complex network of gutters and drains that feed every drop of water landing within its walls into pools and cisterns dug into the rock. The cities also contain the remains of oil and wine presses and wheat mills. But where did they get these crops in the desert? Below the ramparts of Avdat, in the valley bottom, are a series of stone-walled fields shining green in the desert. This is an ancient Nabatean farm excavated and renovated in the 1970s by an Israeli archaeologist from the Hebrew University in Jerusalem, Michael Evenari. When I paid a spring visit to the Avdat desert farm, they hadn't had rain for six weeks, but the soil was damp, a field of wheat was growing fast, almond trees were in leaf and pistachio trees would follow any day. 'We have tried to grow the crops mentioned in the Bible,' said research scientist Pedro Berliner. 'And most of them will grow here in the desert.'

The secret of the Nabateans' agricultural success is capturing rainfall. Above the farm, six lines of stone walls, each about half a metre high, wind round the next hill. They collect occasional rain as it falls off the slopes and divert it to the fields. The story is the same at Shivta, where the ruins of the Nabatean city and the lush grass and fig trees on its renovated farm may soon be overshadowed by a nuclear power station. Ironically, one of the station's prime tasks will be to provide electricity to keep in operation the pumps of the Israeli water grid, which takes a fifth of the nation's electricity.

As Berliner took me round his blooming farm, Israel was facing a water crisis; the pipeline from the Sea of Galilee was shut and orchards everywhere had been told to face heavy price increases for water, plus a 70 per cent cut in supply. 'Until now, our pistachio nuts have not been economically viable,' said Berliner, 'but as water prices rise for modern farms out here in the desert, this kind of run-off farming is going to look increasingly attractive.'

Researchers from round the world marvel at what the Israelis have recreated in the desert. Its example has helped successful rain-capturing projects in several African countries.

But the Bedouin couple driving their goats along the hillside past the Avdat farm are not so impressed. The farm was once their land and without the scientific fanfare, they too farm the ancient Nabatean fields of the upper part of the wadi. The water collected by many of the stone conduits passes over their fields before reaching the Israelis' farm.

Berliner and his colleagues curse their neighbours. 'They have no right to be here. This is government land – and they take our water. We are trying to stop them farming,' he told me. This attitude seemed odd for a scientist. He showed no interest in how the Bedouin farm. But in Israel, science is political, and most political of all is the science behind the nation's founding vision, that it can turn the 'desert' of Palestine into a garden.

The Bedouin have been farming in the valley outside Avdat since long before the Israelis arrived. Their crops are not so attractive commercially – just a few acres of fodder to supplement their goats' meagre diet of desert grasses. But perhaps, for all the Israeli claims to have rediscovered the Nabatean farms, these fields never were totally abandoned, or their secrets forgotten.

Once stone walls are pointed out to you in the Negev, you spot them everywhere. The desert is marked by long lines of rocks, hugging the contours of hillsides and spanning wadis. Some of the walls, says Arie Issar, head of hydrology at the Institute for Desert Research, once took water to farms. Some still do, ensuring that small patches of green barley survive as emergency pasture for the Bedouin herds, even in the driest years. Typically, 20 hectares of hillside can provide enough water for one hectare of fields. Other lines of walls fill cisterns, caverns dug into the chalk hillsides to provide drinking water for flocks of sheep and goats, as well as for their shepherds.

Yehuda Nevo, an Arabist at the Institute for Desert Research, says the cisterns were the basis of survival in the Negev a thousand years before the Nabateans built their cities, and right up until the present. 'There are hundreds, maybe thousands, of cisterns in the Negev,' he says. The Bedouin continue to clean and use them, even though conduits are often allowed to silt up and some cisterns are filled from water trucks. 'There are no drinking water problems anywhere in the Negev.'

The Israelis are not alone in their failure to appreciate the ancient ways of water in the desert. Nor are stone walls the only invisible technology. One of the most extraordinary devices for capturing water in the desert is the *qanat*. Seen from the air, the *qanats* look like a series of large mole-hills arranged at regular intervals down a mountainside. And that is roughly what they are, except that the moles who dug the long underground tunnels and vertical shafts to the surface are human. In Iran, the home of the *qanat*, they call these human moles *mughani*. They are a close-knit caste of people who for more than 2,000 years have dug and maintained their tunnels, some tens of kilometres long, deep into the hills.

Qanats are on an altogether grander scale than the spring tunnels of Palestine. Tunnel lengths are measured in kilometres, not metres. They underpinned the grandeur of the great Persian empires of old, and even today the *mughani* can claim much of the credit for Iran's healthy agricultural industry. Until the middle of this century, *qanats* supplied three-quarters of the water in Iran. More than peacock thrones or mullahs, the *mughani* made Iran.

The interior of Iran is mountainous, snow-covered in winter but blistering hot in summer. Rainfall is scarce, mostly falling on high mountain slopes and running down short streams before disappearing into huge 'fans' of alluvium that skirt the mountains, and collecting in underground layers of gravel. So ancient Iranians dug for water, chasing signs of seepage back ever further into the hillside.

Qanats are gently-sloping horizontal tunnels that slant through the alluvial fans to the water-containing gravel beds beneath. The gradient may be little more than one in a thousand and the tunnels sometimes have to be 10 kilometres long to reach a reliable source of water. All are dug with simple hand tools.

It is engineering on a heroic scale. There are around 40,000 *qanats* in Iran, enough to pass 20 times right through the centre of the Earth. Perhaps half were still in operation within the past 20 years. The earth moved and the sweat and lives expended in their creation is hundreds of times greater than in the construction of the pyramids of Egypt. But, being buried deep underground and with the name of no great king as their regal architect, they have been ignored by archaeologists and tourists alike.

Most *qanats* gush their water at all hours in all seasons to the gardens of mountain villages. But they can equally well serve whole towns. Details of their current use are sketchy, but before the revolution of the Ayatolla Khomeini, around 400 *qanats* supplied the central Iranian town of Yezd, where some extended 50 kilometres into the hillside. Water for Isfahan, a city of more than a million people, arrived through a tunnel more than 80 kilometres long. Teheran, the capital, was supplied from three dozen large tunnels and more than a hundred smaller ones. One gushed its water into the grounds of the British Embassy. The water was once prized by the British community in Teheran, to whom it was delivered on horse-drawn cart.

Wherever the empire of the Ancient Persians expanded between 500 BC and AD 600, there are *qanats*. They pepper the landscape of southern Afghanistan, western Pakistan and western China (where they are known as *karez*), and the war-racked Kurdish lands of Iraq. Egyptians once used them to collect water from deep in the sandstones of the Western Desert. They are the 'unfailing springs' of legend in Oman. After Arabs conquered Iran in the seventh century, they took *qanats* to Cyprus, Morocco, northern India and as far as Spain, where they once helped water Moorish Madrid. Spanish explorers even took them to northern Chile, where there are 15 tunnels among the nitrate mines of the Atacama Desert.

Qanat is a Semitic word meaning 'to dig' and probably has the same origin as the word canal. *Qanats* are also called 'chains of wells' because of the vertical shafts that penetrate the main tunnel from the surface about every 50 metres along their length. The shafts provide a route for the removal of excavated earth, as well as access and ventilation for digging and repairs. One giant tunnel dug 500 years ago near Gonabad has a well more than 300 metres deep.

Qanats require constant repair to remove falls of soil inside the tunnels. As late as the 1950s, one in seven of the population in some areas of Iran were *qanat* diggers. But, despite efforts by Islamic fundamentalists to revive their craft during the 1980s, the *mughani* are today a disappearing band of village underdogs. Many abandoned their tunnels in the 1950s after land reforms released them from their duties to local tribal chieftains. Those *mughani* that continue their ancient underground craft are in constant fear of pockets of bad air that may suffocate them, of a sudden rush of water or of cave-ins. Arie Issar, the Israeli hydrologist, worked in Iran repairing *qanats* after an earthquake in the early 1960s. He described the perils thus:

> To the foreigner working in Iran, the lack of precautionary measures, as well as the fatalistic approach of the diggers to loss of life is shocking, especially in regions where the composition of the soil makes the likelihood of a collapse greater. In such regions, they have boys to help them carry the excavated material from the tunnel, thus its diameter can be kept to a minimum. In one area in central Iran where there was a high risk of accidents, the *mughani* worked in their burial clothes, so that if the tunnel collapsed on them their comrades did not have to dig them out and wash and dress them in order to give them a proper burial.

Whatever the horrors, the *qanats* provided the water for millennia of successful farming in a hostile environment. They survived into the present century without either loss of flow or visible damage to their environment because, says the German hydrologist Gunter Garbrecht, 'they tap the groundwater potential only up to and never beyond the limits of natural replenishment. They are self-regulating and do not unbalance the hydrological and ecological equilibrium of the region.'

Even so, when foreign civil engineers arrived in Iran in the 1950s to advise the newly installed Shah on the future of his country, they barely noticed these 'unfailing springs'. The British engineer Henry Olivier dismissed *qanats* in a single sentence in his memoirs. They looked like 'bomb craters' from the air, he said, and mentioned being in a light plane that crashed into one. They had no place in his prescription for creating a new water supply for Teheran, a city traditionally dependent on *qanats*.

Since the 1950s, modern Iran has adopted petrol-driven pumps, which can raise more water than *qanats* ever did. But, unlike the *qanats*, the pumps have no built-in self-regulation. Unless prevented by the authorities, farmers 'mine' underground water, taking more water than is replenished by rainfall. As a result, water-tables beneath the *qanats* fall and the tunnels dry out.

Peter Beaumont, a British geographer, watched 50 *qanats*, a fifth of the total, dry out on the plain around Teheran within six years in the 1960s as mechanised pumps and dams in the hills dried out the aquifer. He warns that: 'A traditional system of irrigation in balance with the environment will go out of existence, replaced by a modern system which will prove easy to abuse.' Garbrecht adds: 'Sooner or later, the water potential will become exhausted and the agriculture and economy will fall back to its original level.'

By contrast, in western China, in the province of Xinjiang, 2,000-year-old *qanats* (known there as the *karez*) are undergoing a revival. There are more than a thousand *karez*, with a total length of more than 5,000 kilometres, providing a third of the region's water supply.

In Iran, *qanats* have fallen out of favour partly because of the danger of the work involved: 'It's slave labour,' one Middle Eastern water engineer told me. But need it be that way? Smaller tunnels may be narrow and perilous, but in many larger *qanats*, the *mughani* and their equivalents in other countries have developed relatively safe and bearable methods of tunnelling. It is no worse than coal mining, and the boring could be mechanised. One estimate made in the early 1980s put the commercial cost for a civil engineering firm to dig a new *qanat* eight kilometres long at around a million US dollars, and concluded: 'At that price, the *qanat* would be paid for in some 30 years.'

Issar's compromise, when he visited Iran to help with

earthquake relief efforts, was to encourage villagers to renovate the well shafts of their *qanats*, and then to insert motor-
pumps in them to bring out the water. New well/*qanat*
hybrids have been dug in this way, with the shaft dug first and
tunnel galleries excavated for a few hundred yards to raise
water output. Having seen ancient *qanats* in cliffs south of the
Dead Sea, Issar also dreams of developing mechanised systems
of *qanat*-digging beneath the Negev. The desert's huge stocks
of underground water are currently uneconomic to exploit.
But modern mining technology, using machines rather than
mughani to drive the long tunnels into the rock and bore
shafts could revive the technology.

Mexico City is today the largest metropolis in the world, with
a population exceeding 20 million. Its squatter slums sprawl
across the dried-out beds of lakes that once filled the Valley of
Mexico, a landlocked basin in the middle of the country.
These lakes were once home to *chinampas*, floating gardens,
a 2,000-year-old system of farming that remains one of the
most productive in the western hemisphere. The city is now in
the process of engulfing the last of these lakes, Lake Xochimilco, and with it the valley's last, still flourishing, floating
gardens.

Five hundred years ago, the *chinampas* of the Valley of
Mexico fed the Aztecs when their capital, Tenochtitlan, was
probably the largest city in the world. Before the Aztecs, the
floating gardens fed the Mayans. And before the Mayans,
2,000 years ago, they sustained the vast pyramid city of Teotihuacan, whose pottery remains have been found in the mud of
Xochimilco. When Hernan Cortés arrived in Mexico in 1519,
he found a quarter of the Valley of Mexico covered in a series
of vast shallow lakes each summer. The Aztecs called the
valley the Lake of the Moon. Within one lake, Texcoco, stood
an island containing the Aztec capital.

The Spaniards described the Aztec capital as another
Venice, a city of tens of thousands of canoes and crossed by
myriad canals. Around it were tens of thousands of 'tillers
who dwelt in the middle of the swamps'. They lived in houses
made of reeds and branches, which were built on artificial

land made of similar materials. These tillers, called *chinamperos*, had turned the shallow lakes into a patchwork of floating gardens, each around 100 metres long and perhaps 10 metres wide, surrounded by waterways. A few years after Cortes's arrival, a missionary, Father Acosta, described how 'gardens that moved on the water have been built by piling earth on sedges and reeds . . . and on these gardens they plant and cultivate, and plants grow and ripen, and they tow these gardens from one place to another.'

Today, most of the lakes have been drained. Texcoco is a remnant fetid pond between the city's largest squatter colony and its international airport. But, to the south, Lake Xochimilco, though only a sixth of its former size, survives as a living museum of how the valley's great civilisations once fed themselves.

Properly maintained, floating gardens produce six or seven crops a year and remain fertile for centuries, until they are towed away and replaced. To keep them fertile, the *chinamperos* paddle down the waterways in their narrow flat-bottom boats before each planting season, scooping mud from the lake bottom on to the gardens with buckets attached to the end of long poles – looking for all the world like students on a lazy afternoon's punt down the river. Other sources of manure once included human night soil and bat manure, collected by Indians from caves and brought to the city in mule trains.

The gardens are stocked from seed beds with beans, maize, tomatoes, peppers, a local grain called amaranth and, since the arrival of the Spaniards, European vegetables such as cabbages and onions. They now also grow flowers, such as marigolds and Mexico's national flower, the dahlia, for tourists.

When not tending their plots, the natives of this extraordinarily productive environment could once spear carp and salamanders, which were prized for their tender meat, in the canals – that was until about 1950, when pollution from Mexico City began to kill the fish. But despite the pollution and the urban encroachment, which have reduced the floating gardens of Xochimilco to 200 hectares, the *chinampas* are still hugely fertile, producing a significant proportion of the city's vegetables.

For many years, the fecundity of the *chinampas* was regarded as a unique phenomenon in the Americas. But the continent was far from being a backwater before Columbus set foot on the shores of what he christened the 'New World'. The Americas had approaching a third of the world's population, as many as lived in China and certainly more than in Europe. Many places supported more people than they do today, and South America in particular has yet to recapture the agricultural productivity that it enjoyed before Europe's barbarians set foot there.

In the Andes, the Incas and others had created magnificent systems of stone-walled terraces that covered some one million hectares in the steep valley sides of Peru. Today more than half of these terraces lie abandoned. The Chimu empire in the northern coastal desert of Peru constructed hundreds of irrigation canals and underground conduits bringing water from the Andes. Its hydraulic engineers fought for several centuries to maintain the gradients of these canals as movements in the Andes tilted their plain, cutting off the canals from the Moche River. That land too now lies waste, but other canal systems still water fields.

Archaeologists have praised the prowess of the empires that left behind great monuments: the Chimus' headquarters at Chan-Chan, Teotihuacan in the Valley of Mexico, the Incas' lost city of Macchu Picchu. The monuments of these 'empires of the sun' resembled those of the early civilisations of the Old World. But the researchers missed the even larger earth works, systems of raised fields that transformed huge areas of waterlogged pampas into farms that sustained the great majority of the 100 million or so inhabitants of the Americas.

Like the stone walls of the North American Desert, the raised fields of South America remained invisible to outsiders for almost five centuries until 1960. That year, oil prospectors took their swamp buggies out across the *llanos* de Mojos in remote northeastern Bolivia, a grassy lowland, cowboy country across which several tributaries of the River Amazon flooded each year. What the oil men thought was a flat plain turned out to be corrugated, an endless landscape of shallow ridges that gave the buggies a distinctly bumpy ride. The ridges, each no more than a metre high, cover 200 square kilometres. Raised a little higher are 1,500 kilometres of causeways and what could be burial mounds and villages.

Local Indian peoples dug the ridges perhaps 2,000 years ago to create drained soils on which to grow their crops. Several hundred thousand people probably once lived on land that now has many times more cattle than people. The fields, canals, causeways, dykes and artificial lakes, the remains of a once-thriving technology, now lie abandoned. These ancient people had engineered their landscape in a way that leaves modern researchers gasping.

Once identified, raised fields have cropped up everywhere. In Ecuador you can see them over the river from Guayaquil international airport. A few are still cultivated, with rice grown in the ditches and maize on the ridges. There are more on ancient beaches along the coastline of Surinam. In northern Colombia there is a flat low-lying basin near the town of San Marcos that floods for half the year. 'When the waters retreat, the grass appears as stripes for several weeks, with the ridges brown and the ditches bright green,' says Clark Erickson of the University of Pennsylvania, who has spent several years uncovering raised fields. He says there could be many more sites all over South America – in the Pantanal, the great wetland of southern Brazil, or even within the Amazon rain-forest, where researchers are beginning to uncover highly sophisticated farming systems. Small versions have been uncovered in North America around Lake Michigan and in Indiana. Many more have been ploughed up in the Mississippi valley.

The most intensively studied raised fields are not on the lowlands but on the shores of Lake Titicaca, in the cold *altiplano* of southern Peru. 'To the contemporary agrono-mist,' says Erickson, 'the *altiplano* is a marginal landscape for agriculture. The soils are heavy and waterlogged on the plains and thin and poor on the steep slopes. Killing frosts, severe droughts and heavy flooding are frequent. Crops generally have a low productivity.' Yet this is probably where the potato was first cultivated. And sometime about 3,000 years ago, lakeside communities of Aymara and Quechua Indians laboriously began digging long ditches and piling the earth into ridges across at least 800 square kilometres of the plain.

The whole system appears to have been abandoned around AD 300, but rebuilt between 1000 and 1450. Today, the Quechua tending their cattle on the plains call the ridges *waru waru*. Some say the ridges were left behind by some 'first race' who ruled the area before the Incas. At the beginning of the 1980s, the Quechua agreed to take part in an audacious experiment to redig a series of ditches across the marshes, using traditional tools. By 1990, they had drained more than 100 hectares of marsh and planted the ridges with Andean potatoes and grains, which they have farmed as their ancestors once must have done.

The results were spectacular. The fields raised crops clear of ground frosts, kept salt at bay and, like the *chinampas* of Mexico, created fertiliser in the form of mud and algae that grew in the ditches each summer. During the severe drought of 1982–3, they produced crops when nearby conventionally managed fields failed. Three years later, when there was massive flooding on neighbouring fields, the ridges kept plants dry. In more typical years, yields of potatoes are 10 tonnes per hectare – three times the yield of neighbouring farms. As a bonus, the farmers found that the ditches attracted fish, birds and turtles for the pot.

Erickson has a photograph of the 30 Quechua farmers and their families who dug the ridges. Grinning beneath headgear ranging from baseball caps to traditional wide-brimmed Andean hats, they brandished the tools of their new trade, including the *rawkana*, a short-handled stone hoe, the *waqtana*, which looks like the shaft of a primitive plough, and the *chakitaqila* or footplough. So successful was Erickson's experiment that local churches and political parties now want to include raised fields in their aid projects. One party constructed a large block of fields in the shape of its logo.

South America is a depopulated landscape today. But prehistorically, it was a land of terraced hillsides, corrugated lowlands and floating gardens that supported great civilisations.

Today it is Peru and Bolivia, the countries with some of the most impressive abandoned agricultural and hydrological remains, that have the worst problems of poverty and under-development.

Erickson pleads for his lessons from the past to be adopted widely. Yields on his Peruvian farms could theoretically allow 1.5 million people to live in the Lake Titicaca basin, many times its current population. The revival of thousands of raised fields could provide farmers all over South America with a good living growing cash crops as well as staple foods, in a region where several ambitious projects to import Western farming methods and genetically 'improved' crops have failed.

PART II

Transformations

6

IRRIGATING INDIA

There are old habits and old prepossessions, old methods and old means to be contended with.

John Colvin, Lieutenant-Governor of the Northwestern Provinces, inaugurating the Ganges Canal, 1854

Arthur Cotton sailed for Madras, the capital of the south India state of Tamil Nadu, in 1819. He was aged sixteen, had completed an induction in engineering at the East India Company's college outside Croydon, and was destined to become imperial India's foremost irrigation engineer. In old age, he remembered:

> When I first arrived in India, the contempt with which the natives justly spoke of us was very striking; they used to say we were a kind of civilised savages, wonderfully expert about fighting, but so inferior to their great men that we would not even keep in repair the works they had constructed, much less even imitate them ... There are multitudes of old works in India [which] show both boldness and engineering talent. They have stood for hundreds of years.

Much of India was irrigated from tanks, shallow mud-walled reservoirs in valley bottoms that captured the monsoon rains each summer. Around Cotton's new home in Madras, the state of Tamil Nadu had the densest assembly of tanks in a land full of them. Cotton found more than 30,000 tanks. Most were small, covering a hectare or so and irrigating perhaps 20 hectares of paddy. But the largest covered 100 square kilometres and had more than 20 kilometres of embankments.

Taken together, they covered several per cent of the land surface.

Tanks date back to the earliest flowering of civilisation in the Indian subcontinent. Large tanks, employing sophisticated methods of water control, were an early feature of life from the far south to the banks of the Ganges in northern India, where archaeologists have uncovered a huge brick-lined structure dating back 2,700 years that passes river water through settling tanks to remove silt before collecting clean water at its base. In southern India, as in Sri Lanka, a dense patchwork of small, independent village tanks and irrigation systems was overlain by a network of great reservoirs, to feed imperial cities, armies and parks.

While the British largely ignored the village tanks and irrigation channels, they were full of admiration for the great canals and weirs built by previous rulers of the land. Some of the earliest and most successful British feats of water engineering in India were the renovations of such ancient waterworks. Thus Arthur Cotton rebuilt the Cauvery Anicut, a 300-metre-long weir that had zigzagged across the shifting mud-flats of the delta of the River Cauvery south of Madras for 1,800 years. It was the central feature of an irrigation network that, though largely silted up by the nineteenth century, had once watered some 2,500 square kilometres of the coastal plain.

Cotton found that European engineers did not know how to hold the new weir fast on the sandy delta. He said later that 'it was from the [native Indians] we learnt how to secure a foundation in loose sand of unmeasured depth. In fact, what we learned from them made the difference between financial success and failure. With this lesson about foundations, we built bridges, weirs, aqueducts and every kind of hydraulic work.' This ancient expertise, as old as the aqueducts of Rome, turned his team of imperial engineers into the creators of what he boasted were 'the greatest financial successes of any engineering works in the world. We are thus deeply indebted to the native engineers.' However, in later years, Cotton appeared to forget this early lesson. Once he had finished renovating old works and begun to build his own,

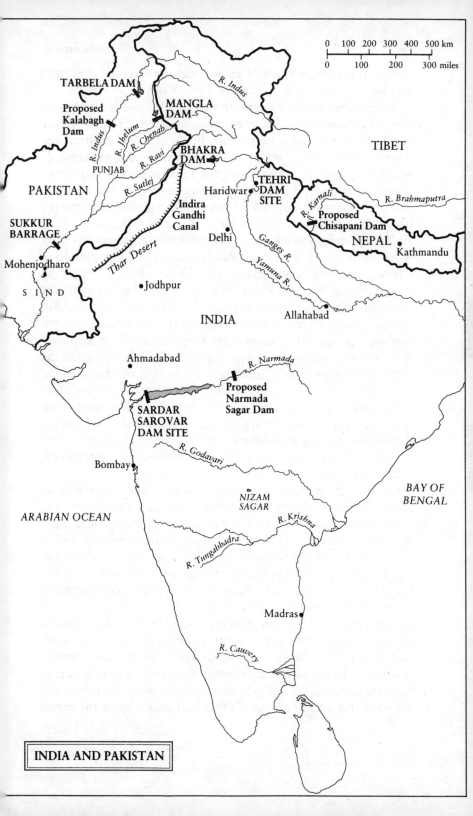

INDIA AND PAKISTAN

disasters overtook him and he became responsible for most of the biggest irrigation failures in British India.

British engineers also rebuilt the canals of the great plain of the River Ganges and its smaller cousin the Yamuna, in the shadow of the Himalayas. Until the fourteenth century, the entire Ganges plain was covered in forests. Tigers harassed wayfarers on what is today one of the most densely populated areas on the planet. Then the Mogul emperor Feroze Shah Tughlaq began to clear the forests and dig what became the largest network of canals in India.

Two hundred years later, Emperor Shah Jehan, the man who built the Taj Mahal at Agra, extended the canals to Delhi, where he was constructing the Red Fort overlooking the Yamuna. It is not clear how much of Jehan's canal was built for irrigation, since villagers in the plain had dug hundreds of wells to reach abundant underground water. But the British described the extension to Delhi as 'for the adornment of his palace and gardens and to supply the inhabitants of the city'. Shah Jehan built a second canal on the east bank of the Yamuna to water his hunting lodges and palace gardens. The east-bank canal silted up within a few years and the west-bank canal, plagued by waterlogging, was abandoned a few decades before the British arrived on the plain.

From the 1820s, the British set about restoring the canals, learning the ancient skills and codifying them until they reckoned they knew more about what made a successful irrigation canal than any engineers on Earth. They learnt how too steep a gradient caused the water to run out of control, scouring the canal bed and eating away at banks and bridges. And they learnt that if the slope were too shallow, the muddy rivers would fill the canals with silt. In the process, says the technology historian Daniel Headrick, 'they laid the foundations of modern hydraulic engineering'.

But again, when they started to build from scratch, things began to go wrong. The first canal the British built for themselves was the Ganges Canal, designed by Proby Cautley, a self-taught engineer. It irrigated the Doab, a long corridor of fertile land about 100 kilometres wide between the Ganges and Yamuna rivers. The canal took almost the entire dry-season flow from the Ganges at Haridwar, where the holy river emerges from the Himalayas. At its opening in 1854, it was the largest canal system anywhere in the world with more than 1,300 kilometres of waterways, built at a cost of £2 million, largely by coolies carrying soil in baskets on their backs.

The canal was a model of Victorian engineering: grand, beneficent and imposing. It had gardens of mango trees and ghats for religious bathing at every bridge. It leapt across the River Solani at Roorkee on a giant masonry aqueduct with 50 spans each of 50 feet – again, the largest in the world. And it was here at the foot of the aqueduct that an audience of 50,000, made up of the British Indian aristocracy and the peasants of the plain, gathered one April day in the sweltering pre-monsoon heat, to hear the opening ceremony conducted by the Lieutenant Governor of the Northwest Provinces, John Colvin.

Colvin's speech was also a Victorian epic of bombast, thoughtfully translated into several local languages and handed out to the peasants. Despite the evidence round him of a huge local population who for hundreds of years had tended their bullocks and raised water from their wells, Colvin explained that, owing to the canal, 'great tracts of country once desert and without inhabitants are now filled with people'.

Colvin explained to the multitudes at the canal's inauguration that it would prevent a recurrence of the great famines of 1837 and 1838. Nobody knew how many people had died then but, he told them, it 'caused government a direct loss in money spent and revenue remitted exceeding one *crore* (10 million) rupees. No government can endure a repetition of such sacrifices.' But seven years later, after the 1860–1 famine, the official report found that the Ganges Canal had been of little use in protecting the people of the area.

There were two reasons. The entire system had been built on too steep a gradient, causing flooding in the wet season and, worse, dry canals when water was needed most, when flows in the river were low. And, despite the threat of famine, the British had encouraged farmers to replace some of their traditional food crops, such as millet, with cash crops – wheat, cotton, sugar cane and indigo – that were in strong demand back in Britain.

Trade between India and the rest of the empire grew fast after the completion of the Suez Canal in 1870. From then on, says the environmental historian Donald Worster, 'India began exporting its wheat to England via the canal, sending food that had once been stored against times of scarcity and hunger.' Scandalously, during the next famine years of 1876–7, India exported record quantities of grain to its European markets.

Colvin had boasted that: 'There are old habits and old prepossessions, old methods and old means to be contended with, but these have in some measure even now melted away beneath the influence of European science, wisely and considerately displayed.' But it was unclear whether the new colonial habits and prepossessions, methods and means, were serving India better than the old.

Perhaps the most misplaced of Colvin's promises to the peasant farmers along the Ganges Canal was that it would 'remove those unsightly swampy tracts of land . . . to drain all of these and so purify the air they now taint – to fill their basin with a rich cultivation'. In practice, far from helping to drain the land, the canals played havoc with natural drainage. They overflowed, leaked water into the soil and cut off gulleys that had carried away the monsoon rains. Through the 1870s, fields became quagmires.

Where the canals went, and where waterlogging was worst, mosquitoes gathered, and fever was rife during the years of heaviest floods. Malaria was endemic in India then, as now. But the local sanitary commissioner reported a 'general and intense' level of fever along the tracks of the Ganges and Yamuna canals, which were 'very much' to blame. Annual death rates among peasants along the canals exceeded one in ten in the worst years, such as 1879. That year, the sanitary commissioner reported that fuel for crematoria had run out, and there were no able-bodied people to tend the fields. Travellers recorded very few children about – partly because they died in greatest numbers, and partly because impotence is a side-effect of malaria among men. For a decade, more than three-quarters of all deaths were from fever.

At Kosi, fever cut the population from 12,000 to 7,000 in the two decades following the arrival of the canal. It was as bad in Meerut. Once described as 'the healthiest station in the provinces' before the canal came, by the 1870s government officials reported that there were no farmers fit to harvest the fields, and they seriously considered abandoning it. To doctors, the malaria came as no surprise. In the 1840s, a medical committee had warned that the Ganges Canal should go ahead only if the land around it was properly drained.

Eventually, most of the drainage problems were alleviated. But were such sacrifices justified? The colonial authorities gained a financial return and so, presumably, were satisfied. But there has been little serious research into the overall effects of the British irrigation projects along the Ganges. Detractors, such as Nirmal Sengupta of the Madras Institute of Development Studies, have pointed to the serious effects of waterlogging. Besides the malaria, they suggest that rising water-tables undermined and destroyed thousands of wells, the traditional water supply for irrigated fields in the area. And the switch to cash crops increased vulnerability to famine. A tried and tested farming system, in tune with local needs and customs, was jettisoned in order to grow crops for the empire.

But a counter-attack has been launched by, among others, Ian Stone of Sunderland Polytechnic who, in a thorough study of *Canal Irrigation in British India*, tried to draw up a balance sheet. The malaria was appalling, he says, but the water-logging was sorted out. Most wells were not destroyed. People rushed to take the new canal's water because it was cheap, probably as reliable as their old wells, increased their credit worthiness at banks, and raised their potential income from cash crops such as sugar cane. Small farmers were squeezed out, and turned into farm labourers, but he concludes that: 'The water trickling into the fields was as tangible as any of the Western innovations which filtered down to village level – and more tangible and more pervasive than most.'

Win or lose, the imperial irrigation engineers had moved on to their biggest prize. The Punjab is a broad flat alluvial plain formed by five rivers – the Indus, Jhelum, Chenab, Ravi and Sutlej – as they cascade out of the Himalayas. The rivers, which coalesce to form the main stem of the Indus, flow west to the Arabian Sea.

When the British surveyed the Indus valley in the nineteenth century, they saw a near-replica of the Nile. The climate was much drier than the Ganges plain, but the annual snowmelt in the Himalayas provided summer floods to cover fields with silty water and wash away salt. Inundation canals dug 5,000 years before during the Harappa civilisation had been extended and improved by the Moguls. But the British decided that they could do better, providing year-round irrigation that could grow two or even three crops each year.

As ever, the British, while dreaming of imperial splendour, seemed to be driven more by the prospect of immediate fiscal gain. The canal builders had to pay their way, by supplying water to create a granary out of the Punjab and so to provide instant tax revenues. They built weirs and barrages across the great river and its tributaries, first in the Punjab and then, much later, further south in the white-hot desert of the Sind. They extended long canals across the flat arid plain, which stretches unbroken for 1,600 kilometres from the Himalayas to the Arabian Sea, and eventually created the largest continuously irrigated area of land on Earth. Out of a 'gloomy wasteland' without towns, villages or roads and peopled only by 'disputatious nomads who made a living by cattle-thieving', wrote James Morris in *Pax Britannica*, 'the British created a new country'.

Colonisation by handpicked farmers, many of them from the Ganges region, was far from smooth. Besides facing nomads, angry at the theft of their land, the early colonists often lacked sufficient water for their taps. Cholera struck more than once. The turning point came in 1892, with the construction of the Lower Chenab Canal, which carried six times the flow of the River Thames and irrigated around 10,000 square kilometres. Soon after came the Triple Canal Project, an ingenious scheme built between 1905 and 1917, which linked by canal the waters of the Chenab, Jhelum and Ravi to allow extra irrigation of land further south in the driest lands.

The water was brought to the land; then the people were brought to the water. Administrators handed out land in small squares – 11 hectares each in the Lower Chenab colony, for instance. At regular intervals along the canals there were villages, and then market towns. At its heart was the new city of Lyallpur (named after the local governor, and today called Faisalabad), which was laid out in the pattern of a Union Jack.

No Stalinist social engineer could have ordered things more tidily, though the British added their own element. There were three clearly delineated classes of people among the settlers: peasants, whose small plots predominated, then yeomen and finally gentry, who got bigger plots and were expected to be natural leaders. The British allocated each neighbourhood to a particular religious group: Sikhs, Muslims or whatever. The colonies' planners instructed farmers in the planting of wheat, cotton and sugar cane and at Lyallpur they constructed what remains one of the largest agricultural colleges in Asia.

But many of the lessons from the Ganges Canal had not been learned. The project had aimed to irrigate as many acres as possible, to maximise tax revenues. By spreading water thinly across land, this maximised the risks of seepage from canals, waterlogging and salt accumulation. Yet they dug no drains to carry away excess irrigation water. Sure enough by 1908, just 16 years after opening, the Lower Chenab colony was reporting newly waterlogged soils, and widespread salinisation has followed.

Later, it was claimed that the Punjab public works department had all along intended to carry out drainage works. But it never did and, in truth, according to historians of the colonies such as Aloys Michel, there was a strong 'anti-drainage lobby' inside the department. Certainly the overriding obligation of engineers to make money from the colonies led to a very short-term view of a long-term problem, and allowed no spare cash for drainage construction.

Nevertheless, despite feuding, engineering setbacks and a

host of hostages to ecological fortune established for the post-independence era, the extraordinary British drive to irrigate India did produce results. They spent as much money on canals as they did on railways and ended their rule with more than 100,000 kilometres of canals cut and more land under irrigation than there is land in the whole of England. In the space of a hundred years, they had matched irrigated acreage from traditional techniques such as tanks. When they left, one in every eight irrigated fields round the world was in India.

7

THE GIFT OF THE NILE

One day, every last drop of water which drains into the whole valley of the Nile ... shall be equally and amicably divided among the river people, and the Nile itself, flowing for 3,000 miles through smiling countries, shall perish gloriously and never reach the sea.

Winston Churchill, after a military campaign on the Nile with General Kitchener, 1908

Mohammed Ali was a small-time Macedonian tobacco merchant when in 1799 he was press-ganged by the Turkish Sultan in Constantinople to join forces attempting to repulse a French invasion of Egypt, which was under nominal control of the Sultan. His small detachment was repulsed before it landed on African soil, but four years later, he returned to Egypt with a band of Albanian mercenaries. They marauded through the land, which was by now abandoned by the French and disintegrating into chaos. He gathered adventurers and fighting men as he went, and, after two years, was proclaimed viceroy of Egypt by the Sultan.

The effective rulers of this chaotic country were not the Ottoman Turks themselves, however, but the Mamelukes, a ruling caste of former Ottoman soldiers who had arrived in Egypt as slaves six centuries before. So, after building up his army, Mohammed Ali invited 500 Mameluke leaders to his official residence, a walled city overlooking the Nile near Cairo. There, he slaughtered them. So began the career of the man who created modern Egypt and tried hard to recreate the Nile.

Mohammed Ali wanted to Westernise and industrialise

Egypt and saw water as the key to this. He restored the
Mahmoudieh Canal, a silted-up relic of Ancient Egypt which
connected Alexandria to the Nile. The job took three months
and 20,000 forcibly conscripted labourers lost their lives in the
process. Next, he sought to tame the Nile and the farmers
who had captured its flood and planted crops in its silt for
7,000 years. He wanted to convert the farms of the Nile valley
and delta to year-round irrigation, so that they could grow
both a food and a cash crop each year. To do this, he once
again press-ganged hundreds of thousands of peasants to dig
canals to provide, for the first time, a permanent flow of water
to the fields. The canals were in places eight metres deep so
that they could take water from the Nile outside the flood
season. He then installed 38,000 water-wheels, driven by oxen
and camels, to lift water from the bottom of deep canals and
into fields.

The new canals successfully provided water all year round
to some parts of the delta, but in others they rapidly filled with
Nile silt. So in 1833, he built barrages on the main branches of
the Nile delta. 'Give me regulators at the heads of the delta
canals, and I am master of Egypt,' he said. His intention was
to keep the water-level constant in the river, four metres
above its dry-season level, so that the canals did not have to be
dredged each year to keep water in them.

Barrage building proved a gargantuan task, however. At
one point, frustrated by slow progress, Mohammed Ali had to
be persuaded not to order the demolition of the pyramids to
provide building stone. The barrage on the Rosetta branch
was finally completed in 1861, more than a decade after his
death, but was so badly built that it was another 30 years
before engineers dared raise the water-level in the river by
more than half a metre.

The hidden hand behind Mohammed Ali's activities was
French. Napoleon Bonaparte had dispatched French invading
forces to the country in 1798 and in 1800, and he had then
commissioned a survey of the country's agricultural potential.
His surveyors estimated that Egypt could grow more than
France. The Rosetta barrage was constructed under the super-
vision of a French engineer, Linant de Bellefonds, and it was

the French who first recommended to Mohammed Ali that he should grow cotton, then in great demand in France. Mohammed Ali saw production of cotton as the springboard for creating a textile industry in his country, though this placed him in conflict with the French, who wanted raw cotton for their own factories to process. After a military skirmish against his forces in 1841, the French insisted on opening the country up to foreign trade. While this led to increased foreign investment in cotton production, it ruined Mohammed Ali's budding industries and the crop from then on left the country unprocessed.

After his death in 1848, his grandson Abbas, a rabid anti-foreigner, abolished schools, sent French doctors and engineers home, and then attempted to destroy the half-completed delta barrage, which he described as 'a colossal crime against the laws of nature'. But Europe's economic grip on Egypt was tightening, and after this interlude, Egypt swiftly became what Daniel Headrick, the technology historian, calls 'a slave of cotton'.

Despite the failures with the barrages, by the mid-nineteenth century, the Nile delta was far more heavily engineered then it had been fifty years earlier. Mohammed Ali had dug three wide canals right across it, largely replacing the old branches of the river. The new man-made hydrology spread year-round irrigation through much of the delta – just in time to reap the benefit from soaring cotton prices during the American Civil War, which drastically cut North American production.

By now, the avowed purpose of irrigation of Egypt was to turn the country into the cotton-growing capital of the world. And it was this – more even than the Suez Canal, completed in 1870 – that attracted the British, the greatest consumers of raw cotton in the world. In 1882, while in theory still under the rule of the Ottoman Empire, Egypt came under the effective control of Britain and the British consul-general, a member of the Baring banking family, Lord Cromer.

So lofty he had earned the nickname 'overbaring', Cromer brought with him from his previous appointment in India a large personal staff of civil servants and irrigation engineers, and raised loans on behalf of the British government from his banking contacts to build new irrigation works and rebuild the Nile barrages. In 1890, the delta barrage for the first time held water four metres higher than its dry-season norm. Cotton yields soared and the Treasury saw a return on its first investment of a million pounds within four years. By 1895, however, the delta farmers were again running short of reliable water and Cromer called on his director-general of reservoirs, William Willcocks, to find a solution.

Willcocks has become a legend among imperial water engineers. Born in a tent beside the West Yamuna Canal in northern India, where his father was in charge of the canal's headwaters, Willcocks spent his early years supervising stretches of the nearby Ganges Canal on horseback. A sallow, permanently ill-dressed man with hooded, half-closed eyes, he was a colonial misfit in the narrow social world of British India, a man who regarded 'dinners, dances, visits and such-like as a wicked waste of time'.

In his first five years in Egypt, according to one account, Willcocks 'spent every day and slept every night in the fields and villages' along the Nile. He surveyed more than a thousand kilometres of the river and riverside communities from the Mediterranean to the Sudan, and appears to have been better loved by the farmers, or *fellahin*, along the Nile than by his superiors. He was certainly better known there. It was said that 'every *fellah* in Egypt knows the name of Wilguks'.

While Cromer epitomised the mercantile streak that drove much imperial engineering, Willcocks represented the missionary zeal of many empire-builders to improve the lot of the natives. Irrigation was for him the oldest applied science in the world and a cause of order and civilisation that began on the Euphrates and the Nile. He wrote of his adopted country:

> Once people took to irrigation, they had to form laws and respect them, for disobedience and wilfulness spelt ruin not only to their neighbours but also to themselves. When the water that irrigates your field has to flow in a channel which passes the fields of all your neighbours, and cannot be maintained in a state of efficiency unless all do their duty, it

is easy to understand how method, order, and obedience to a properly constituted authority very soon developed themselves.

Willcocks proposed and then designed the greatest British endeavour in Egypt, the first Aswan Dam. He built the dam 600 kilometres upstream of the delta. It was 3 kilometres long, 27 metres high and contained 40,000 cubic metres of granite blocks. Nothing like it had been built before. Like a huge weir, it let the early silt-laden floodwaters from the Blue Nile pass over its top each summer. Then it captured up to one cubic kilometre of the clear water from the slightly later and smaller flood of the White Nile in a reservoir behind the dam. The reservoir's water was released gradually during the dry season, increasing the Nile's meagre flow. Downstream of the dam, Cromer's engineers built new barrages and dug new canals to carry the extra water to fields. This greater control over the Nile offered the prospect of both more summer maize to feed the fast-growing Egyptian population and – of greater importance for Cromer's bankers, who had produced £5 million to build the dam – a greatly increased cotton crop each spring.

Willcocks, who fell out with Cromer and left the Egyptian service before the dam was finished, received a knighthood for his efforts and on his death the *Spectator* called the dam 'as great a memorial as Cheops' Pyramid, and of considerably more use to Egyptians'. The chief beneficiaries, however, were the bankers of London and the textile magnates of Lancashire, for whom Egypt was a source of raw cotton second only to the USA.

Egyptian cotton was regarded as the best in the world, commanding prices 50 per cent higher than American cotton and twice those of Indian cotton. There were investors aplenty to pay for the raising of the dam in 1912 and 1913, and again in 1933. An American pioneer of international agribusiness, Leigh Hunt, described the fields of the Nile delta as 'the highest priced agricultural land in the world'. But while rivals for the accolade, such as the Central Valley of California, were able to take their profits and invest them locally, the wealth being generated by the cotton grown in Egypt never found its way home.

By the eve of the First World War, Egypt's ancient irrigation system had been transformed into a vital cog of the British Empire. It was also showing signs that its sudden productivity might not last indefinitely. Having abandoned the flood irrigation system in favour of canal irrigation, Egypt found that the fields of the Nile began to suffer the great bane of this system – salt.

The sheer profusion of water supplied by the canals to cotton crops ensured that water-tables rose into the surface zone of soils, where evaporation sucked out the water and left behind a crust of salt on the surface of the soil. The destroyer of the fields of southern Mesopotamia was beginning, slowly, to poison the longest-lasting hydraulic civilisation of all, on the Nile.

As early as 1882, when the British first assumed control of Egypt, Sir Donald MacKenzie Wallace, *The Times* correspondent in Constantinople, wrote after a visit to the Nile delta of 'white nitrous salts covering the soil and glistening in the sun like untrodden snow'. In 1909, the Egyptian cotton crop failed, partly because waterlogging from the exceptionally strong flood that year brought salt to the surface. A report commissioned by Cromer recommended that the acreage under cotton crops should be reduced by two-thirds, though the proposal was never implemented. By 1947 another British report concluded that rising water-levels and salt had combined to reduce cotton yields along the Nile to half their potential. Long before then, however, the imperial spotlight had moved from Egypt.

In the final years of Cromer's reign in Egypt, British attention had begun to stray south towards the heart of Africa. Engineers dreamed of controlling the entire Nile, the longest river in the world, and of building dams far upstream to tame the mysterious floods that Egyptians had been content to wonder at.

The military men were looking upstream, too. In 1898, General Kitchener had secured British control of the Sudan by his victory at the Battle of Omdurman, and then saw off a French expeditionary force on the upper Nile in the Sudan at Fashoda, one of the critical moments in 'the scramble for Africa'.

Between Fashoda and the great equatorial lakes from which the White Nile rises, there lies the Sudd, an impenetrable marsh, which in wet years can grow to the size of Scotland. 'This horrible region of everlasting swamp', the nineteenth-century British explorer Samuel White Baker called it. For Willcocks it was several cubic kilometres of water which 'stands well above the level of the flat plain as though it were congealed'. Its waterways were 'blocked by masses of living vegetation, 15–20 feet thick, half a mile long and the full width of the river'. These masses of reed, grass and papyrus – known as *sudds*, the Arabic for obstruction – were so solid that herds of elephant could walk across them.

Kitchener, knowing that he could not take his ships through the Sudd, felt militarily exposed. He dispatched Sir William Garstin, Cromer's head of public works, to investigate. Garstin reported that for Britain to control the Nile and its waters, it had to clear the Bahr al-Jabal, the largest of three weed-clogged waterways through the Sudd. By 1904, the job was done and encouraged by the military, the hydrologists pursued their plans to control the entire river. Garstin made three survey trips to the far south and produced what became the definitive British plan for harnessing the Nile. Almost a century later, British hydrologists still subscribe to it in almost every detail.

The first part of the Garstin plan was to raise dams at the mouths of the great equatorial lakes, Lake Victoria and Lake Albert at the head of the White Nile, and Lake Tana, the source of the Blue Nile in Ethiopia. This would allow the engineers to control the lakes' outflows and thus regulate the entire flow of the river. The second part of the plan began from Garstin's observation (originally little more than a hunch, but subsequently proved to be correct) that around 60 per cent of the water entering the Sudd was lost to evaporation as it meandered slowly through the marsh in the fierce tropical heat.

The Bahr al-Jabal, said Garstin, should be by-passed with a canal. If water could pass through the region in a few days, rather than a few months or years, evaporation would be much reduced. It was the logical next step in increasing Egypt's water supply, and suddenly Kitchener's military imperative to control the upper Nile embraced the hydrological imperative to win this 'lost' water.

Within two years of Garstin's report, published in 1904, one of his subordinates was in the US studying dredging on the Mississippi, and the Treasury had found the money to buy dredgers, steamers and barges for the Sudd Canal project. However, construction never began, as first Cromer and then Garstin left Egypt, and Kitchener, after succeeding Cromer as consul-general, later moved to other duties in the First World War.

After the war, Garstin's successor, Sir Murdoch MacDonald, became embroiled in a bitter feud with Willcocks. Willcocks accused MacDonald of falsifying and suppressing hydrological data on the Nile at the bidding of cotton magnates who wanted to dam the Blue Nile at Sennar in Sudan in order to feed a big new cotton-growing project at El Gezira near Khartoum. MacDonald had, according to Willcocks, 'grossly exaggerated' the official figures for river flows during drought years such as 1914, in order to pacify Egyptian fears that the abstractions for Sudan could damage the Aswan reservoir. In a future drought, Willcocks feared, 'the Aswan reservoir will have to be filled in flood'. Because the first waters of the flood are laden with silt, the reservoir would soon clog up and 'its days will be numbered'. Thus, not only would 'Sudan be stealing Egypt's water', but Willcocks's greatest creation would be destroyed.

It was a bizarre interlude. The vendetta ended in 1921 with Willcocks found guilty of criminal slander and libel in a Consular Court. If there was a conspiracy then it persists, for MacDonald's figures still stand. Gezira and the Sennar Dam were both completed by 1925, but there was no risk to Willcocks's dam. The succeeding decades were unusually wet and the first drought only came in the 1980s, by which time Willcocks's dam had been buried beneath the new High Aswan Dam.

Despite his victory, MacDonald emerged from the dispute with his reputation among Egyptians so tarnished that he retired to Britain and set up a water-based engineering consultancy. The cotton magnates meanwhile had moved into El Gezira, an alluvial plain just south of the confluence of the Blue and White Niles, which Garstin had called 'the richest alluvial deposit' in the country.

The security of supply of raw materials for British industry was a prime concern of government then and none was more important than cotton. British mills had more than a third of all the world's spindles, and cotton goods made up a third of British exports. But the locals at El Gezira were not too keen on their land being taken over by cotton plantations and had hidden from Garstin when he first showed up in their villages. In 1908, as the first experimental farming schemes were started by the British, they stormed the office of the deputy inspector of the Blue Nile Province and killed him. The British responded by killing 35 rebels in pitched battle and hanging a 'ringleader'. The following year, the Egyptian and American cotton crops both failed, and a crescendo of lobbying from the cotton mills pushed an initially reluctant British government towards funding the project.

Work on the Sennar Dam and 50,000 hectares of irrigated cotton plantation in the heart of Africa began the following year. The dam and first irrigation canals were completed in 1925, at a price of £14 million.

Meanwhile, Egypt had become independent and a constitutional monarchy in 1922. British engineers and scientists stayed behind to compile volume after volume of statistics on harnessing their beloved Nile. The Sudd Canal project was renamed the Veveno-Pibor scheme and the Garstin Cut, though nothing was ever built. The only lasting change was the signing of the ridiculously one-sided Anglo-Egyptian Nile Waters Agreement of 1929, in which the Egyptians (represented by British hydrologists) were granted 48 cubic kilometres of the Nile's annual flow, and the Sudanese (represented by another team of Britons) received 4 cubic kilometres.

Nobody else, including Uganda where the White Nile

began, and Ethiopia from where the Blue Nile rose, was granted anything. The main effect of this agreement, intended to protect the interest of Egypt, was to set nationalists and British administrators in every upstream nation against any cooperative water management projects on the river for the future. Garstin's plan, to supply Egypt with water regulated behind dams in these upstream nations, was dead, and Churchill's dream of 'smiling countries' sharing the river had turned sour.

8

HOW WATER WON
THE WEST

What do we want with this vast worthless area – this region of savages and wild beasts, of deserts of shifting sands and whirlwinds of dust, of cactus, of prairie dogs?

Daniel Webster on the American West

The Hoover Dam on the Colorado River, in the heart of the American West, was the first superdam and it is one of the most beautiful and awe-inspiring pieces of engineering ever executed. It towers more than 200 metres above the bottom of the Black Canyon, close to the Grand Canyon. The dam became the centrepiece of the development of the Great American Desert, and without it, Los Angeles and Las Vegas today would be unrecognisable. There would have been many fewer American war planes to bring victory on the western front in the Second World War, and dozens of large dams raised in its image round the world since its completion in 1935 might never have been built. The Hoover Dam, as icon and engineering, as a temple to its age, stands beside the Great Pyramid and the Great Wall of China. It is, quite simply, hard to be sure what the world would have been like without it.

The dam sits astride the artery of the Great American Desert, the 2,300-kilometre River Colorado, which flows through rapids and deep canyons from Wyoming to the Mexican border. When in 1857 an army lieutenant, Joseph Ives, wrecked his steamboat at the foot of the Black Canyon, close to where the Hoover Dam now sits, he wrote in his report: 'The region is, of course, altogether valueless. Ours was the first, and will doubtless be the last, party of whites to visit this profitless locality.'

He was already wrong. Early gold and mineral prospectors, spurred by the discovery of gold on the American River in California in 1848, had been followed by cattle ranchers. Urged on by the *Herald Tribune* in New York, which had entreated the nation's youth to 'Go West, young man', farmers began populating the lands between the Mississippi and the Pacific, and irrigating its soils. Among the first were Mormons who ended their great trek west on the shores of the Great Salt Lake in Utah in July 1847. Almost on the first day of their arrival, they began building small dams in local streams to irrigate the soil. While later cowboy mythology held that in towns such as Laramie and Cheyenne it was the gun that won the West, in truth it was water. Irrigation was the key to the colonisation of the Great American Desert.

In the days of the Wild West, water was a commodity to be hoarded and used for personal profit. And as rich farmers and corporations gained large estates and the water rights that went with them, they wanted to preserve their holdings from interlopers upstream, who might steal 'their' water.

The first man to bring some order to water rights in the West was John Wesley Powell, a geology professor from Illinois who had lost an arm in the American Civil War, but who in the 1860s became a national hero by shooting the Colorado's rapids from Wyoming to Nevada. He proposed in 1876 that river water should not be captured piecemeal by individual farmers or communities to irrigate their fields, but should be managed for the good of all and, in the case of the Colorado, captured behind giant reservoirs.

Powell's ideas languished during his lifetime, but in 1902, the year of his death, President Theodore Roosevelt created the Bureau of Reclamation, which from the first concentrated on the 'taming' of rivers as Powell had envisaged, with large dams and even larger laws. The bureau which, in the succeeding decades, was to build more dams and irrigation schemes than any other in the American West, was then, as now, dominated by Mormons, the first irrigators of the Great American Desert. One of its earliest and biggest tasks was to

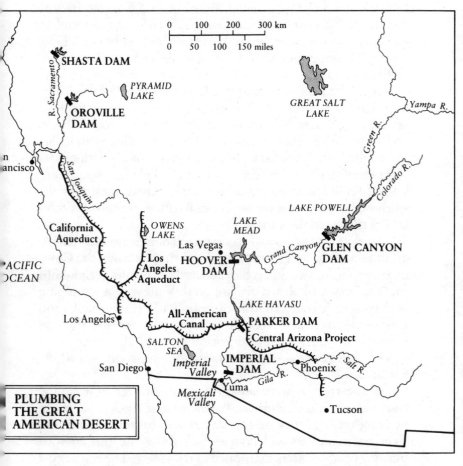

PLUMBING
THE GREAT
AMERICAN DESERT

evolve a plan to control and use the river that had made
Powell famous, the Colorado. The logic of those deliberations
led to the eventual adoption of most of Powell's ideas and,
almost inexorably, to the construction of the Hoover Dam.

By the early years of the twentieth century, it was clear that
public control was needed over the nation's major rivers, and
especially over the Colorado, on which millions of people
were dependent. Adventurers were threatening the West's
greatest resource. Two such men were George Chaffey and
Charles Rockwood, a man with a vision to make the desert of
California bloom. In 1901 they dug a canal from the Colorado

near the small town of Yuma, Arizona, and diverted part of
the river's flow west to California's Valley of the Dead, a
virtually rainless expanse close to the Mexican border. They
renamed it Imperial Valley before inviting farmers to move in.

The river had been this way many centuries before, and the
Valley of the Dead was an abandoned meander of the Colorado. Its soils were fertile and it had a 365-day growing
season. All the two men needed in order to make their fortune
was water, and within months of the canal filling with Colorado water, the Imperial Valley was criss-crossed with canals
and fences. Within three years, settlers had planted 600 square
kilometres with barley, sorghum and alfalfa. Such was the
spirit of the times that the Southern Pacific Railroad was soon
laying rails into the valley.

However, the canal and its diversion dam were ramshackle
affairs. In 1905, an early spring flood rushed down the Colorado, washed away the feeble dam and took a sharp right into
the channel and down to Imperial Valley. The tumbling
waters, which over millions of years had created the Grand
Canyon, took only weeks to deepen the small irrigation
channel so much that the entire flow of the river came
careering west, creating a new inland lake, soon named the
Salton Sea.

Only in 1907, when almost two years of high flows in the
river subsided, did Southern Pacific freight trucks succeed in
pouring enough rock and mud into the breach to force the
river back into its old course and allow the sun to start
burning off the waters marooned in the valley. The rescue cost
nearly $3 million, and never dried up the Salton Sea, which
continues today as a salty drainage sump for the valley's fields.

Rather like the efforts of the hapless Henry Shreve to
straighten the Mississippi a few decades before, the works of
Chaffey and Rockwood appeared to destabilise the river.
Modern tax-payers spend hundreds of thousands of dollars
each year now, keeping it shackled to its current course.

Floods and then a series of drought years in which there
was not enough water to irrigate the Imperial Valley, fuelled
calls for the government to tame the Colorado. By this time,
all across the American West dams were the rage. By 1930,

there were 25,000 dams and barrages for diverting and storing water in the American West, and more than 120,000 kilometres of main canals, a feat only comparable with British efforts in Egypt and India. Individually most of these projects were small, but controlling the Colorado would require something big, said the engineers, something to put the British-built Aswan Dam in the shade.

The Bureau of Reclamation was anxious to fulfil the dream of Powell for a large dam to control the river's turbulent lower reaches. As luck would have it, from 1914, the bureau had as director one Arthur Powell Davis, nephew of the one-armed visionary. For Davis and Francis Crowe, who first surveyed the Black Canyon site for the dam and later left the organisation to help work for the construction company that built the dam itself, the plan became a grand obsession. 'I was wild to build this dam – the biggest dam built by anyone anywhere,' said Crowe.

This was not the language of the technical reports, which spoke of a dam in the Black Canyon as the optimal method of controlling floods and providing permanent water supply and hydroelectric power. But it was perhaps the truer reflection of the motivation behind the construction of the Hoover Dam. A Senate committee, endorsing the Hoover Dam project in 1928, spoke with zeal of how 'a mighty river, now a source of destruction, is to be curbed and put to work in the interests of society'. Donald Worster of the University of Kansas and author of *Rivers of Empire*, wrote in the 1980s of these men:

> All wanted, with a desire that knew no bounds, to dominate nature. Only a river as wild and full of life as the Colorado could satisfy their desire. Always under the statistics there was an unfathomable layer of irrationality, a vague unspecified longing, a will to power. If the river had a fanatical zeal about it, the men who came to it were fanatics too. They would not be satisfied until the river was under their total domination, from headwater to mouth – until the river was dead.

It was a forbidding challenge. The federal government eventually spent $48 million in a gorge hundreds of kilometres from anywhere, where temperatures could exceed 50 degrees Celsius. The bill included building an entire town, Boulder City, to house the 5,000 construction workers, a railway line, and the largest aggregate works anywhere in the world.

The dam was larger than the Great Pyramid of Egypt and taller than a 60-storey skyscraper. It contained enough concrete to pave a two-lane highway from San Francisco to New York. Behind it, stretching upstream for 160 kilometres, the gorge filled with the clear blue waters that they called Lake Mead. The lake holds 36 cubic kilometres of water, more than twice the Colorado's average annual flow.

The Hoover Dam transformed the bureau, turning it into a mass producer of large dams. The bureau remade the hydrology of California, by tapping the Sacramento River to irrigate the Central Valley in the largest irrigation project in the world, and soon became the largest producer of hydroelectric power in the world.

The image of the white concrete plug in the Black Canyon became part of the New Deal world of President Franklin Roosevelt, for large dams were embraced by 1930s environmentalists and social campaigners as much as by engineers. They were a source of clean, cheap electricity for the masses, and of water for the pioneers described by Roosevelt as the '*Grapes of Wrath* families of the nation'. Writers such as Britain's J. B. Priestley lauded the new dams. It was a brave new world.

Drawing on the ideas of John Wesley Powell, who had first suggested organising the development of the West according to river basins, the New Dealers wanted to plan every feature of the landscape and the nation. Roosevelt wanted a string of dams along the Columbia River in the northwest of the country as the basis for a planned society based around agriculture and small industry. He began with the Grand Coulee Dam which, on completion in 1942, was more than twice the size of the Hoover Dam.

The same ideal lay behind the creation of the Tennessee Valley Authority. The authority had wide powers to build dams, buy up private property and impose rules on farmers to halt soil erosion over more than 2 million square kilometres of the Tennessee valley. Like the Hoover Dam, the authority became a model for much else proposed by the Americans for the rest of the world after the Second World War, such as the creation of the Volta River Authority in Ghana.

Even before Roosevelt was replaced in 1945, the dream was changing, however. For one thing, the Bureau had discovered hydroelectric power in a big way. As long ago as 1906 it had persuaded Congress to allow it to keep income from the sale of electricity generated at its dams for ploughing back into irrigation schemes, and with the Hoover Dam, it had created a huge money-making machine for itself. Soon the money-making became an end in itself. Early ideals that electricity should be preferentially offered to cooperatives and municipal authorities gave way in the 1940s to a series of massive contracts with private utilities.

In addition, war had intervened. The Hoover Dam powered the armaments industry and the manufacture of aircraft. On the Columbia River, where the Grand Coulee was completed just after the nation went to war, the first priority was to provide the unparalleled amounts of electricity needed in the manufacture of the first atomic bomb, and the Tennessee Valley Authority too provided power for the Oak Ridge nuclear plant. After the war, the Tennessee Valley Authority, which had been set up with the aim of harnessing natural forces to social equity, diversified with breathtaking ease from building hydroelectric power plants to building nuclear power stations.

Democratic instincts also faltered in the supply of irrigation water. Roosevelt's '*Grapes of Wrath* families' soon lost their places in the queue for water to corporate farmers. From the $440-million Central Valley Project in California, the Bureau's great scheme of the 1940s, to the Deep South, 'New Deal policies enabled large landowners to invest in new technology, consolidate their holdings and dislodge their tenants,' says Clayton Koppes, former president of the American Society for Environmental History.

The Hoover Dam was built for California. The Act of 1929 which authorised the dam also approved a replacement for the old Imperial Canal, a much larger waterway 70 metres

wide to be called the All-American Canal. Even more urgent
were the demands for water and power emanating from the
fast-growing city of Los Angeles. They were, however,
demands rather than needs. As Worster points out, the Colorado did not so much supply as help to create that city, for the
benefit of the people making their fortunes from its growth.

William Mulholland, the legendary chief water planner for
the desert city, once said: 'If we don't get the water, we won't
need it.' As long as the city, and others such as Las Vegas, had
water they would persuade farmers and office workers alike
from the east to join their sunbelt world. So the Colorado
turned into a staircase of reservoirs. After the Hoover Dam
came the Parker Dam in 1938, which supplied Los Angeles
and San Diego via the California Aqueduct; then the Imperial
Dam, further south again, which filled the All-American
Canal.

The irony was that the river was being harnessed increasingly for the benefit of a state through which it did not pass.
For many years, the state of California received a third of the
Colorado's waters. Other states through which the Colorado
did pass, wanted something to show for their rights to part of
the flow, granted in a Colorado Compact signed by those
states in 1922. They too wanted federally funded engineering
projects. So they were given the Navajo Dam, followed by the
Flaming Gorge Dam in Wyoming and many more, before the
creation in 1964 of the largest lake of all on the Colorado.
Lake Powell flooded tens of kilometres of spectacular gorges
close to the Grand Canyon, and increased the storage capacity
on the river to 68 cubic kilometres, more than four years'
flow. Today, the river is the most heavily managed on Earth.
But is it managed sensibly?

Those who say not point to Phoenix, Arizona. The city was
given its name by an English traveller, Darrell Duppa, because
it rose 'like a phoenix' from the remains of a large community
of Hohokam Indians, who until the fifteenth century diverted
the Salt River there into a network of irrigation canals. In
1867, a former soldier in the confederate army, Jack Swilling,
revived the ancient canals and established the new town. Soon
afterwards, the construction of dams in the headwaters of the

Salt River secured its future, and a century later Phoenix was the capital of the booming sunbelt, attracting high-tech industry and the rich and retired from the east. It now has around 2 million inhabitants and is sprawled across more than a thousand square kilometres of desert.

Phoenix is as profligate with its water as it is with its land. The residents of private estates in smart suburbs such as Scottsdale and Paradise Valley water their football-pitch sized lawns daily. The sprinklers are almost permanently in operation at the city's 70 public golf courses and numerous parks. Nearly every home has a swimming pool. Developers compete to include the tallest fountains and largest lakes on their estates. On the south side of town, by a nice irony, is the US government's Water Conservation Service. Scientists there record the fact that each resident of Scottsdale consumes around 4,000 litres of water a day – about 20 times the typical consumption in Europe.

The Salt River has long since ceased to meet the city's demand. All its waters are collected and, except after a major flash flood, the riverbed through the city is dry. The local red light district is built right across it. Wells tap underground water, but overpumping is routine. Phoenix is frantically buying up farmland all around, shutting off the irrigation channels and appropriating the water rights that go with the land for the use of the city. In the battle between fountains and alfalfa, the fountains win every time.

The Bureau of Reclamation has come to the rescue with the $4-billion Central Arizona Project, one of the world's largest and most expensive water supply systems. The project is a huge concrete-lined canal that zigzags for 500 kilometres through the Arizona desert bringing up to 2 cubic kilometres of Colorado water, an eighth of the river's average flow, from the Parker Dam to Phoenix and Tucson. To reach these overgrown oases, Colorado hydroelectricity powers 97 pumps that raise the water almost 1,000 metres. It is a graphic illustration of the American water planners' cynical maxim that 'water flows uphill to money'.

In size and cost, the project bears a remarkable resemblance to the first phase of Colonel Gadaffi's Great Man-made River in Libya. And it, too, will be financed largely from central government coffers. Two-thirds of the $4 billion bill to fill Phoenix's swimming pools and irrigate its golf courses is being met by federal subsidies from the federal government.

The Central Arizona Project is the result not of one man's obsession, but of American politics. It is the apotheosis of what they call the 'pork barrel', the art of assembling a local and vocal bandwagon for an expensive project that can attract large federal funding. Compliant congressmen in Washington, with an eye to where the next slice of campaign fund contributions is coming from in their home state, support schemes that will keep local construction companies happy – and gang up to vote through each others' pet projects.

Water schemes show the pork barrel at its most bloated. The history of American politics is littered with political careers and business fortunes that water made. Among the most illustrious was the partnership formed in the late 1930s between Lyndon Johnson, then an ambitious young congressman, and two small-time engineering brothers, George and Herman Brown, proprietors of Brown & Root. Johnson used his contacts in Roosevelt's White House to ensure that the brothers won contracts to complete a dam outside Austin, Texas. The dam made the brothers' fortunes. Their company went on to become among the largest civil engineering firms in the world – winning, for instance, the contract from Gadaffi to design and supervise construction of the Great Man-made River. And the dam made Johnson's career, when the grateful brothers showered campaign contributions on him as he fought his way to a seat in the Senate in the 1940s, and ultimately to the White House.

The Central Arizona Project (CAP) was one of the most protracted, and certainly the most lucrative, exercises in the art of the pork barrel. First proposed in 1927, it was added to the Bureau of Reclamation's massive waiting list of projects in 1949. Then followed 17 consecutive years during which Arizonan farmers, miners and housing developers, whose future fortunes hung on the scheme, travelled annually to Washington to press their case. Backed by local politicians Barry Goldwater and Carl Hayden, who at a crucial point in deliberations was chairman of the House Appropriations Committee, they eventually pushed through their crazy project and construction began in 1973.

The politics were rough, and local opponents faced a big stick. More than a decade later, academics at the University of Arizona in Tucson still talked of a former colleague, Robert Young, who was 'railroaded out of town' for his vocal opposition.

The nerve centre for the CAP sits between Dynamite Road and Happy Valley Road, amidst a landscape of giant saguaro cactuses on the northern outskirts of Phoenix. The control room, which runs the entire network of sluice gates, pumping stations, storage reservoirs and water treatment works, looks like something out of Cape Canaveral. This is because the computers, from Johnson Controls, are identical to NASA's. Everything is duplicated: there are back-ups for every pump; one computer stands by to take over from the other; two data collection networks collate millions of bits of data every day, one by cable, the other by microwave link. There are even two men employed to fish drowned deer out of the concrete-lined aqueduct.

This grand folly does not even guarantee water. Lake Havasu is one of the last out-take points on the river's route to the sea – past the great lakes Powell and Mead. And, while the Colorado Compact, which divided up the river's flow between the states, decrees that the river's annual flow was 20 cubic kilometres, nature has ever since steadfastly failed to live up to this expectation. The average for the past 70 years has been 16.7 cubic kilometres. In 1934, at the height of the 'dust bowl' 1930s, it managed just 6.9 cubic kilometres. A few dry years in the Midwest and the aqueduct to Phoenix could be as dry as the Indian canals that Jack Swilling dug out to found the city.

It sounds as if there is a water crisis, and that is the way they describe it out in the West. But can this be so while the fountains are high in Phoenix? Or when half the water extracted from the Colorado goes to irrigate crops currently in surplus? The watering of the West is founded on a myth, a kind of mirage which sees purpose in the purposeless. Sanity suggests that the city sprinklers should be turned off.

Economic logic suggests that the fields should be left dry. As
Dick Shaefer at the Bureau of Reclamation's head office put it
to me: 'Historically, we established a base for a stable population in the West. It has allowed today's cities to grow. The
question now is whether we should dump the farmers.'

This is a thorny question for an agency that still prides itself
on having a special mission. It publicises its activities with a
leaflet carrying a photograph of a poor Midwest farmer, one
H. J. Mersdorf, standing in the midst of the dust bowl of the
1930s next to a sign bearing the legend: 'Desert ranch: have
faith in God and US Reclamation.' But the picture of the
pioneer is another Western myth. It is a long time since the
main occupation of the Bureau of Reclamation was to provide
water for poor farmers. It was usually the big farming com-
bines that gained the most. Down in the Imperial Valley of
California, it may have been pioneers that were flooded out by
the Colorado's unscheduled detour in 1905, but once the
Bureau had completed the All-American Canal in 1940, it was
the big commercial farms that benefited.

It is men such as Bud Antle with his 8,000 hectares of
irrigated fields in the Imperial Valley and Arizona that owe
the greatest debt to the bureau. Says Frank Gregg, who once
ran another federal agency, the Bureau of Land Management:
'No Bureau [of Reclamation] project was ever built that satisfied its original ideas. None of them met the efficiency targets
and few of them were dedicated to providing water for the
sturdy yeoman pioneers.' In truth, subsidies were vast because
large corporate landowners were charged next to nothing for
their water. A detailed study in the mid-1980s by the World
Resources Institute, an influential environmental group based
in Washington DC, found that across 140 large irrigation
projects the average effective subsidy was 83 per cent of the
cost of the project. There was 'a total subsidy to the farmers
that use bureau water of a billion dollars a year'. Not even
Gadaffi will match that.

The West, far from being thirsty, is awash with so much
water that it has no idea what it can sensibly do with it. The
swimming pools of Scottsdale show that, and so does the
decision to create Lake Powell behind the Glen Canyon Dam,

a copy of the Hoover Dam a few tens of kilometres upstream. It was built where it was not for hydrological reasons, but to satisfy political demands when the upstream states complained that they were not being allowed to extract the water allowed to them under the Compact. Yet the Bureau wanted a reservoir far enough downstream for it to generate large amounts of hydroelectric power to supply to Los Angeles and Las Vegas. The result was the creation of a lake which took 15 years to fill and from which roughly a tenth of the Colorado's flow evaporates each year in the hot desert sun.

9

COMMISSAR COTTON

Only in cement and iron can the fraternal brotherhood of all
mankind ... be forged.

V. Zazubrin at First Congress of Soviet Writers, 1926

Just as the American Dream has revolved around 'going
West', so the Soviet theme of peopling the virgin lands of the
East has resonated through the present century. While
Roosevelt's New Dealers in the 1930s almost lusted after the
taming of nature, so Stalin sought a similar domination. But if
the aims in the USA and the USSR were similar, the means
were very different. Stalin combined brutality to the landscape
with unprecedented brutality to his people.

Stalin's first great project was the construction of the
Belomor Canal between the White Sea off the Arctic northern
shore and the Baltic. In the twenty hectic months of construction through the winters of 1931 and 1932, the 200-kilometre
canal was blasted through rock and ice across northern Russia
under the orders of the Hydrological Planning Agency. Tens,
perhaps hundreds, of thousands of virtual slaves from Stalin's
prison camps lost their lives through exposure and disease.

Stalin intended the canal to provide a possible escape route
for the Baltic fleet to an Arctic refuge. But, in their haste, his
engineers dug a path that was too shallow to allow large ships
to pass. The canal never served much of an economic function
either. But its central purpose, says Charles Ziegler, a professor of political science at the University of Louisville, Ken-
tucky, 'was political – to impress the citizenry with Stalin's
and the Party's ability to achieve impossible victories over
nature'.

Ze'ev Vol'fson, a senior Soviet official who in the 1970s smuggled to the West a manuscript called *The Destruction of Nature in the Soviet Union*, says the canal was remembered mostly as a picture on a million cigarette packets. In his book, written under the pseudonym Boris Komarov, he argued that: 'The more such projects contradicted the laws of nature, the more highly they were regarded ... the more brilliantly the illusion of their success demonstrated the power and wisdom of the new leaders of the country.'

Stalin's war against nature was fought by generals. Just as the USA brought in the US Army's Corps of Engineers, so Stalin created his Hydrological Planning Agency as an offshoot of the State Political Administration – his all-powerful secret police. The agency's managers who ran the canal project had the rank of major-general.

Few dared doubt that nature had to be subdued. Maxim Gorky, a leading apologist for Stalin's excesses, led a team of writers who went to see the completed Belomorsk Canal. *Izvestia* recorded his view of his leader's canals: 'They are big rivers, my lord, and sane. Before, rivers were mad.' More chilling still is the exhortation of V. Zazubrin, a delegate to the First Congress of Soviet Writers in 1926, quoted by Vol'fson:

> Let the fragile green breast of Siberia be dressed in the cement armour of cities, armed with the stone muzzles of factory chimneys, and girded with iron belts of railroads. Let the taiga be burned and felled, let the steppes be trampled. Let this be, and so it will be inevitably. Only in cement and iron can the fraternal union of all peoples, the iron brotherhood of all mankind, be forged.

In the late 1940s came the Great Stalin Plan for the Transformation of Nature. Following Lenin's dictum that 'Communism is Soviet power plus electrification', he announced plans to build great hydroelectric dams to power industrial development along the Volga and Dneiper rivers.

The Americans built most of their dams in gorges, to collect the most water and generate the most power from the least loss of land. But Soviet engineers ignored such natural features

and worried nothing about drowning wide fertile river valleys with shallow reservoirs behind huge earth dams. In all, they flooded an area roughly the size of France. Typical was the Kuibyshev Dam on the Volga, finished in 1953, the first great post-war hydroelectric scheme on the river. The construction of the 4-kilometre barrier across a shallow valley involved moving more than 30 million cubic metres of debris, and created Europe's largest man-made lake, 490 kilometres long and up to 40 kilometres wide. Round the coastline of the great lake, reports Vol'fson, there are '11,700 square kilometres [of] silted, impassable swamps, where masses of algae multiply in the summer and then rot'.

Apart from keeping the inhabitants of the labour camps occupied, it is hard to see the sense of many of Stalin's large dams. The Kuibyshev flooded almost half a football pitch to provide enough generating capacity to run one single-kilowatt electric fire. In 1952, his engineers finished the Tsimlyansk Dam, a barrier 40 metres high and 13 kilometres long across the valley of the River Don. It flooded 2,700 square kilometres of farmland, drowning more than two football pitches to run a one-kilowatt electric fire. Vol'fson says that if the land flooded in the 1930s for the lower Dneiper hydroelectric project had instead been planted with hay, the annual harvest could have been burnt to produce more energy than the hydroelectric plant.

There is today very little left of the original valley of the Volga, the largest river in Europe. There are altogether nine large hydroelectric plants along the Volga and its major tributary, the Kama. The reservoirs have increased the surface area of the river's waters sevenfold. The plants don't quite have the romantic names of their counterparts in the American West. In place of Flaming Gorge and Savery-Pot Hook and Blue Mesa and Silver Jack, the Russians had the V. I. Lenin Hydropower Plant and the 22nd Party Congress Station. Lyricism comes instead from the dams' opponents. In 1989, a Public Committee to Save the Volga, headed by the veteran Russian writer Vasily Belov, who for 30 years had extolled the virtues of Russian peasant life, won official approval for its campaign slogan: 'If the Volga is ailing, so is Russia.'

Much of the pressure came from Russian nationalists opposed to the abuse of the 'mother of Russia', the River Volga, and the loss of the sturgeon in it, which had all but died out along the polluted and canalised river. Writers of Belov's 'village school' had mourned the drowning of rural communities beneath reservoirs on the Volga. Valentin Rasputin in his book *Farewell to Matyora* described the flooding in the 1960s of an old village as waters rose behind the Bratsk hydroelectric dam near Lake Baikal. Now the Russian environmentalists see their chance to undo some of the damage, and are calling for the destruction of the Volga-Kama cascade of dams, starting with the Rybinsk reservoir which inundated 4,500 square kilometres of meadows, oak groves and other forests, along with almost 500 villages, north of Moscow.

During the 1980s, Soviet engineers, having completed the transformation of European rivers envisaged by Stalin, switched to the huge fast-flowing rivers of Siberia and to the mountainous regions of Central Asia where deep gorges offer attractive new dam sites. The wastes of Siberia are now home to four of the ten most powerful hydroelectric complexes in the world. Two, the Krasnoyarsk and Sayano-Shushensk, are on the Yenisei, a river with six times the flow of the Nile that hurtles out of Mongolia and heads north to the Arctic Ocean. The other two complexes, the Ust-Ilim and the Bratsk, are on a tributary of the Yenisei called the Angara, which flows out of Lake Baikal. The power generated at these dams is used for new industrial enterprises, such as aluminium smelters along the Trans-Siberian Railway, as well as being exported along high-voltage cables to the west.

Meanwhile, on the River Vakhsh in the mountains of Central Asia, beyond Samarkand and close to the borders with Afghanistan and China, Soviet engineers have built the two highest dams in the world, the Nurek at 300 metres and the Rogun at 335 metres. Other giants, such as the 255-metre Kambaratinsk, were planned for the River Naryn upstream of Tashkent in the 1990s. But there are serious seismic problems in this region, and the Rogun Dam is said to be vulnerable to earthquakes, while the 272-metre Inguri Dam in Georgia, which was finished in 1980, may be demolished because of growing official concern about its stability.

The Soviet Union finished the 1980s with almost 400 cubic kilometres of water stored behind dams. It boasted three of the world's ten largest reservoirs and four of the ten largest hydroelectric plants. It had more installed hydroelectric capacity, at around 70 gigawatts, than any other nation, bar the USA. In the immediate aftermath of the Union's breakup in 1991, there were few signs that the pace of dam-building would slacken. In its first few months, one of Russia's best sources of foreign exchange was aluminium, smelted by power from its dams. Russian aluminium reached foreign markets in early 1992 in such quantities that prices slumped and several Western smelters closed.

For the 1990s, the eyes of the Russian engineers have turned even further east. They announced plans for a new 'cascade' of seven dams to be built jointly with the Chinese down the River Amur, which forms the border between the two countries through Manchuria before pouring into the Pacific Ocean. And they are designing what could become the largest hydroelectric dam on Earth, a 20,000-megawatt giant construction at Turukhansk on the Tunguska, an eastern tributary of the Yenisei.

While hydroelectric power was always the prime purpose of most Soviet dams, they also provided water for irrigation. Soviet management of the Volga diverted roughly a quarter of the river's flow for irrigation. This may have gone some way to making good the farm output lost in the drowned valleys – but not far. Crop yields from irrigated fields mostly remained low, typically only a half those predicted in successive five-year plans. The reasons are familiar: inefficient use of water followed by waterlogging and a build-up of salt in the soils. One study, quoted by Eugene Podolsky, a scientist with the Association for Ecology and Peace in Moscow, found that half of irrigated Soviet farmland was taken out of production within seven years of the first water reaching the fields.

Farming has not emptied the River Volga in the way that the irrigators of the American desert have sucked the Colorado dry. This is as well since the Volga drains not into the open ocean but to the Caspian Sea, where it provides 80 per cent of the inflow. None the less, since the 1930s, engineers have planned to increase the flow of the Volga by diverting to the south water from rivers that currently flow north into the Barents Sea and the Arctic. For the Soviet landscape plumbers, water flowing into the Arctic is wasted water.

One scheme would barricade off Onega Bay from the Barents Sea and reverse the river so that it flows uphill and over into the Volga basin. There it would top up the Rybinsk reservoir, the 'top step' of the Volga hydrological stairway, with up to 20 cubic kilometres of water each year. The extra water would raise the output of hydroelectric plants all the way down the Volga, feed ambitious irrigation projects on the dry lands around the Caspian Sea, dilute pollution and, if necessary, help refill the Caspian Sea when, as happened in the 1970s, its coastline retreats.

Stalin's successor, Nikita Kruschev, embraced the diversion plan as part of his grand vision to reclaim 'virgin lands', but it was ditched in the mid-1960s in the face of opposition from Russians who feared that it would damage the north of their country. The idea was revived again in the mid-1970s and approved by ministers in 1984 but thrown out by Mikhail Gorbachev in 1986, again following strong Russian opposition. The dissolution of the Union makes its revival for the moment improbable. Even so, there remains a widespread Russian fear that the 'technocratic bureaucracy' will outlive the eclipse of the Kremlin and is biding its time before resuming its diversion scheme.

Even more dramatic than the Russian river diversions to help out the Volga was a parallel scheme to divert major rivers of western Siberia, such as the Ob and the Irtysh, south to the southern states of former Soviet Central Asia that border the Caspian Sea's smaller brother, the Aral Sea. This was the 'project of the century', designed at least in part to halt the 'ecological disaster of the century'. The project of the century fell foul of Gorbachev's new realism, but the ecological disaster shows no signs of going away.

Since the end of the Cold War, many airliners en route from

Europe to India and the Far East have flown across the former Soviet Union – over the Ukraine, the great Volga basin, the Aral Sea and Samarkand. In clear weather you can spot the reservoirs glinting along the Volga and in the southern mountains. But the real landmark of this route is the deep blue waters of the Aral Sea.

Especially on a moonlit night, the aerial view of the sea, until recently the fourth largest inland sea in the world, is disorientating for anyone following the journey on one of those maps printed in the back of airline magazines. You can follow the route of the railway line from Moscow to Tashkent, then pick out the lights of Aralsk, the port on the northern shore of the Aral Sea. But instead of waves washing up to the town's harbour and promenade, there is a vast expanse of barren desert glinting white in the moonlight.

The shoreline itself is now 60 kilometres to the south, and the white expanse between is salt: crystals of calcium carbonate, sodium chloride, sodium sulphate and magnesium chloride. Since 1960, the surface area of the Aral Sea has shrunk by 40 per cent and its volume has fallen by more than 60 per cent.

Out of the aircraft window on the other side, there are the lights of Muynak, once a great fishing port and harbour for steam ships plying the 330-kilometre crossing to Aralsk. In the 1950s, Soviet government film-makers portrayed the heroism of fishermen in the Aral Sea, who caught 50,000 tonnes of sturgeon, carp and bream each year. Today, most fish are gone. The last trawler was left to rot on the dry seabed in 1984. And several times a year since 1975, great dust storms up to 500 kilometres across have blown out from the exposed seabed, lifting each year an estimated 75 million tonnes of salt, laced with agricultural chemicals, and depositing it across the landscape. Winds that once brought moisture from the sea now bring only a lethal dust that destroys soils and blankets vegetation.

Cosmonauts, who take off from the nearby Baikonur cosmodrome, watch the storms from the Soviet space station in orbit. Scientists can measure the fall-out of dust along the shores of the Arctic Ocean and the River Ganges. It spreads as perniciously as the radioactivity from the nuclear testing ground at Semipalatinsk, another local enterprise. The region's population, meanwhile, is suffering from epidemics of throat cancer, brought on by inhaling Aral Sea salt and pesticides such as the weedkiller Butifos in the dust. They suffer a high incidence too of anaemia, probably caused by polluted drinking water, of typhoid, hepatitis, gallstones, kidney diseases and TB.

What has caused this ecological and human catastrophe? The answer is cotton, irrigation and Soviet planning. The desiccation of the Aral Sea was arguably the greatest single folly of the Stalinist state; the single most unambiguous example of the failure of central planning.

Irrigation began in the desert lands round the Aral Sea thousands of years ago. In the Kopet Dag mountains, which mark the Soviet border with Iran, farmers diverted rainfall into shallow depressions, which they ploughed and planted. They dug *qanats* here too, to tap the water in the fans of alluvium on the valley sides. In the late 1980s, Turkmenistan's minister of health, K. Chagylov, told the Soviet press:

> I remember the inimitable taste of the water of my child-
> hood. In our small village in the desert, water came to us
> from the mountains via a system of *kyariz* [*qanats*] con-
> ceived and built by our forefathers, and the water was
> crystal clear and fresh. The mountains were then covered
> with forests; now they are bald and there is no water. The
> *kyariz* have crumbled and fallen in.

Almost from the first day of the revolution in far-away Petrograd, the Bolsheviks had eyed the Aral basin for agricultural development. Lenin wrote that: 'Irrigation will do more than anything else to revive the area and regenerate it, bury the past and make the transition to socialism more certain.' Under Stalin's first five-year plan in 1928, the region's wheat farms were turned into centrally-run 'collectives' growing cotton for the textile mills of European Russia. Soviet Central Asia became the most northerly cotton-growing area in the world. The water-guzzling plants were fed by an ever-expanding network of irrigation canals connected to the two great rivers running into the Aral Sea, the Syr Darya and the

Amu Darya. By 1932 Stalin declared the Soviet Union self-sufficient in cotton, but expansion continued.

Local officials objected to this diktat from afar. The prime minister of the Uzbeks, F. Khodzhaev, complained, 'You cannot eat cotton', and his first party secretary, A. Ikramov, drew up alternative plans for developing irrigation to supply local needs. Both men were executed in 1938 for 'bourgeois nationalism'.

By 1960, after several decades of obedience to 'Commissar Cotton', irrigation water reached 50,000 square kilometres of fields in the Aral basin. The amount of water diverted from the two rivers was 40 cubic kilometres. None the less, the Aral Sea was at this time as full as at any time in the recent past. This was partly because rainfall had been unusually high for several years, and partly because most of the diverted water eventually found its way back into the rivers, and so to the sea. The sea was also remarkably resilient to changing river flows. Under normal circumstances, only half the water in the two rivers reached the sea. The rest was lost to evaporation from the rivers and their large deltas at the sea's edge. The first effect of the diversions was to begin to dry up the deltas, so reducing this evaporation.

Then, starting in the late 1950s, Soviet engineers began to dig the Karakum Canal. The canal, the longest in the world, runs for 1,300 kilometres due west from the upper reaches of the Amu Darya right along the Iranian border. It takes water out of the Aral Sea basin altogether, over the watershed and almost to the shores of the Caspian Sea. It was the construction of the Karakum Canal, and the creation along its route of one of the largest and least efficient irrigation systems in the world, that began in earnest the desiccation of the Aral Sea.

It was a classic Soviet blunder, combining several Stalinist obsessions. There was the Soviet love of giant construction projects. There was the obsession with security: this canal along the remote Soviet-Iranian border was built to provide socialist prosperity for a region thought to be vulnerable first to Western and then to Muslim influence. And there was the particular love of water projects, the taming of nature.

Between 1956, when it delivered its first water, and the

mid-1980s, the annual 'take' of the Karakum Canal from the waters of the Amu Darya rose to 14 cubic kilometres – making it almost as large a waterway as the virgin Colorado before Americans began to dam it. In its first 30 years of operation the canal abstracted 225 cubic kilometres of water, roughly two-thirds of the water currently stored in the Aral Sea. Most crucially, and unlike other irrigation systems in the area, none of that water even found its way back to the Aral Sea.

Water from the Karakum Canal disappears into the sand causing waterlogged fields and huge pools of salty water across the desert landscape. Seepage from the canal has created a new saline lake that covers 800 square kilometres in the midst of the fields of the Karakum. The desert city of Ashkhabad is now surrounded by swamps.

Without the Karakum project, the Aral Sea would certainly have diminished. For one thing, rainfall in the region has fallen since the early 1960s. For another, water withdrawals for irrigation have soared everywhere under the insatiable demand for cotton, and cotton's insatiable demand for water. There have been more new irrigation projects, such as the Golodnaya Steppe along the Syr Darya, and there have been a series of giant dams in the headwaters of the two rivers to further regulate their flow and ensure that even in wet years little water reaches the Aral Sea.

By the mid-1980s, the average flows of water into the Aral Sea from the two rivers fell from an average of 50 cubic kilometres a year between 1930 and 1960 to half that figure by 1970, just 10 cubic kilometres in 1980 and less than 5 cubic kilometres in the 1980s. Though heavy rains allowed a small recovery at the end of the decade, for several years in the mid-1980s the operators of the dams and sluice-gates removed every drop of water from the two rivers. Nothing at all was left for the Aral Sea.

To make matters worse, the collective farms had found themselves in a vicious circle. Straining to reach production targets imposed in Moscow under crude slogans such as 'Produce millions of tonnes of cotton – at any cost', they over-irrigated their fields. As a result, according to Soviet research published in *Izvestia* in 1985, two-thirds of the fields of Uzbekistan and Kazakhstan by then suffered seriously from salinisation. The figure reached 80 per cent in Turkmenistan, the land of the Karakum Canal. Fields along the canal had accumulated an estimated 62 million tonnes of salt, approaching 1 kilo per square metre, and could, the article warned, become useless for cotton farming within a decade.

In Uzbekistan during the 1980s, 5,000 square kilometres of cotton fields were abandoned to salt. The region's cotton yields dipped from more than 2.8 tonnes per hectare in the late 1970s to 2.3 tonnes in the late 1980s. Overall 7 per cent less cotton was being produced on 15 per cent more land served by the irrigation canals. The orgy of cotton production is all ending in very salty tears.

It appears that the Soviet authorities deliberately decided to drain the Aral Sea in order to boost cotton production. A former president of the Academy of Sciences of Turkmenistan has been quoted by Soviet authors as saying:

> I belong to those scientists who consider that drying up the Aral Sea is far more advantageous than preserving it. Good fertile land will be obtained. Cultivation of cotton alone [on the seabed] will pay for the existing Aral Sea with its fisheries, shipping and other industries.

In 1975, a special commission set up by the State Committee for Science and Technology concluded that 'current practice ... foreordains the reduction of the Aral Sea to a small, saturated salt solution, a residual reservoir'. Thus, the fishing industry was written off. So was the value of the river deltas, where hay fields and pastures have disappeared along with the forest and shrublands that supported wild boar, deer, jackal, the occasional tiger and enough muskrat to allow a harvest of 650,000 pelts in 1960.

However, other things were not predicted or allowed for. Central planners blundered badly by assuming that a crust would form on the exposed seabed, preventing dust storms and allowing farming there. And they were wrong to dismiss the idea that the loss of the sea could upset the climate on which the growth of the crops depended.

Today salt poisons humans and wildlife alike, and prevents the growth of any kind of vegetation on the seabed. The climate, too, has changed as much as 300 kilometres from the former shoreline. Without the moderating influence of a large body of water, summers are hotter than ever and winters colder; spring frosts are later and autumn frosts earlier. At Kungrad, on what was once the Amu Darya delta but which is now 100 kilometres from the sea, the growing season has been reduced so much that cotton will no longer grow and fields are being switched to rice.

So what is to be done? V. M. Kotlyakov, director of the Soviet Institute of Geography in Moscow, said in 1990 that 'the Aral region is in a state of ecological crisis ... so serious that the human population can no longer live and work as it once did. Only a short time remains ... before life and work in the region become impossible.'

The only solution, say local officials, must be more water. The first priority when the scandal hit the headlines in the late 1980s was to reduce disease by bringing in fresh drinking water. A 200-kilometre pipeline, built at a cost of £350 million, takes fresh water from the headwaters of the Amu Darya to towns on the southern fringes of the sea. But the farmers and officials want more water to irrigate more fields to grow more cotton and, as an afterthought, to refill the Aral Sea. This water, they say, must come from the north, by diverting part of the flow of the Siberian Arctic rivers, the Ob and its tributary the Irtysh.

The temptation is obvious. These are vast rivers running, as hydrologists see it, to waste in the Arctic Ocean. The combined flow of the two rivers is almost 400 cubic kilometres per year, more than four times that of the Nile.

The environmental effects of diverting the Siberian rivers would be immense. In places on the Irtysh, river flow would fall by 60 per cent. Perhaps a quarter of the fish in the Ob and Irtysh would disappear, as wetlands in which they breed disappeared and ice flows increased. There could even be dangerous effects on the Arctic Ocean if 2 per cent of the flow of fresh water to the Ocean was suddenly diverted south. However, several Western studies have concluded that any upset to world climate is most unlikely.

The diversion would involve the construction of a new canal the size of a large river and more than 2,000 kilometres long. Even somebody sympathetic to the scheme, such as the American geographer Philip Micklin, admits that leakage from a long unlined canal across an arid landscape would waterlog and salinise large areas of land 'of considerable agricultural potential'. But this is only part of the case against construction of the canal. In reality, the former Soviet states of Central Asia have no need of outside water. Dry though the Aral basin may be, it naturally contains huge amounts of water. As recently as 1960, its two rivers carried into the Aral Sea annual flows approaching four times those of the virgin Colorado.

Where has all this water gone? There is no doubt that the collective farms of the Aral basin, which live on in the independent states, have been hugely profligate in their use of water. In Uzbekistan, irrigation in the early 1980s provided an annual covering of water of 1.75 metres, reaching 3.6 metres in some areas. Here, too, large amounts of drainage water collect in local depressions and evaporate. The largest such depression, Lake Sarykamysh, held 30 cubic kilometres of salty drainage water by the end of the 1980s, making it one-tenth the size of the Aral Sea itself.

A 20-year emergency programme, announced by Moscow in 1988, called for repairs and modernisation to irrigation systems and drainage. The aim was to cut water consumption on farms by a quarter within a decade. There were also plans for two giant new canals to drain salty water away from depressions and take it directly to the sea. The blueprints show one drainage canal flowing all the way from Termez on the Afghan border. It would, said the planners, cost $2.4 billion and take 15 years to build. Together they were intended to raise the flow of water into the Aral Sea to 21 cubic kilometres by the year 2005. But even this would be little more than a third of the pre-1960 flow, and only half what hydrologists say is necessary to maintain the sea at its present much-reduced state. The Aral Sea, therefore, would continue to shrink.

In any event, in 1991 the independent states won control of their own cotton fields. Uzbekistan, source of two-thirds of the Soviet crop, laid plans to expand the industry and boost exports. It was clear that, while Moscow's control had gone, Commissar Cotton lived on in Tashkent. Agricultural priorities will have to change if the Aral Sea is to be saved. As Peter Rogers of Harvard University puts it: 'Water and salt are not the fundamental causes of the Aral basin's problems. The real cause is the demands placed on the ecosystem by local people and the larger Soviet population. The cause is economic development and how it has been implemented.'

Meanwhile, up in the mountains at the headwaters of the Amu Darya, on the Vakhsh tributary, they are still building dams. The aim is to increase the amount of water that can be captured during wet years, when the Aral Sea might otherwise be replenished. One approaching completion in 1991 was the Rogun, the highest dam in the world at 335 metres. It will, say the authorities, permit the irrigation of another 4,000 square kilometres.

Many emerging nations around the world, and especially in Africa, sought in the 1950s and 1960s to follow the Soviet path of remaking their nation in 'cement and iron'. But even if they turned to the alternative American model of economic development, the messages were much the same. The urge to tame nature was at its height. And so too was the belief that the harnessing of natural forces could be translated swiftly and painlessly into national transformations.

The two nations that made the first and boldest attempts to mortgage their futures each to a single grand water project were Egypt and Ghana. Egypt, under Colonel Nasser, decided to exert absolute control on the Nile by creating the world's largest dam. Ghana, under Kwame Nkruma, determined to create the world's largest reservoir, covering an area of land the size of the Lebanon in the centre of the country, in the hope of creating an industrial state overnight.

A SOURCE OF
EVERLASTING PROSPERITY

Here are joined the political, social, national and military battles of the Egyptian people, welded together like the gigantic mass of rock that has blocked the course of the ancient Nile.

Colonel Nasser, at the impoundment of the High
Aswan Dam, 1964

The Egyptian revolution of 1952 ousted King Farouk and brought to power an army colonel, Gamal Abdel Nasser. His generals were not of a mind to listen to British hydrologists with their plans to secure Egypt's water behind dams in the far-off headwaters of the Nile. They could not countenance being dependent for their water on Kenya, Sudan or Uganda, all of which were still ruled by the British. And, having just achieved a revolution themselves, they were equally fearful of independence upstream, because of the many declarations being made by nationalist movements in these countries, all of whom wanted a share of the Nile's waters.

The Egyptian commanders wanted control of the Nile for themselves. And they wanted a very visible symbol of that control. The answer, suggested to them by two very un-British engineers from Greece and Italy, Adrien Daninos and Luigi Gallioli, was the High Aswan Dam. They proposed a giant barricade across the river at Aswan, many times the size of the original British dam, that could halt the annual floods in their tracks and store almost two years' flow of the river in a gigantic lake. The dam would tower more than 100 metres above the river and weigh 17 times as much as the Great

Pyramid. From Egypt being, as Herodotus put it, 'the gift of the Nile', the waters of the Nile would now be in the gift of the Egyptian government. Moreover, the High Aswan would be the largest, most dramatic dam in the world, a huge affirmation of the aspirations of a newly independent nation, in a continent about to free itself from the colonialist yoke.

When Daninos and Gallioli first brought their proposal for the dam to Cairo in 1948, it had been dismissed by King Farouk's adviser on the Nile, the Briton Harold Hurst. He warned that a giant shallow reservoir in the hot plains of southern Egypt would be a constant victim of evaporation. In this, he was completely correct. When full, the completed reservoir loses an estimated 15 cubic kilometres of water a year, almost a fifth of the river's annual flow and not far short of the loss from the upstream swamps of the Sudd that have so infuriated generations of hydrologists. Besides wasting water, the evaporation also increases the saltiness of irrigation water even before it reaches fields. Since the construction of the High Aswan, river-water reaching the Nile delta has contained a third more salt than before the dam was built.

Hurst, like his predecessors, wanted instead to hold water in the equatorial lakes at the head of the White Nile, partly because this would get round the evaporation problem. The lakes were deep and the climate less hot than at Aswan. But for Nasser 'the largest lake ever shaped by human hand' would be 'a source of everlasting prosperity' for Egypt, and after 1952 Hurst was forced to go along with this view. Under Nasser there was, said one Egyptian critic, Professor Ali Fathy, effectively a High Dam Covenant that prevented opposition. To oppose the dam was to oppose the revolution and independence itself.

At first, neither the West nor the Russians were prepared to put up the funds for construction of the High Aswan Dam, but Nasser refused to be put off. In July 1956, with the summer floodwaters racing down the Nile, he announced to a huge rally in Alexandria that he was taking over the Suez Canal and that 'the canal will pay for the dam'. In the ensuing confusion of the Suez Crisis, which destroyed for ever British influence in the region, the Soviets agreed to fund the High

Aswan after all. For them, too, the dam was more symbol than engineering project. It became a sign of their growing influence in Africa and their association with liberation and anti-colonialism.

In order to complete the dam, Nasser had to reach a new agreement with Sudan over the Nile's waters. This was because the dam would flood land in Sudan, including hundreds of Nubian villages and the town of Wadi Halfa. But Nasser, like the British before him, determined that to control the Nile, he had to control Sudan, which won its independence in 1956. There was more than a suspicion of Egyptian involvement when, two years later, with negotiations on a new Nile Agreement going badly and vitriolic propaganda emanating from both sides, there was a coup in Khartoum. Months afterwards, Nasser and Sudan's Major-General Ibrahim Abboud signed a deal under which Egypt was granted 55.5 cubic kilometres of the river's annual flow and Sudan 18.5 cubic kilometres.

The Cold War was, meanwhile, heightening Egypt's fears as well as its hopes. While superpower rivalries had persuaded the Russians to help Nasser build the High Aswan, they persuaded the Americans to take a new interest in the Nile. The dam-builders of the Bureau of Reclamation went to Ethiopia to draw up a master plan for damming the Blue Nile, the source of the majority of Egypt's water. The builders of the great Hoover Dam proposed four giant hydroelectric dams on the Blue Nile, starting at its source, Lake Tana, in the Ethiopian highlands.

Together, the dams would have held back 51 cubic kilometres of the Blue Nile's flow. Egypt, which had refused to include Ethiopia in the Nile Agreement with Sudan, suddenly felt its control of the river threatened. Political change in Ethiopia, with Haile Selassie replaced by the Marxist government of President Mengistu, ultimately ensured that no large dams were built in Ethiopia, but 30 years later, Egypt still declares that it would go to war to prevent 'its' waters disappearing behind somebody else's dam. Egypt could not, and still cannot, countenance dams upstream over which it does not have control.

Nasser shut off the flow of the Nile for the first time in May 1964. From now on, the great river would form a lake bearing his name. At the ceremony, Nasser told the world: 'Here are joined the political, social, national and military battles of the Egyptian people, welded together like the gigantic mass of rock that has blocked the course of the ancient Nile.'

Has the project, which eventually cost $1.5 billion, fulfilled its expectations? For such an unambiguous construction, the answer is extraordinarily hard to divine. Almost 30 years after its completion, claims that it is both 'a disaster' and 'a crowning success for large dam construction' are routinely made as if they were self-evident. The truth probably has more to do with the trade-off between long- and short-term gains.

The plus side is mostly short-term. Dangerous floods have been staunched, while the dam helped protect Egypt from the drought of the 1980s that devastated upstream countries such as Sudan and Ethiopia. Constant high water-levels in the Nile have meant that most fields now produce two or three crops of high-yield grains or cash crops, with water-guzzlers such as sugar cane and rice joining cotton. There is spare water for the development of 'new lands' in the desert, and attached to the dam is a hydroelectric plant with a capacity as great as the Hoover Dam.

But there is a substantial 'down-side' to the dam, which will inevitably grow with the passing decades. The first is the fate of the 120 million tonnes of silt brought down annually by the river. The silt is the fertile product of upstream soil erosion, much of it in the Ethiopian highlands. Once, a tenth of this silt ended up on fields. Today, the silt is building up uselessly in Lake Nasser. It will be hundreds of years before the silt seriously reduces the reservoir's capacity. But, coupled with the more intensive cropping, the loss has deprived many soils of vital nutrients and trace elements contained not just in the silt, but also in the organic matter that it contains.

When William Willcocks built the first Aswan Dam he ensured that the silty flow passed over the dam and on downstream to the fields. He warned that: 'The rich muddy water of the Nile flood has been the mainstay of Egypt for many generations, and it can no more be dispensed with today than in the past.' Since the completion of the High Aswan, which trapped all the silt, Egypt has become one of the heaviest users of chemical fertilisers in the world. It applies 175 kilograms to every hectare of farmland each year, some of it manufactured near Aswan with hydroelectric power generated at the dam. Even so, many trace elements in the soil are in increasingly short supply.

The Nile delta, a creation of silt deposited as the river reached the sea, ceased to grow more than a century ago, when the first barrages were built. But since 1964, it has been in full retreat. The former village at Borg-el-Borellos, at the mouth of one of the main channels out of the delta, is now 2 kilometres out to sea. Beyond the delta, in the eastern Mediterranean, the silt and the algae in it once fed a fishery that yielded 30,000 tonnes of sardines a year. But that disappeared almost overnight when the dam was closed.

Nile silt served a number of less obvious purposes. Bricks were made from it. Now, as a result of the High Aswan Dam, the people who built the pyramids are running out of bricks. The river bank is pitted by brick pits that the river has never refilled. Between 1964 and 1984, brick makers desperate for new supplies bought up an estimated 1,000 square kilometres of fertile farmland, and stripped it of soil. In 1985, the government legislated to halt the practice, but with little success.

The Nile no longer brings silt to the fields of Egypt, but it does bring salt. The white crystals first seen in the delta a century ago, are now spreading fast in the hot Egyptian sun. Abundant water has vastly accelerated the process. Each year, six million tonnes of salt now accumulate in the fields of Egypt, one tonne per hectare. The country spends tens of millions of dollars each year laying the largest piped drainage network in the world, in an attempt to keep water-tables low and prevent salination of soils. Even so, two-thirds of fields have drainage problems and on more than a third of the fields, which the Nile once flushed clean every summer, salt is reducing crop yields.

But Egypt's worst problem, the greatest poison distributed by the dam along with its water, has been to believe Nasser's boast that it would be a 'source of everlasting prosperity'. This engineering hubris has led the country to spend huge sums of money chasing absurd dreams that succeed only in pouring the dam's expensively won water into the sands of the desert.

Since 1964, the top priority of Egyptian agricultural planners in dispensing the Aswan Dam's waters has been to reclaim 'new lands' from the desert. The programme was foolish from the start and has proved disastrous in practice. According to one study, only around half of the land 'reclaimed' from the desert since the revolution by the provision of irrigation canals, has ever been cultivated.

Liberation Province, the first effort, was an almost complete failure. Then came the biggest area of new lands, 5,000 square kilometres west of the delta in an area named Nubaria. Engineers built canals, roads, new villages, electricity lines and 2,000 pumping stations. There were wheat fields and rice paddies, even fish ponds. But almost as soon as the new Nubaria Canal brought water to the land, fields became waterlogged. Large numbers were abandoned as the engineers moved on to the next scheme.

The trick, as much self-delusion as anything else, is to show off the new land before it returns to the desert. And so, around new towns such as Intelaq, journalists are occasionally taken to visit the blooming of the Western Desert. In November 1987, *The Times*'s Ian Murray wrote of a former sand dune at Intelaq where: 'Birds now flit through the eucalyptuses, oranges and grapefruit glow in the green citrus orchards, and even mushrooms push up through the wild strawberries on the floor of the pine forest.'

Even allowing for journalistic exaggeration, it was a fine picture, though spoilt somewhat by the discovery that the farm Murray had visited was a research station. Farmers down the road could produce only a fraction of the fruit needed to be profitable. 'They began arriving a year ago, but already some of their farms looked doomed,' said Murray later in his piece. The 'most successful' such scheme, he said, was the 20,000 hectares of the El-Salhia project, a privately owned desert plantation where 'barley and beans, gladioli and

peanuts are flourishing'. But even here 'the price of the irrigation exceeds the value of the crop'.

All over the Western Desert, poor sandy soils with the
texture of granulated sugar have been expensively equipped
with irrigation canals, and then forgotten about a few years
later. Some determined farmers have dug up mud from the
banks of the Nile and brought it by truck to spread on their
desert fields. But meanwhile, good fertile soils in the delta
have been under-used because of inefficient water distribution
or allowed to degenerate to salty quagmires for want of
drains. More still has been buried beneath the advancing
suburbs of Cairo, the largest city in Africa, whose growth the
hydroelectricity generated at Aswan made possible.

The actual amount of land under cultivation in Egypt is
falling. It peaked around 25,000 square kilometres in the early
1960s and, despite plans to raise the irrigated area to 30,000
square kilometres after the completion of the dam, it has since
fallen back. Murray was able to begin his paean from Egypt's
Garden of Eden with the observation that 'the map still shows
this as desert', though it now begins to look as if the map-
makers knew best.

Despite the disasters, the ideological juggernaut of watering
the 'new lands' rolls on. Egypt is already using more water
than it is entitled to under the 1959 agreement with Sudan, but
it intends to pour another 9 cubic kilometres of Nile water
each year on to some 6,000 square kilometres of new land to
be wrenched from the deserts during the 1990s. High on the
list of crops to be expanded is rice, which requires 6,000 times
its own weight in water to produce a successful harvest.

Middle East water expert Tony Allan, from the School of
Oriental and African Studies in London, detects the same
madness that he also sees in Soviet water projects. 'Unviable
projects have been sustained as national fantasies, and once
established, cannot be gainsaid without an intolerable loss of
face by the national leadership,' he says.

Despite the dam and the new lands Egypt does not feed
itself. In 1972, months after the completion of the dam, it
became a net importer of food. In the 20 years since, the
country has become ever more dependent on food imports

and on aid from the USA and Saudi Arabia. A combination of salt problems, urban sprawl from Cairo and the destruction of farmland to provide bricks has reduced the amount of farmland faster than it is being 'reclaimed' from the desert. A more important reason is the country's growing addiction to using its irrigated fields for export crops. Most of its extra output from the High Aswan's water – a result of growing more crops on the same land – has been devoted to this task.

Egypt remains one of the world's major exporters of cotton, growing around half a million tonnes a year. Besides cotton, the country produces more than 2 million tonnes of water-hungry rice, much of it for export, and more than 9 million tonnes of an even more thirsty crop, sugar cane. The water that can irrigate one hectare of sugar cane can sustain five hectares of cotton or rice, 10 hectares of wheat, 15 and 30 hectares respectively of two traditional grain crops, sorghum and millet.

Since the days of Mohammed Ali, Egypt has harnessed its irrigated fields to the production of water-hungry crops required by other countries, whether imperial masters or trading partners. It has, with or without the High Aswan Dam, sufficient water to feed its own people, but not to meet its wildly ambitious plans for export production.

The tragedy is that in order to meet its current export targets, it may have fatally mortgaged its future, reducing the fertility of soils that have been bountiful over millennia, but are now deteriorating year by year. To maintain those soils, its most prized natural asset, it must spend ever more on fertiliser and drainage. And to pay for that will mean selling more and more export crops, and working the soils ever harder.

Once Egypt fed itself by blindfolding oxen and making them walk a treadmill, endlessly turning thousands of water-wheels to raise water to its fields. Now it is the nation itself that appears to be on a treadmill, forced to walk ever faster to maintain what once came free of charge on the annual flood from the 'mountains of the moon' – a gift of the Nile.

'I noticed on entering the narrow gorge below Ajona that it

was an ideal place for a dam.' So wrote Sir Albert Kitson, director of the Gold Coast Geological Survey, in his diary in April 1915, during a canoe trip down the River Volta. Of such observations are national tragedies made. Fifty years later, the dam was built, more than a twentieth of the newly independent state of Ghana was under its waters, and, partly because of the false hopes placed in the dam, a nation which had been the brightest star among the emerging countries of Africa, was bankrupt.

For many decades the British regarded the Gold Coast as a model colony. The country became the British Empire's main source of cocoa, and white men travelled freely in the interior, boating along the several branches of the River Volta as they flowed through a country of forests and savanna grasses. Kitson discovered his gorge, near the small town of Akosombo in the lower reaches of the Volta, only a year after finding a large deposit of bauxite, the raw material for aluminium, not far away at Mpraeso. He soon began dreaming of harnessing a dam in the gorge to provide cheap hydroelectricity for smelting aluminium, a new metal that found extensive use in the aircraft industry.

In 1924, Kitson proposed a 15-metre dam at Akosombo. He got nowhere then, but two decades later, the prospects had been transformed by the success of the Hoover Dam in the American West. Britain had mined Gold Coast bauxite to manufacture its own planes, but after the war found itself hostage to an American near-monopoly in smelting capacity. The government consequently encouraged the British Aluminium Company and its Canadian equivalent Alcan to buy into the African Aluminium Syndicate, a company set up to build a dam, now to be 75 metres high, at Akosombo.

The British became ambitious. A civil servant, Sir Robert Jackson, drew up a comprehensive development plan for the Gold Coast, based around the dam. It was like an African version of the Tennessee Valley Authority and envisaged creating a single body, the Volta River Authority, to supervise the transformation of the country. The dam would now be 113 metres high and have a capacity of 165 cubic kilometres, almost exactly the same as Lake Nasser in Egypt, though it would drown an area of fertile land as large as Lebanon in the centre of the country.

To justify such a loss, Jackson planned a massive development of bauxite mining to feed smelters, and of irrigation on the nation's surviving farms. He foresaw a bustling traffic of ships across the new lake and dozens of factories powered by hydroelectric turbines at the dam. The hook was the dam, the bait was cheap power for aluminium smelting, but the big fish was the investment to transform Ghana into a modern industrial nation.

By this time, Ghana's independence was only two years away. The battle to control the new nation was between Joseph Danquah, a radical activist and lawyer with good connections everywhere from the Inner Temple in London to the tribal chiefs of his own land, and Kwame Nkrumah, a charismatic and brilliant populist with strong Marxist leanings.

Danquah sensed danger in the Akosombo project. He declared that 'the Volta River is not for sale'. A colleague, K. A. Busia, warned that 'it is against our interest as a nation to mortgage our entire economic future' to the international aluminium industry. Danquah favoured more modest plans to irrigate the farms that were the country's prime source of wealth, and to build small dams to generate electricity for the farmers.

But Nkrumah saw Ghana and himself in the vanguard of a modern Africa based on rapid industrialisation. Marxist or not, he desperately wanted foreign investment to build the dam and make his dreams come true. And he wanted a single, giant project – a symbol around which his new country could unite and display as evidence of Ghana's arrival in the modern world. That symbol was the dam. He had none of Danquah's forebodings. The Soviets had thought nothing of flooding huge areas of fertile river valley along the Volga to generate hydroelectricity, and after Nkrumah visited that country and saw these great works, it became a badge of pride that his dam on the Volta would create the world's largest man-made lake.

When the British pulled out of the project in 1957,

Nkrumah sought help from President Eisenhower to persuade US companies to fulfil the Jackson plan for comprehensive development of his country. Eisenhower was anxious to make up for his political mistake the year before in allowing Moscow to build the High Aswan Dam in Egypt and take the political high ground in Africa. But there was a world surplus of aluminium smelting capacity and when Nkrumah met Edgar Kaiser of the US aluminium combine the Kaiser Corporation in New York in July 1958, Kaiser had the whip hand. He did not need the extra capacity offered by Nkrumah and could name his terms.

Through subsequent negotiations, leading up to the eventual signing of the Master Agreement between the two men in 1962, talk of comprehensive development of the Volta basin disappeared. Nkrumah was forced to abandon all idea of large irrigation projects. Investment in fishing and shipping was dropped. Finally and most humiliatingly, though a new survey had confirmed Ghana as having one of the largest bauxite reserves in the world, he had to agree that Kaiser would import its raw material for smelting from Jamaica.

Only the dam and the smelter survived the negotiations. And even then the final contract was hedged around with numerous promises. Ghana agreed to maintain cripplingly low electricity prices for three decades, to exempt Kaiser from taxes on imports for smelting, and not to nationalise or interfere with the smelting plant in any way. It even agreed, in order to gain a loan from the World Bank, not to use revenues from electricity sales in any sector of the economy other than power generation.

Moreover, Kaiser, in its role as consulting engineer to the project, insisted that the dam was designed with a spillway so high that there was little or no chance of its future use to irrigate farms downstream of the dam on the Accra plains. This was despite a study by the US government that showed irrigation to be at least as profitable a use for the water as hydroelectric power, and despite the fact that the downstream farmers would be desperate for water once the dam stopped the annual flow of silty floodwaters across their fields each summer.

Danquah, the one leader to oppose the dam from the start, was defeated for the presidency by Nkrumah in 1960 and sent to prison, in 1961, where he died in leg-irons in 1965. That year, Nkrumah, growing increasingly demagogic as his dream died around him, published a book damning the role of foreign capital in the failure of Africa's dream of development. On 22 January 1966, he inaugurated the Akosombo Dam. But the next month, while on a visit to China and perhaps considering a switch to Maoist policies of self-sufficiency and rural development, he was overthrown in a coup.

It is far from clear whether Ghana gained anything at all from the plant. With half of the electricity from the dam tied to Kaiser's smelter until the mid-1990s, Kaiser was, by the early 1980s, buying electricity from Ghana at one-twentieth of the average world price. The World Bank concluded that Ghana would not recoup its expenditure on the £100-million dam until the contract expired in 1997. As a major rebuilding of the dam took place in 1991, it emerged that, even after rehabilitation, it would only provide reliable power for a further 20 years.

The waters of the River Volta had been sold – and sold very cheaply. They had taken with them what was once one of the brightest political careers in independent Africa. More important, however, they had spread disease across the countryside, brought chaos to stretches of the coastline and drowned the homes and farms of 80,000 people.

As the waters of Lake Volta rose, Ghanaian officials belatedly woke up to the fact that all these people would have to be rehoused. Eventually, they herded the bulk of the residents from 700 villages by boat and along hastily constructed roads to 52 new villages. Because there were not enough lorries, many people had to leave their possessions behind. The evacuees found that there were not enough houses in their new villages, that soils were often poor, that promised farmland had not been cleared, and that farm equipment had not arrived. Within months, the United Nations was bringing relief food aid to the evacuees, and eight years later, a UN study found that most had fled: while 64,000 people had been taken to the villages only 25,000 remained. The dam had turned independent peasant farmers into a dispossessed rural under-class dependent on the state for food, shelter and work.

Lake Volta has left many other legacies that will long outlive even Kaiser's 30-year power contract. The worst may be schistosomiasis. This sometimes fatal disease, the bane of African water projects, is caused by a parasitic worm har-boured by certain types of snails that live in stagnant tropical water. Before the creation of Lake Volta, the general infection rate in the rural population of central Ghana was 1–5 per cent, mostly in pockets of water on the river delta and some upland streams. Since the dam created 5,200 kilometres of stagnant lake shoreline, where algae and weeds attract large numbers of snails, infection rates have risen to 80 per cent. Farmers tempted to farm the 1,500 square kilometres of mud-flats created when the reservoir was drawn down during the drought years of the 1980s were especially vulnerable.

Fish stocks have remained high in the lake above the Ako-sombo Dam, with landings averaging around 30,000 tonnes. According to one review, income from fish sales during the 1980s exceeded that from power sales. But below the dam many species of commercial fish have disappeared, along with oyster beds and a once-thriving shrimp fishery. Since the dam was built, there has been a steady migration of people from villages downstream. Along with the fishermen, thousands of farmers too have departed as the annual flood cycle that once fertilised their fields has failed.

If anything, life on the coast around the mouth of the Volta has been damaged worst of all. The Volta's silt, trapped behind the dam, no longer reaches the coastline, which has begun to retreat under the constant scouring by strong Atlan-tic Ocean currents. Keta, a town of 10,000 people built on a sand spit around a lagoon at the mouth of the Volta, has disappeared into the sea. The coast of neighbouring Togo is being eaten away, too. A chunk of the main Ghana-Benin highway along the West African coast has disappeared, and a harbour jetty is threatened.

None of these hidden costs to the lives of Ghanaians from construction of the dam appear in government calculations, partly because they are hard to quantify and partly because most affect the masses of rural poor who are unable to make their case in government circles. This may be one reason why the Ghanaian government under Jerry Rawlings seemed set at the beginning of the 1990s to repeat its mistakes by building a new dam, even larger than Akosombo, on the Black Volta a few miles above where it enters Lake Volta.

The British once had great hopes that, even without state investment, Lake Volta would become an important shipping thoroughfare. Kaiser had told Nkrumah that, within months of the dam's completion, hundreds of thousands of tonnes of goods would be transported across the lake. Instead, it took a big aid loan before a single ship, the *Akosombo Queen*, set off upstream from the dam in 1973. The ship never did much business and was scuppered six years later.

PART III

Age of the Superdam

11

TO SUBDUE THE EARTH

Big dams and water projects have not only failed to achieve
their basic objectives, but are also leaving a legacy of un-
surpassed cultural destruction, disease and environmental
damage.

Brent Blackwelder, Environmental Policy Institute,
Washington, 1984

There is an unnerving fervour about dam-builders – especially
when assembled en masse at meetings of the International
Commission on Large Dams (ICOLD). For one thing, they are
almost all men. I counted three women at one gathering of 500
engineers at their triennial conference in Vienna in 1991. For
another thing, many of these remoulders of the planet, the
begetters of hundreds of structures the size of the Great
Pyramid, have a messianic fervour for their calling. To suggest
that their creations, by interfering brutally in the flow of great
rivers, might be doing harm as well as good is to invite an
inquisition of your motives. To question their own motives is
to bring blind incomprehension. Mankind needs water; water
is in rivers; therefore the rivers must be tamed, runs their
creed.

Since the construction of the High Aswan and Akosombo
dams in the 1960s, they have pursued their vision and their
contracts with hardly a look over their shoulders. Large dams
remain today an experimental technology, in part because few
studies have ever attempted to assess their ultimate impact.
Nobody has quantified the cost to Ghana of the lost farmland
and fisheries, the increased disease and eroded coastline.
Nobody in Cairo has tried to balance the lost silt and

encroachment of salt to Egyptian fields against the increased water supply and hydroelectric power. Still less has anyone attempted to gauge the warping effect on political and economic life of harnessing small undeveloped nations to the success or failure of a single giant dam.

The 1991 ICOLD conference was held in Vienna in a conference centre beside an artificial channel of the River Danube. A meander of the Old Danube, abandoned by nineteenth-century water engineers, dawdled by unnoticed several hundred metres away. On stage the opening ceremony featured musical celebrations of a rustic Austrian past – a time when, according to the master of ceremonies, the Danube floodplain was a land of 'wide pastures and dense woods'.

There appeared no flicker of recognition from his audience that it was their efforts that had obliterated most of these features with dykes and weirs, constructed in the cause of improved navigation and flood protection. Nor did they recall that five years before, they had lost a bloody battle with environmentalists who wanted to preserve the last great riverine forest of the middle Danube, the Hainburg Forest. The dam-builders had wanted to flood the forest in order to generate hydroelectricity for Vienna.

On their way into the conference centre, the delegates had smiled at the chants of protesters calling for 'No Dams' and 'Free the World's Rivers'. For them, the world's destiny was bound up with dams. The conference host, Wolfgang Pircher, declared that the world's 36,000 large dams, each with a height greater than 15 metres, were 'the key to our management of the lifegiving waters of the rivers', and the means to defeat 'nature's scourges ... droughts, floods and epidemics'. They were 'essential to our very way of life ... many more have to be built'.

ICOLD's President, Jan Veltrop, after 37 years of dam-building, revealed none of the fashionable modern doubts about technological advance. 'Science fiction has become reality,' he declared with a fierce joy, though there was much work to be done. 'Eighty nations face a serious shortage of water; 1.2 billion people are without safe drinking water ... The management of the world's water is the greatest challenge facing mankind in the decades ahead.'

The keynote address from Professor Otto Hittmaier, past president of the Austrian Academy of Sciences, called for sound environmental management of rivers, but charged the environmentalists outside with being 'ideological dogmatists whose purpose is to prevent rational planning'. Rational planning had been the making of mankind, he said. On the Tigris, Euphrates, Nile and Indus, the 'design and construction work required to harness water could only be carried out in the framework of an ordered society'.

It was straight out of Wittfogel's texts on hydraulic civilisation, though Hittmaier made no mention of the down-side of Wittfogel's idea – that such ordered societies were inherently despotic and, ultimately, unable to adapt or evolve – the dinosaurs of civilisation. Large dams, said Hittmaier, 'are a visible symbol of efficient and responsible environmental management' and 'the very basis for a civilised existence'. Nature was all very well, but 'man's first duty is to his species. We should obey the biblical command to go forth and subdue the Earth.'

This urge, evident in the works of engineers from the time of ancient Sumer, through classical Rome to nineteenth-century Victorian endeavours, has been pursued in this century with greater vigour and greater technological facility than ever before. In the post-war years, the Soviet and American models of harnessing rivers in the cause of economic advance provided the backdrop, and much of the expertise, for what happened in the Third World.

After the High Aswan and the Akosombo dams came an avalanche of massive projects designed to catapult nations emerging from the colonial yoke into the modern world. In India, Nehru launched one of the most ambitious dam-building programmes, starting with the 226-metre Bhakra Dam, which was completed in 1963 on a tributary of the Indus. Four years later Pakistan completed the Jari and Mangla dams on two of its Indus tributaries.

Nigeria, the most populous nation in Africa, built the Kainji on the River Niger. On the Zambezi, the British colonial authorities had completed the Kariba Dam, and the

Portuguese followed downstream with the Cahora Bassa. Brazil was busy too, while in Iran the young Shah decided to replace traditional *qanats* with dams in the hills above Teheran. Only guerrilla warfare prevented the Americans from building a staircase of dams down the Mekong in southeast Asia.

A technology barely tested in the landscapes of Europe and North America was being unloaded on to foreign lands with very different and more vulnerable environments with a reckless disregard for the possible consequences. Dams were built to irrigate already highly productive farmland, to generate electricity where none was needed and to end seasonal floods on which millions of farmers and fishermen depended.

Sometimes, it seemed, they were built for little discernible purpose other than as a symbol of nationhood. Like a national airline, or an international conference centre, no modern nation could be without one. Whatever travails had to be borne, whichever babies had to go unfed, it was a necessary sacrifice. But a generation later, we can begin to count the cost and assess whether the promised benefits were delivered. Have we tamed nature; and if so, has it benefited us?

Today worldwide there are more than a hundred 'superdams', with a height of more than 150 metres, subduing some of the world's greatest rivers. Three-quarters of the world's superdams have been built in the past 35 years; around fifty of them were completed during the 1980s. Their reservoirs have a total capacity of 6,000 cubic kilometres and they cover almost 600,000 square kilometres. That makes them, in aggregate, roughly the size of the North Sea. Their capacity is equal to 15 per cent of the annual runoff of the world's rivers. Already those dams are holding back so much water that they artificially lower by a few millimetres the tides on every beach in the world. By early next century, if the dam-builders get their way, two-thirds of all the flow of rivers to the oceans may be controlled behind large dams.

In the 1950s, large dams were still heralded by environmentalists as the gleaming wonders of the modern age, as the source of cheap, clean, unending hydroelectric power promised by the dam-builders of the American West. The first man to glimpse a different truth was David Brower, a Californian

loner who enjoyed walking the mountains of the Sierra
Nevada, and who in 1952 became the first paid executive
director of the leading conservation group of the day, the
Sierra Club. In those post-war years, with the dam-builders
anxious to construct new Hoover dams across the American
West and round the world, Brower declared that 'no work of
man violated nature as completely, as irrevocably, as a dam'.

Brower's favourite spot in the American West was Echo
Park, a desert canyon in the upper Colorado basin where the
Green River supported lush meadows and willow trees. So it
was probably a mistake for the Bureau of Reclamation to
decide in the mid-1950s to dam the canyon and flood the
meadows to generate hydroelectric power. Blazing with indig-
nation, Brower testified before Congressional subcommittees
and demonstrated that, in its arrogance, the Bureau had manipulated the data for the hydroelectric and other benefits that
would flow from the dam. So persuasive was Brower in his
testimony that he was eventually supported by some leading
dam engineers, such as the head of the rival Corps of Engineers, General Ulysses Grant. The Bureau, outgunned,
dropped the project.

The victory inspired another of much greater significance,
the preservation of the Grand Canyon from a proposal by the
Bureau's engineers for a series of dams – including the Bridge
Canyon Dam, which would have cost 20 times the price of the
Hoover Dam and been the first billion-dollar dam.

For some, this triumph in the mid-Sixties was a turning
point for the whole American, and perhaps worldwide,
environment movement. Certainly it allowed people such as
Brower, whose interests lay more in the mountains of California than the dope-strewn streets of Haight Ashbury, to alert a
new generation of student radicals and counter-culture gurus
to green issues. As rock stars began to sing country songs and
the flower power people took their free love and tepees into
America's wild open spaces, the meeting of unlike minds
seemed complete.

Brower's growing radicalism led to his expulsion from the
Sierra Club and to his forming a new organisation, Friends
of the Earth, the first truly international environmental

organisation. Through its various chapters round the world, it became one of the driving forces behind opposition in the early 1970s to dam schemes such as the vast James Bay project in the Canadian Arctic.

While the first phase of the James Bay project went ahead, the fire of opposition to dams continued to burn. The 1930s dream of managed river valleys providing clean power to the toiling masses began to dissolve into a nightmare of obliterated landscapes – nature defiled rather than tamed, bludgeoned rather than managed.

In Britain in the 1970s, opponents succeeded in preventing the construction of water-supply dams in national parks on Dartmoor and the North Yorkshire moors and in Kent, the 'garden of England'. In the early 1980s, the Austrian greens awoke from their love-affair with dams in the Alps to prevent the drowning of the Hainburg Forest. Then in 1983, in one of the most heavily publicised and successful protests of all, demonstrators led by the Australian Bob Brown and Britain's 'television biologist' David Bellamy sat down in front of bulldozers to halt the Franklin Dam on the Gordon River in Tasmania. The dam would have flooded a large area of rainforest that had been uninhabited since white men hunted Tasmanian aborigines to extinction a century before. After their victory, the protesters set up the world's first green party.

As engineers moved their attentions to the developing world, greens followed. Indian campaigners proved just as resourceful as their first-world counterparts and prevented the damming of the Silent Valley in the Western Ghats and the inundation of its rich virgin rainforests. As in Tasmania, the sacrifice of forests to make electricity had proved a potent force to move public opinion.

Not all environmentalists were opposed to large dams. As late as 1981, the respected Worldwatch Institute in Washington DC, run by Lester Brown, looked forward to a quadrupling of world hydroelectric production by early next century and concluded in a lengthy and enthusiastic report on hydropower that: 'Developing countries cannot afford to miss the opportunities offered by large dams, despite the human and ecological disruption that their introduction can bring.'

As with most successful environmental campaigns, however, public concern was drawing from a well of academic concern. While most dam projects continued to be built, biologists, economists and hydrologists and even engineers were all voicing worries that the dam-building juggernaut was out of control. Some schemes, such as the Hoover Dam, were regarded as successes by all but the most hostile. But now the dam industry was earmarking less good sites and hoping to rely on its great financial and lobbying muscle, backed up by the endless retelling of a handful of success stories, to push through its schemes. The great icons of the movement, the Hoover and Grand Coulee dams, the schemes of the Tennessee Valley Authority, were receding memories.

The bad news was pushing out the good. The Akosombo was one horror story. The Kainji Dam, completed two years later in Nigeria, was another. This intended 'pillar of economic and social development' for Africa's most populous country threw 40,000 people off rich floodplains on the River Niger to generate electricity for national industrial development. Like Akosombo, it did extraordinary damage for a puny gain: its installed generating capacity is just 760 megawatts. As the floodplain dried out, fish catches and dry-season harvests fell by more than 50 per cent right down to the river delta, more than 600 kilometres downstream. Thayer Scudder, an American academic with thirty years' experience of watching the failures of African water projects, concluded that Kainji had 'more negative impacts on riverine production systems than any other large-scale dam in tropical Africa'.

There was a litany of failure too from India, where an estimated 16 million people have been moved from their land to speed the largest dam-building programme in the world over the past 25 years. Dams became harbingers of drought rather than plenty across the arid lands of Africa and, as at Cahora Bassa on the Zambezi, became targets for guerrilla warfare. Crazy schemes in the Amazon jungle yielded more mosquitoes and more poisonous gases from rotting vegetation than power.

By the start of the 1990s, governments were growing fearful of the long lead-times and soaring costs for large dams. Even the banks had begun to say no. Just 20 major dams had been completed in the three years before ICOLD's 1991 meeting, compared to 30 in the same period a decade before. Only five more were slated for completion in 1991. One of them, the Rogun Dam in the Soviet Union, the highest in the world, was six years behind schedule and destined only to increase the destruction of the Aral Sea.

Like that other icon of modern energy engineering, the nuclear power station, the project that finished on time and within budget was a rare event. Of the ten largest dams under construction a decade before, four were now more than five years late; three had disappeared off all international lists, apparently abandoned; and only one, El Cajun in Honduras, had been completed on time.

A possible new icon was the Itaipu hydroelectric dam on the River Parana in Paraguay. Completed in 1982, largely by Brazilian companies under the control of the military regime, it could generate 12,600 megawatts. It was comfortably the world's largest hydroelectric dam, ahead of the Guri project finished in Venezuela four years later, and it was likely to remain the largest until the end of the century. Itaipu feeds electricity to Brazil's great cities of Rio de Janeiro and São Paulo and makes Paraguay the largest exporter of electricity in the world. But it suffered from association with the military regimes that built it and Brazil's environmental destruction in the Amazon.

Set for completion in 1996 further downstream on the Parana is the Yacyreta hydroplant. Almost a decade behind schedule, its dams and dykes will stretch for no less than 70 kilometres, linking islands across the floodplain of the river on the Paraguayan border with Argentina. No icon this, it has been plagued with design and construction problems and was described by the Argentine's President Menem as a 'monument to corruption' in the former military dictatorship. Posted costs of a project that will displace more than 100,000 people have risen from $1.5 billion to $6.5 billion, and the final bill may be $12 billion.

The rationale for the construction of dams is straight-forward and powerful. Most of the world's rivers have very variable flow. Either they are highly seasonal, such as the great monsoon rivers of Asia, and rivers that rely on springtime snowmelt, or, as in deserts, a great proportion of their flow comes in sudden storms. To make the best use of the rivers – for generating hydroelectric power, for diverting the water to irrigate fields, or for navigation – the high flows need to be captured and then released slowly during times of natural low flow. Only dams can do this.

In the real world, life has not proved so simple. Rivers are not, as engineers sometimes imagine, simple conduits by which water reaches the sea. They have floodplains which, if left to their own devices, will flood. They recharge groundwaters and permanent wetlands. They have back-waters where fish spawn. They bring silt from the mountains to the sea, where it may create fertile deltas, and so on.

These processes are often the basis for natural wealth – of forests, fish and other wildlife – on which millions of people in a single river valley may depend. Dams disrupt the rivers and often destroy this natural wealth. Many dam-builders now concede that they should 'mitigate' such damage where possible. Some, such as the chairman of ICOLD's environmental committee, the British consulting engineer Ted Haws, would agree that the precise size and site of a dam should depend on such considerations. What few can even contemplate is that, in any but the most exceptional case, dams could, by disrupting river valleys in this way, do more harm than good.

Nor, in their devotion to dams as symbols and engines of progress, can many understand that their projects may be politically and socially undesirable, rewarding the wealthy city-dwellers and depriving the rural inhabitants of the natural wealth of the river valleys – the fish and meadows, silt and free irrigation. Because this natural wealth is rarely turned into cash, and is more often part of the cash-less 'subsistence economy' of the rural poor, it is too often invisible to econo-mists and government ministers. Few Ghanaian officials are even aware of the harm done to the countryside and its inhabitants by the Akosombo Dam.

A river valley sustaining millions of people may produce virtually no 'gross national product' in the sense that economists understand it. But its 'gross *natural* product' may be immense. The first time national planners may contemplate this distinction may be when thousands of refugees from the floodplains, their fields dried out by the dams and their fisheries gone, appear in shanty towns around capital cities. These people, rather like the 'poor commoners' created by the draining of the English fens 300 years ago, are refugees from a war between the cash economy and traditional subsistence economies. Says the British hydrologist Philip Williams: 'Dams are essentially a weapon in the expropriation of a common resource by special interests.'

Williams is an interesting figure in the debate. An Englishman who emigrated to California, he runs a successful consultancy, advising local authorities on how to turn the concrete-lined drainage ditches and water channels of that most engineered of states back into real rivers, with reed beds and lily ponds, mayflies and mud. Doubling as president of the International Rivers Network, an anti-dam pressure group, he arrived in Vienna in June 1991 both to demonstrate outside the ICOLD conference and to speak at its sessions.

In the besieged world of ICOLD, conference officials were flummoxed by this banner-wielding, tie-wearing, carefully spoken, rabble-rousing fifth-columnist. The commission's environment committee rounded on the demonstrators for being opposed to progress and anti-rational. 'They want the electricity, but they don't want the dams,' as one put it. But Williams stood by his assertion that nobody need enter into a debate about the aesthetic value of a landscape or put a price-tag on a submerged Indian temple, still less need they debate the philosophy of 'small is beautiful'. Almost every large dam ever built, he said, would have been ruled uneconomic if the true economic cost of their destruction of natural wealth had been placed in the balance.

He probably exaggerates. All forms of energy round the world are subsidised in some way. Nuclear power stations do not pay for the vast research expenditure involved in their development (which was mostly paid for by the military), nor the likely ultimate waste disposal costs. Coal- and oil-fired power stations do not pay for the cost of the acid rain and global warming that their emissions produce. If they did, then all electricity would cost more. And that would improve the 'benefit' side of the cost-benefit equation for hydroelectric power.

But what is certain is that, if customers for all sources of energy paid the full environmental costs of its generation, then energy saving would be an even more attractive alternative to building new power plants of all kinds than it currently is. We don't, after all, actually want the electricity itself; we want the services it can provide. We don't even want the water in the irrigation systems; we want the food that they can produce. But engineers have somehow persuaded us that all our investment should go into generating electricity and providing water, rather than making more efficient use of what we have. This makes increasingly little sense.

Besides Williams, ICOLD's members heard just one speaker able to utter some home truths about large dams. He was Ernest Razvan from the International Hydraulics Institute at Delft in the Netherlands. He was no fundamentalist opponent of dams and had harsh words for some environmentalists. But he agreed with them that dams 'are damaging the state of natural equilibrium that results from millions of years of evolution. It's not just butterflies or fish or reptiles, it's groundwater, soils and vegetation.'

He called for ICOLD to produce a new environmental code of conduct for its members, to stop engineers cutting environmental corners in their designs in order to make the cheapest bid. Dam engineers cannot take this kind of talk. Haws was on his feet from the platform. 'I don't think it is necessary to impugn the ethics of consultants,' he said angrily. Haws refused to accept for publication in the conference proceedings a paper submitted by Razvan in which the renegade Dutchman presented his thoughts even more sharply. Large dams were 'exceeding the adaptation capacity of environmental systems', he said. Setting his face against the hydrologists' article of faith that any water left untamed in a river was running to waste, he went on: 'To be environmentally compatible, a project should observe some limits. The concept of the protection of water resources becomes parallel to the use of water resources. It follows that the idea of maximising the use of river flow should be abandoned.' He continued:

> When I proposed such an approach in a feasibility study of one particular dam, my associates flatly rejected it. By presenting our client with a more expensive solution, they argued, we will nullify our chances of receiving new orders. Our competitors would probably follow the conventional approach and thus deliver much cheaper solutions. Professionally I was frustrated, but I accepted their decision. The environmental compatibility could become a design criterion only if observed by all consultants involved ... It is a matter of professional ethics ... It is time for professional organisations such as ICOLD to take a stand on such an issue.

But not only did ICOLD fail to take a stand, the guardians of its environmental flank refused to allow Razvan to make his case. ICOLD's creed is to improve the construction and effectiveness of large dams, but never, it seems, to question their virtue. Perhaps they understand where the argument leads. Razvan certainly does. 'The new approach', he said, 'requires an abandonment of a basic concept of Western civilisation, that man is the master of nature and not a part of it. It is a long way from this old conception, deeply rooted in the human mind, to the new ideas about environmental protection. An ideological shift must take place, and rapidly.'

The enclosed world of the dam-builders, the great engineers of nature, seems unable to make that ideological shift. And that is why this bastion of the age of reason suddenly seems to many not so much thrusting and modern as arcane and out of touch. When Williams told the members of ICOLD that he was no infidel, and was merely asking them to extend their rational thought to encompass the impact of their creations, they reacted with incomprehension. They equate rationality with human mastery of the planet, and still believe that only greater mastery, in the form of more huge bludgeoning structures, will allow humanity to thrive and prosper. They see no prospect or purpose in a new, softer, more harmonious form of living. They look forward to a new generation of mega-projects, of a fully plumbed planet, with awe and expectation. Could they be right?

Before examining in more detail the world that the super-dams and other large hydraulic projects of the late twentieth century are creating, we look first at what it means to a single valley when the dam-builders move in.

12

A RUMBLE IN THE HILLS

A new caste system has evolved around the new temples of India.

Jayanta Bandyopadhyay, Indian Institute of Management,
1985

There are new occupants in the palace high above the town of Tehri in the western Himalayas. Until 1949, the palace was the home of the kings of Tehri-Garwhal. By the late 1980s it had fallen into the hands of the Tehri Hydro Development Corporation and its Soviet technical advisers, who wanted to drown the valley below for 45 kilometres by building the largest dam in Asia.

The yellow building is perched above the spot where the rivers Bhagirathi and Bhillunguna, tributaries of the sacred River Ganges, join. Far below, they are building the first stages of a 244-metre dam. On the facing hilltop sit a series of concrete barracks. These are the first phase of Tehri New Town, homes for some of the 80,000 people who will be moved from the old town of Tehri and from 23 nearby villages when the valley is flooded. Tehri, a bustling market town, has been turned into a huge construction site in the midst of the Himalayas. Day and night, the town is rent with the noise of trucks rumbling across the bridge over the Bhagirathi at the entrance to the town, and on to the dam site. From a couple of kilometres away comes the sound of blasting, as workers dynamite the hills to provide the rocks that will make up the core of the dam. Dust covers everything; armed guards carrying fixed bayonets stand on street corners; and huge arc lights peer down through the night from the surrounding mountainsides. The river is filled with silt from earth-moving works.

This is what dam construction means to hundreds of communities all over the world, where inhabitants of remote towns and villages suddenly find that dam-builders want to flood their valleys. The residents of Tehri are told nothing of what is going on and are lied to contemptuously. For weeks in the autumn of 1990 construction managers denied what everybody could hear with their own ears: that their men were blasting rock from the hillsides at night. The denials only ended when, early one morning, a large rock flew over the hill and crashed through the roof of a house next door to the local chief of police.

During almost twenty years of fitful construction activity at Tehri, since the dam was first approved, diversion and overflow tunnels have been dug through the mountainsides. By the end of 1990 the river itself had been turned aside by a coffer dam, which was intended to keep the riverbed dry while the main dam was built. Few Indian politicians have visited Tehri during all this time to see what their decisions are inflicting on this Himalayan valley. The town is remote, and the nearest airport and railway stations are in the lowland towns south of the Himalayas, such as Dehra Dun.

The bus ride from Dehra Dun to Tehri is instructive. Everywhere the valleys are starved of investment. Agriculture is on the wane. Only a few communities along the valleys that funnel into Tehri have the small weirs and diversion channels that can take stream waters the few yards to irrigate their fields. Still fewer villages have electricity. Magnificent systems of terraces climb for 500 metres and more up the hillsides. They are the product of centuries of effort in rearranging soil to create fields from steep slopes, while preventing soil erosion. But most terraces lie abandoned. As their walls crumble, soil falls to the valley floor.

Village men work instead in the gangs that are widening the road to Tehri, another cause of soil erosion in the valley. Or they take the bus to work in the towns. The women left behind work 18-hour days in the fields, and the children, deprived of local schools, look after the goats. 'It's a money-order economy. Most families depend on cash earned in the towns to survive,' says Vijay Negi, a local writer who left the hills some years ago with his parents to live in Dehra Dun. 'Even now, my mother thinks largely of the old village.'

Much of the natural wealth of the valleys has been destroyed during the past century as the hill forests have been chopped down. Lately, foresters have met opposition from the Chipko movement, which is based here. Large signs on the hillsides announce the spending of European Community funds on tree-planting projects, but just past one sign, there is only a large clump of cactuses. Many hillsides have become rocky, soil-less and barren. A region with 120 days of rain each year is dotted today with cactus plants and in places looks little better than a desert.

As a result of these changes the hill soils can no longer store as much rainfall as they once did. Streams that once carried water all year long now dry up outside the monsoon season, while the monsoon floods have become more intense. Outside Dehra Dun, there are stony riverbeds hundreds of metres wide that dry up completely for nine months of the year. Traversing them are bridges that are washed away by the violence of each summer's floods.

This ecological decay is in the interests of neither the villagers nor the country. Negi laughs at the incompetence that allows a nation to destroy its mountain soils, a natural water reservoir, while spending billions of dollars to create new reservoirs behind giant dams.

The Geological Survey of India first identified the Bhagirathi gorge at Tehri as a possible dam site in 1949, and its survey report recommending the construction of a dam was completed by 1969. But progress since then has been slow. Work began in the mid-1970s, but ceased in the early 1980s as construction workers moved to another dam site. Then in 1986 Mikhail Gorbachev, carrying an open cheque book for funding energy projects, visited India for a summit with the then prime minister, Rajiv Gandhi. Indian officials had hoped to direct roubles into nuclear power, but negotiations failed. According to reports at the time, the Tehri Dam was picked up at short notice to fill the diplomatic gap and provide a deal to be signed at the end of the trip. Soon, Soviet engineers and equipment arrived in Tehri, and work began in earnest.

All the electricity generated at Tehri will be carried away by pylon to join the state grid at Meerut, 250 kilometres away – largely to power industry in the lowland cities. The dam will also provide extra water for state irrigation canals along the Ganges and Yamuna (the canals constructed by the British almost 150 years ago) and for taps in New Delhi. As water and electricity head south, villages in the Tehri region will remain without power to lift water the two metres from the local rivers that would allow them to irrigate their own fields. The Tehri dam has, like most dams round the world, been imposed on the locals with little or no consultation. But opposition has been intense and vocal. The Tehri Bandha Virodhi Sangharsh Samiti (Anti-Tehri Dam Struggle Committee) has had the support of the town offices of all the political parties since its formation in the mid-1970s, even while their state and national parties support the project.

The central figure in the opposition throughout that time has been a Tehri lawyer, Virendra Saklani, a former freedom-fighter who carried a gun as Indians fought the British for independence. Saklani became an activist with the Chipko movement to preserve the hill forests and, like many Indians, felt a strong spiritual attachment to the Ganges. 'The sanctity of the Ganges water is revered by millions,' he says. 'I have a bottle of Ganga water in my home. I drink it on special occasions. This water is unique because it never goes off. It has great purifying powers, even cleaning up industrial pollution.' He is convinced that a dam at Tehri will change the chemistry of the Ganges.

When I met him in November 1990, Saklani was in his mid-seventies, frail and suffering from bouts of asthma. But he was defiant. Days before, his campaign had been dealt what appeared to be a fatal blow. The Supreme Court in New Delhi had turned down his five-year-old application for dam work to be halted on the grounds that the government had not properly considered critical seismological evidence. That evidence pointed to the danger of a large earthquake in the region that could destroy the dam and drown towns downstream such as Rishikesh and Haridwar, where some 200,000 people live.

The judges, while ruling themselves not competent to decide on the merits of the seismological case, found that the government had gone through the proper procedures. Now Saklani held a counsel of war in the front room of his Tehri home. His fellow activists included town stall-keepers and the local hotel manager. It was their first meeting since the court decision. 'I am not depressed,' he told them. 'We shall just have to go back to the local courts and try again.'

The campaign's second major figure was Sunderlal Bahuguna, the leader of the Chipko movement, who found international fame with their tactic of hugging trees to prevent them from being chopped down. Bahuguna lives in Serian, a small village which is to be drowned by the Tehri Dam. He pledged to stay, whatever happens.

In December 1989 Bahuguna embarked on a ten-day hunger strike at the dam construction site, aimed at halting the project. The strike won plenty of publicity, helped in part by his son, who is the Tehri correspondent for several national newspapers. But locally the strike was not an altogether happy affair. When he spoke to students at the small Tehri campus of the University of Garwhal, he was howled down. And days later, supporters of the dam ransacked the camp set up by him at the dam site itself. There were persistent rumours that student leaders had been 'bought' by the Hydro-Development Corporation or contractors; but it was equally true that many students and townspeople no longer required bribes to support the dam.

For 20 years, Tehri has been blighted. The local hospital, which serves villages for many miles around, desperately needs investment. So does the university campus, much of which is housed in tin huts. The town's main hotel is an unswept flea-pit. The sewage and water supply systems have been left untended. Says Negi:

Nobody will invest in the town. Many people now just want the dam to go ahead. They say the indecision is unbearable. People want new hospitals, roads, shops but

until the uncertainty is ended and the move to New Tehri
made, they fear that no investment will come. The
uncertainty has affected the character of the people. There
is a sense of resignation; even the annual whitewashing of
walls is not done and people have grown used to unhygienic
conditions.

Few locals are employed on the dam site because contractors
prefer to truck in labourers with no local ties. But for some
the dam is a honey pot, a rare instance of money from central
coffers penetrating the hills. The prime local contractor, formerly an official in the state irrigation department, has
become a millionaire even before work begins on the main
dams. Bribes and fiddles proliferate.

Close to the village of Serain, landowners built a series of
ramshackle houses. Locals claim that the houses were built
solely in order to claim compensation from the authorities for
their eventual inundation. Once the cheque arrived, the
houses were taken apart and rebuilt down the road, ready for
a new round of compensation claims. The corruption runs
deep. Says one implacable member of the anti-dam committee, Kailish Uniyal: 'The dam is a form of madness. Most of
the politicians are puppets in the hands of industrialists and
businessmen who want to build the dam.' There is a new
local saying: 'As the Ganga of money is flowing, let's take a
dip into it.'

Uniyal is contemptuous of those who say that the dam is
essential for economic growth in the region. In the neighbouring province of Himachel Pradesh they have plans to generate
large amounts of power from small 'run-of-river' schemes that
rely on the natural flow of streams. 'Few people are displaced
and up to 60,000 local people can be employed to build them,'
he says. 'These schemes fit in with the local people and the
local ecology. They can be built on small rivers and at waterfalls. There is great potential in the Tehri area too for run-of-
river schemes.' In fact, a run-of-river hydroelectric project on
the Bhagirathi, which would have been generating power for
some years by now, was cancelled to make way for the Tehri
Dam.

Big dam projects develop a life of their own. Originally budgeted at two billion rupees, more than four billion rupees had already been spent on Tehri before work on the main dam even started. The official price-tag in 1986 was 13 billion rupees (then worth about £500 million), with unofficial estimates four times greater by the end of the decade. By a perverse logic, the government was by then unofficially advising that, whatever the pros and cons of the dam, too much money had been spent for it to be cancelled.

Since reviving the project in 1986, the Indian government has been besieged by safety objections, among them the one initiated by Saklani at Tehri. First, Soviet engineers voiced misgivings over the design of the dam, which they feared would not withstand a large earthquake. They wanted a more resistant core and a wider base. Then came a disturbing series of reports from Indian seismologists that the dam site was unusually prone to earthquakes. It is just 15 kilometres from the boundary between two continental plates, one of the 'joints' of the Earth's crust.

The India plate to the south is constantly pushing beneath the Eurasian plate to the north. Over millions of years it has created the Himalayas. The build-up of tension along the boundary is periodically released in major earthquakes. Furthermore, the section of the plate boundary that runs near to Tehri is part of a 700-kilometre-long 'seismic gap' – that is, a section of the boundary where the absence of major recent earthquakes leads seismologists to believe that there must be an increase in tension in the rocks that will eventually lead to a large earthquake. The seismic gap extends along the Himalayas from Kashmir, where an earthquake in 1905 measured 8.6 on the Richter scale, to the state of Bihar, where a quake of magnitude 8.4 hit in 1934.

Most of the government's experts work at the university in Roorkee, the home of a great engineering college set up in 1848 for training irrigation engineers, and the site of the giant aqueduct that carries the Ganges Canal across the River Solani. They have always insisted that their structure will be safe. And the government has relied on their guidance.

But in 1990 the country's best-known seismologist, Vinod

Gaur, joined forces with James Brune, one of the USA's top seismologists, to argue that the Tehri Dam would not be safe. Brune, who devised a formula used by the dam's engineers to calculate the maximum likely shake that an earthquake could impose at Tehri, said that they had misapplied his formula. He warned that there were known faults in the local rocks near Tehri. One lies in the riverbed close to the dam site. Another, the large Mahr fault, probably runs directly beneath Tehri. Such faults might be connected directly to the main plate boundary and could bring the force of a large quake much closer to the dam. The Tehri Dam site was 'one of the most hazardous in the world from an earthquake point of view' and there was a 'high probability' of a major earthquake during the lifetime of the dam. A year later, a quake happened in the hills north of Tehri. More than a thousand people died in villages along the Bhagirathi River from a quake only a tenth the size of that predicted for the area. Brune warned afterwards: 'This could be just a preliminary for the big one. Surely now the government must review its plans before it is too late.' But construction continued, and when Bahuguna began a new hunger strike in early 1992, he and his compatriots were arrested and locked up.

If the Tehri Dam is ever filled, it will be a disaster waiting to happen. In 1967, at Koyna near Bombay, the sudden weight of water imposed on a valley bottom during the filling of a reservoir triggered an earthquake beneath the dam. It breached the dam and the resulting flood killed 177 people and injured 1,500. The issue of the safety of the Tehri Dam had become caught in a bureaucratic web of intrigue that appeared to operate without any regard to the real risks that the dam could pose in the real world, and the potentially catastrophic consequences of a wrong decision. Sunil Roy chaired a government working group looking at the environmental impacts of the dam in the early 1980s, and in a personal letter appended to his final report complained about the failure of the government to institute seismological research projects recommended by his group six years before.

He concluded: 'I have chaired innumerable committees and groups in India and other parts of the world. I have never encountered such an unbending dogmatic approach to all issues which were not positively framed to ensure continued work on the Tehri Dam, whatever the cost.' Perhaps the 1991 quake will shake the government out of its complacency.

'If the Tehri reservoir emptied in half an hour,' warns Shivaji Rao, an adviser to the Indian government's environmental appraisal committee for river-valley projects, 'floods may reach Rishikesh in one hour and Haridwar in another fifteen minutes.' A 40-metre wall of water would rush down the narrow valley. 'Almost all the people in Rishikesh and Haridwar may be killed and all towns and villages up to Meerut [some 250 kilometres from Tehri] may be severely damaged; millions of people will be exposed to epidemics.'

The steep-sided mountain valleys of the world provide refuges for many tribal communities and racial minorities. And, despite the seismic threats, they also offer some of the most prized sites for large dams. The gorges that allow engineers to plug an entire valley also provide defences for isolated groups from hostile outsiders, while the same unfenced land that attracts groups beyond the mainstream of modern societies can also often be inundated without political embarrassment. But where the local groups resist the invasion of their lands, the result can be conflict.

Usually that conflict is 'containable' by the national authorities. The dam is built, the people rehoused and the opposition dispersed. But not always. During the revolt in northern Iraq in 1991, Kurds began to demolish the half-completed Bekhme Dam on the Greater Zab River. The dam was planned to grow to more than 200 metres and inundate the lands of one of the Kurds' leading clans, the Barzani.

In the Chico valley in the forested mountains of northern Luzon, the largest island of the Philippines, a dispute over dams became a recruiting ground for a guerrilla war that eventually caused the downfall of the corrupt military dictator, President Marcos. Still largely untouched by mining and with slopes too steep for commercial plantations, the hills of North Luzon are a bastion for some three-quarters of a million Igorot people. They contain abundant fisheries and some of the few surviving areas of forests in a country that was two-thirds forested only 50 years ago. The Igorot, or 'people of the mountains', have also constructed over the centuries magnificent stairways of irrigated terraces on which they grow rice.

But 300 kilometres away as the pylon struts is the Philippine capital of Manila – an electricity-hungry metropolis. After the oil crisis of 1973, Marcos determined to free his country from dependence on oil imports and to tap the mountains for their hydroelectric power. He had another thought in mind, too. Dams could feed irrigation canals to supply nearby lowland plantations run by wealthy corporations and individuals, including Marcos himself. Marcos adopted a plan to build high dams in four gorges and a fifth dam to divert water for irrigation. The dams would create the largest hydroelectric complex in southeast Asia and provide enough electricity to run Manila. They would also flood 16 hill villages, almost 3,000 hectares of rice paddies, a similar area of fruit trees and coffee bushes, and hunting and fishing grounds.

The Igorot were not impressed by the claim of Marcos's Minister of National Planning and Development that: 'There is a greater good to be derived from the setting up of the dams, for the benefit of the society ... and each group has to be willing to make some sacrifice for the benefit of the entire society.' The sacrifices were all on one side; the benefits all on the other. Moreover, what national benefit resided in spiralling into worsening debt problems in order to sell cheap electricity to foreign mining and manufacturing companies was at best unclear.

The Igorot decided to fight back. They harassed survey teams, adopting such pioneering tactics as sending all-women teams to take off their clothes and block the roads, and defying police and soldiers to evict them. They dismantled campsites and later attacked surveyors – who resorted to the air to finish their work. The normally warring tribes banded together by agreeing to a *bondonq*, a mutual defence pact, to fight the dams. Official efforts to break the alliance by arming traditional foes with high-powered rifles failed.

The Igorot had help from leading figures in the Catholic

Church, such as Bishop Francisco Claver, himself an Igorot. Then came cadres of the New People's Army, the guerrilla wing of the Philippines' Communist Party. At first the Igorot sent the guerrillas away, but according to press reports at the time, by the summer of 1978 'NPA songs could be heard around village camp fires and in children's playgroups, while old men chanted verses against the dams and the government.'

The following year, local militias trained by the New People's Army fought skirmishes with battalions of the Philippine constabulary, a para-military force. In 1980, more than 100 people died, including a popular local leader, who was shot down in his home. This enraged rather than intimidated the dams' opponents, and by 1981 the government had backed off, withdrawing its constabulary and dropping the hydroelectric dams from the national energy programme. In 1990, Philip Hurst, an environmental researcher, reported that:

> The area is still a New People's Army stronghold, but relatively peaceful. It is developing a major tourist industry, which will probably be far more beneficial, by way of providing the region with jobs and infrastructure, than would dams. As the tourist industry increases the provision of electric power will become a problem, but small-scale hydro dams may provide a viable proposition.

Meanwhile the failure to build the dams made the Philippines' debt crisis – the subject of a major renegotiation of credit with the International Monetary Fund in 1990 – rather less severe than it might otherwise have been.

The story of Chico valley illustrates many of the central objections to large dams in the third world. It is the rural poor, along with their environment and the natural resources of remote regions, that suffer in order for a few to benefit. By their nature, large dams and hydroelectric projects are amongst the least likely of 'development' initiatives to generate improvements in the lives of the rural poor. But while the Igorot won their battle, many others have lost.

In India in the past 40 years, an estimated 16 million people have become refugees of dam construction – the majority of them from tribal groups. One estimate is that a third of India's tribal peoples have been uprooted in the past 40 years for large dams or other development projects. In China another 3 million have been displaced, 300,000 to make way for the Sanmenxia Dam, which silted up within two years of completion. 80,000 people made way for Akosombo; 120,000 for the Mangla in Pakistan; 120,000 for the High Aswan; 40,000 for Kainji in Nigeria; 50,000 for the Kariba Dam on the Zambezi; 25,000 for the Cahora Bassa downstream on the same river; up to a million people have been moved as part of the Mahaweli dams and plantation project in Sri Lanka. Some commentators say that the disruption caused by the Mahaweli project was a prime cause of the unrest that saw tens of thousands dead as the Tamil Tigers fought the government's forces in the jungles of eastern Sri Lanka from the late 1980s onwards.

Another bloody dispute in the subcontinent began this way a generation before and still continues. In 1963, the Bangladeshi government forced 100,000 tribal people in the Chittagong Hill Tracts – one of the few hilly areas of that flat delta country – off their land to make way for a large hydroelectric dam project, the Kaptai Dam. It was large in terms of land flooded, taking out long ribbons of two fertile valleys accounting for 40 per cent of the land farmed by the hill tribes. But it was small in terms of power generation – the 426 square-kilometre lake feeds turbines that have a capacity of just 150 megawatts. One football pitch of flooded land could power three single-kilowatt electric fires.

For a country so prone to flooding, it seems perverse to have deliberately flooded hill valleys, but there is little love lost between the lowland Bengalis and the tribal groups, such as the Chakmas. Forced from their land by the reservoir and by an estimated 400,000 Bengali farmers settled by the government, the Chakmas were shunted into large barrack-like villages – very different from their former tiny hill hamlets. In 1991, a team of investigators from Amnesty International visited the hill tracts and reported the 'systematic and calculated wiping out of whole peoples and cultures'. As many as 50,000 people have fled, forming the Shanti Bahini, or

Peace Army, which has become a guerrilla force fighting the Bengalis from camps over the border in India.

The Chittagong Hill Tracts, and particularly the area round the hydroelectric facilities at Kaptai, are today under tight military security. As a result, one of the prime tourist attractions of poverty-stricken Bangladesh has become increasingly unattractive to foreigners. Many areas are now out of bounds, and in others guide books warn that a camera is regarded as an offensive weapon. The contrast with the Chico valley of the Philippines – which has escaped dams to find relative peace and a thriving tourist industry – is striking.

The whiff of conflict is growing stronger around large dam projects in many countries. People who once felt they had no chance of preventing the loss of their lands now hear about victories elsewhere and stay to fight. On the Indonesian island of Java in 1989 some 7,000 people remained behind when the Kedung Ombo Dam began to flood the homes of 20,000 farmers. More than 600 families were still there, some living on rafts, when two years later President Suharto was forced to abandon an official inauguration of the project.

In Thailand in the summer of 1991, hundreds of villagers were arrested for occupying a dam site at Pak Mun on a tributary of the Mekong. In the Bihar state of northern India sporadic protests by the Ho tribe, culminating in the arrest of 200 people in April 1991, continue to disrupt work on the Icha High Dam, a project that could dispossess 75,000 people. That summer, too, waters lapped at the first villages on the Narmada River as construction work continued on the Sardar Sarovar Dam, the first of several superdams planned for the valley. The $2-billion dam, funded partly by the World Bank, is on the largest west-flowing river in India. With 90,000 expected to lose their homes as the Sardar Sarovar floods their valley, 200 villagers formed a 'self-sacrifice group' to face the rising waters whenever they reach their village. Meanwhile an international campaign by green groups publicised growing concern among officials at the World Bank that resettlement plans for the evacuees were inadequate.

Months before, protesters had held a long hunger strike. Among its many supporters was Baba Amte, a veteran

defender of tribal groups and the poor, who mocked the
hopes of the dam-builders. 'All those ruthless, monstrous
projects Nehru called temples of development have become
tombs of development,' he said. Far from being a peoples'
project, a sign of national independence, the dam was going
ahead with a military zone imposed around it. Anybody
entering the area 'for a purpose prejudicial to the safety or
interests of the State' faced up to 14 years in gaol.

Besides the dam, engineers have begun digging a canal.
Intended to be the largest lined canal in the world, it was 750
metres wide and might eventually be 450 kilometres long. It
would take water from Sardar Sarovar across the arid state of
Gujarat almost to the border with Rajasthan. Gujarat's
leaders claimed that poor drought-prone villagers, and
especially tribal groups, would receive its water, but in fact
the canal by-passes most of those villagers. Instead, it goes to
districts containing rich landlords growing water-hungry cash
crops, and the industrialists of Ahmedabad. This is not perverse. It is logical, even inevitable. These are the people who
might generate the cash to pay the bills for the dam. But
meanwhile some 60,000 people will lose their land to make
way for the canal.

As the conflict over the half-completed Sardar Sarovar Dam
continued, engineers upstream in Madhya Pradesh were pre-
paring to begin work on a second dam on the river, the
Narmada Sagar. It will be built close to the top end of the
Sardar Sarovar reservoir and will create the largest artificial
reservoir in India, winding back through 500 kilometres of
pastures and forests. Thus two reservoirs will eventually
create a single giant's step in the river covering 700 kilometres.

The Narmada valley project in total is the largest integrated
development project ever attempted anywhere in the world,
many times larger than its distant ancestor, the Tennessee
valley project. As the dams are built, canals dug, forests razed
and fields cleared and planted over the coming 40 to 50 years,
it will affect the lives of more than 10 million people. The
Indian government sees it as a bold plan to transform an
underdeveloped part of India. Objectors see it as an assault on
an unmolested river, on the forests where Kipling set many of

the stories in his *Jungle Books,* and on the millions of tribal people who live along the river's banks and amid the forests.

Far from developing the land, independent scientists have concluded that the Narmada Sagar will waterlog soils in 40 per cent of the 'command area' that it is designed to irrigate. And the Sardar Sarovar may create swamps in the many regions of 'black soils' that it is intended to irrigate in Gujarat.

All the evidence is that the people of the valley, and especially the tribal groups, are prepared to fight to defend their land – and that environmentalists and human rights groups around the world will back them. The dispute over the waters of the Narmada has the potential to become at least as severe a communal conflict for the Indian government to contain as those in Kashmir, Punjab and Assam.

13

A TRICKLE IN THE SAND

The system speaks of the high degree of community sharing, social, moral and religious values built round a desire for 'water for all' in the society.

S. M. Mohmot, University of Jodhpur, on the city's derelict rainwater harvesting system

An ox wallows in the muddy waterhole, taking its fill in the midday heat of the Thar Desert in western India. The waterhole is not a natural feature. The villagers of Jhanwar dug and maintained it to provide water for their animals and to encourage the growth of vegetation. It is one of many traditional water-capturing and -storing devices that still dot the Thar, the most densely populated desert in the world.

Two men walk by in loin cloths and brightly coloured turbans. They glance at the waterhole. It will be dry within ten days, and stay that way for six months until the arrival of next year's monsoon. When it is dry, the men will dig out the fine, fertile mud on its bed and spread it on to their fields. For, while this may be a desert, it is also a land of farms. The Thar is home for 60 people per square kilometre, and almost nowhere in this desert are you out of sight of humans.

For centuries the inhabitants of the Thar Desert have developed devices for harvesting rainwater in the desert. Every village has several *tankas*, simple reservoirs lined with clay that are dug everywhere to collect rainwater. An elaboration is the *kundi*. It is a shallow clay-lined *tanka,* covered to prevent evaporation and keep out animals, and surrounded by a surface of hardened mud about the size of a small suburban garden that funnels rain into the hole after storms.

Elsewhere around Jhanwar, there are small check dams, a metre or so high, that trap silty water in gullies as it flows off slopes after rain. Behind the dams, the silt forms a thick layer of fertile, damp soil ready for planting. These dams also encourage water to percolate into the local aquifers. One dam can ensure that wells stay full as much as three kilometres away.

The largest man-made features in the desert are the *khadins*. They are made by building a low wall across gently sloping land near rocky outcrops. The summer rains pour from the ridges in occasional flash floods, are contained by the *khadins* and create large expanses of green that may incorporate several farms and cover a hundred hectares or more. The first crop is sown in June, after the first rains cover the land behind the wall. It is harvested in late autumn and, if the rains are good and the soil is still moist, a second crop is planted – and sometimes a third crop the following April.

Many of these man-made oases were built 500 years ago by Paliwal Brahmins. Once established, they develop fertile moisture-holding soils, in contrast to the surrounding bare sand. They attract natural wildlife and vegetation, such as the great tree of the Thar, the *khejri*, which taps deep water with its long roots and has leaves that animals eat and fruit for humans. Recent studies have found 500 ancient *khadins*, of which 400 are still in use. The largest are west of Jaisalmer, in the driest western part of the desert close to the Pakistan border. In total, they cover about 120 square kilometres and collect water from almost 2,000 square kilometres.

Throughout the desert, devices such as these can harvest sufficient rainfall to provide water for the population, its animals and its crops. It may be that this peopled desert represents, far more closely than the wastes of the Sahara, the face of the world's arid lands as they were thousands of years ago.

But Jhanwar is only half an hour's drive over a bumpy track and the new tarmac road from the desert city of Jodhpur. The modern world is moving in on Jhanwar and, on the brow of the hill behind the waterhole, there is a new water tower, filled with water pumped by electricity from deep beneath the

desert. Soon, like other nearby communities, the people of
Jhanwar will probably abandon their waterholes, *kundis* and
check dams, and rely on the government's pumps and taps.

A study of the area around Jhanwar found the amount of
land irrigated from rainwater harvesting had halved in the last
30 years. Ravi Goyal of the Indian government's Central Arid
Zone Research Institute, standing beside the Jhanwar waterhole, says: 'Today many waterholes are filled with silt and
abandoned. With the arrival of piped water, people are forget-
ting about traditional methods of collecting rainfall.' 'It could
be the worst thing they ever do, for the new water system, for
all its pumps and pipes and shiny towers, cannot supply the
desert's inhabitants when they need it most, during drought.

The summer monsoon rains are the only source of water in
the Thar Desert. But by the time the rain-bearing winds reach
here, they have crossed many hundreds of kilometres of land.
Some years the rains never arrive. During the dry summer of
1987, the modern tube-wells and dams on local rivers ran dry.
A study for the Centre for Science and the Environment in
New Delhi found that 'the tube-wells had either no water or
no electricity to pump it. But distant villages close to the
Pakistan border, which had not yet benefited from government schemes, had some water to drink as they still had their
traditional systems intact.' Drought was only prevented from
becoming famine by the arrival of convoys of trucks with
water and food.

In the longer term, the changes may spell the end for the
population of the Thar, for the 'new' water is actually old
water, and may not last. The tube-wells that suck water from
beneath the desert are everywhere lowering water-tables and
drying out traditional wells. Meanwhile, because villagers no
longer harvest the rains, the water disappears from the land in
flash floods or evaporates in the summer heat. Much less
reaches the aquifers beneath the ground. 'Groundwater levels
are falling fast and the tube-wells may eventually run dry,'
says Goyal.

The risk of this happening is compounded by the government's efforts to 'green' the Thar by encouraging modern
farming here. These efforts are marshalled by the Central

Arid Zone Research Institute (CAZRI), established at Jodhpur in the 1950s. Big landowners are allowed to mine the water beneath the desert with powerful pump-wells to irrigate thirsty crops such as wheat, rice and even sugar cane. One large land-holding outside Jodhpur is extracting water from the ground three times faster than it is being replaced. A district covering 350 square kilometres will lose its underground water supply within 40 years.

Government planners responded to the 1987 drought with a sudden and sometimes comical conversion to traditional techniques. CAZRI's scientists began a crash programme to build and renovate thousands of check dams, *tankas* and *kundi*, and to clean out abandoned wells. There were some successes. After two years of good rains, one check dam near Jhanwar had collected new soil about a metre deep. The scientists told me with ill-disguised incredulity how it had brought wells back to life.

But they have been unable to resist the temptation to foist on to villagers 'improved' versions of their traditional devices. For a while, CAZRI handed out polythene film and told villagers to lay it over water in exposed backyard *tankas*. The idea, they explained, was to reduce evaporation. Villagers gently explained that they already had their own technique of shading the water with local grasses laid over the water. The grasses worked just as well, and had the added benefit of keeping the water cool.

The scientists spent some time describing to me how they had improved the design of traditional water-capturing walls and dams, and incorporated new materials to extend their lifetime. But when we took the four-wheel drive into the hills, it was quickly clear that most of their structures had been destroyed in recent rains, while the traditional unimproved versions were still stubbornly standing.

The boffins of Jodhpur want to find new sites for *tankas*. They try to identify them by using satellite pictures of the desert. It is a far cry from the villagers' preferred technique of water-divining, which appears to be better at pinpointing the very localised aquifers beneath the desert. The efforts of CAZRI scientists to work with indigenous knowledge about the local environment and how to manage it are welcome, but it is hard for the engineers to accept that they are mere beginners in arts well known to many villagers.

And they have a bigger problem. As the institute's lone sociologist L. P. Bharara explained, survival in such large numbers in the desert requires complex social organisation. Not only that, the social structures are based on that great unmentionable but constant presence in India – the caste system. He showed me a study of a small village outside the desert town of Bikaner. It had a number of *tankas* holding water and six *tobas*, ponds dug amid sand dunes outside the village to provide water for flocks of sheep and goats.

Some castes are usually allowed access to only one of the *tobas*, while other castes can use any they choose. Some *tankas* are for the use of a single caste. It appears thoroughly inequitable but, says Bhahara, the system works to 'ensure not only security, mutual help and cooperation, but also the proper distribution of water available for both humans and animals and grasses'.

Modern systems of social organisation, based on privately owned property without the constraints of caste, may be less fair and leave more people without access to water than before. Among the technocrats at CAZRI, Bharara is close to being an untouchable himself. The director told me irritably: 'I want him to stop doing all this sociology and just to tell me why the villagers won't use many of our inventions.'

The capture of deep underground waters is not the only cause of damage to water resources in the desert. There is also the Indira Gandhi Canal. On paper, the canal and its attendant works form one of the largest irrigation projects in the world. Tapping one of the tributaries of the Indus in northern India, it trails across the Punjab and down into the Thar Desert. It provides water for 13,000 square kilometres of desert from a main canal 450 kilometres long and with 7,000 kilometres of branches. However, after more than 30 years of construction, it is still little more than half complete and has become a byword for bad irrigation planning. Even the technocrats at CAZRI have few good words for it.

Ostensibly the $500 million canal is the key to greening the driest part of the Thar Desert. Actually its main job is political. It was begun to divert water that would otherwise have flowed into Pakistan, and to provide a very obvious Indian government presence in the border region, which has been inhabited traditionally by nomadic herdsmen and, more recently, by smugglers of guns and narcotics.

But nobody wants the canal's water. Few local cattle herders or outsiders have shown any interest in tilling such a hot, inhospitable and remote land. Despite the placement here of 3,500 people flooded out by a dam in the Himalayas, less than half the farms served by the canal had been claimed by the end of the 1980s. At a cost of more than a million dollars per kilometre for the main canal, and $30,000 per square kilometre for irrigable land, the project is an economic disaster.

The canal will eventually end at Jaisalmer, home of the *khadin*, so providing a direct conflict between the new and old ways. But even before it has reached there, many of its distribution canals have been overwhelmed by sand dunes and most of its water runs to waste. Seepage from the canals and crude flooding of fields by farmers ensure waterlogging and a build-up of salt. According to P. C. Chatterji of CAZRI, 'large chunks of the potentially fertile plain are severely waterlogged'. Now there is a 'wet desert' to replace the old dry desert. In some villages malaria is spreading as mosquitoes breed in stagnant pools of drainage water. Little, it seems, has been learned since the days 120 years ago when fever epidemics raged up and down the newly completed Ganges Canal.

If the tragedy at Jhanwar and other desert villages is disturbing, it is matched by the story of the great desert city of Jodhpur. The place that gave its name to riding breeches now has a population of more than a million and grows rich on an unholy mixture of government largesse and the profits from trafficking in drugs from across the border. The desert camel troops so enjoyed by tourists here are important conduits for drugs.

For most of its 500 years' existence, the inhabitants of the desert city and its magnificent fort have slaked their thirst by enlarging lakes in hills outside the city to collect virtually all the rain that falls there. They channelled the water through 80 kilometres of canals to more than 100 reservoirs and wells in the city. The most important reservoir was the Ranisar tank, built inside the ramparts of the fort in about 1460. More than 100 metres long, it overflows into the Padamsar, which was completed 60 years later outside the ramparts.

Water seeps from the bottom of the tanks and is captured by local wells, and by exquisitely decorated step wells that people can walk into to collect their water, or bathe in during religious ceremonies. 'The system is not only an excellent feat of architecture and engineering design,' says S. M. Mohmot of the University of Jodhpur, 'it also speaks of the high degree of community sharing, social, moral and religious values built round a desire for 'water for all' in the society.'

A hundred years ago, Jodhpur still had 50 tanks, 50 step wells and 70 wells. But since then, almost the entire catchment for the city's water supply, once a rolling landscape of forests and lakes covering 120 square kilometres, has been blasted to pieces by quarrying. It is a treeless moonscape, in which most of the water disappears through fissures deep into the rocks. The quarries provide the local *chittar* sandstone, a handsome golden stone that glows in the evening sun and is used for all the big houses and government buildings in the city. But the hills no longer provide water.

With their water supply cut off, the canals to the city have filled with rubbish and three city-centre tanks from which the people of Jodhpur drank as recently as the 1950s are now abandoned and covered in smelly green slime. Many step wells are filled to the surface with refuse.

Most of the tanks and canals were finally abandoned after the construction of a new dam on the River Jawai some 90 kilometres away, which brought new water to Jodhpur. The damming of the Jawai has dried up the river downstream and destroyed aquifers that once filled wells in villages along the river valley. In the drought of 1987, the Jawai reservoir itself dried up, leaving the city dependent on water-trucks.

'We are only now discovering how magnificent a feat of engineering the old system was, and how large its capacity,' says Mohmot. 'If the tanks and canals were cleaned up and catchments renovated, they could still supply up to three months' water for the city each year.' Instead, in 1990, engineers came up with another idea for increasing the city's water supply. They were talking about diverting water to the city from the shimmering white elephant 150 kilometres away on the border with Pakistan – the Indira Gandhi Canal.

The people of the Thar Desert appear caught between two worlds. Their old ways of a strictly ordered caste society, ancient lore and technology, allowed them to live in extraordinary numbers in this hostile environment. Their way of life was not ossified, but it did impose tight limits. Those limits are coming under increasing pressure from outside in the form of roads and water pipes and canals and scientists from CAZRI anxious to help them with 'improved' water technology, or better crops. The eventual result is almost bound to be the depopulation of the Thar. The harder India works to develop and 'green' the desert, the more it seems destined to destroy its life-support system.

14

AFRICAN HARVEST

The floodplain is a vast natural irrigation scheme. It is of great importance and should be preserved.

Ted Hollis and Bill Adams, British geographers, 1990

Some of the greatest disasters for water engineers and development experts have been out in the sandy haze beyond where modern farming can easily flourish and before desert becomes so arid that settled communities give out. Nowhere has this been more true than in the Sahel, the southern fringe of the Sahara.

During the 1970s and 1980s, African governments invested many billions of dollars in aid to rid the Sahel of drought and famine. They took their largesse into territory far removed from the lives of the residents of African capital cities, let alone the corridors of the donor banks and government aid agencies. Like the news of an eighteenth-century war, it took a long time for reports of progress to come home.

The news is that most of their efforts to paint the desert margins green by building large irrigation projects have created more desert than they have reclaimed, have destroyed more farms and more livelihoods than have been improved. One of the most trenchant dispatches from the desert front line came in the late 1980s in an assessment of the causes of desertification in the Lake Chad basin.

This huge tract of the central Sahel is home to tens of millions of people in Nigeria, Chad, Cameroon and Niger. The report, paid for by UN agencies, was largely written by Peter Warshall at the University of Arizona's Office of Arid Lands Studies. 'In the name of anti-desertification,' Warshall said, 'we have witnessed many grandiose projects fail over the past two decades. We have seen huge amounts of international aid wasted in the struggle to fight environmental degradation.'

Most foreign aid in the Sahel goes on irrigation projects. But the donors are usually throwing money at a mirage. Within the Chad basin, says Warshall, 'even in the most optimistic scenarios, irrigated agriculture will only employ 4 per cent of farmers. The needs of the vast majority of peasants go unaddressed. More than that, their needs are damaged when their waters are appropriated for state projects.'

Far from greening empty desert, most irrigation projects take over already productive land for dubious money-making schemes, such as growing water-hungry crops like rice and cotton. The conventional wisdom about the disappearance of trees from the Sahel is that peasants cut them down for firewood, while their animals eat the remainder. In fact, says Warshall, it is 'clear-cutting [of trees] for the large-scale irrigation, dams and reservoirs that is one of the principal causes of large-scale deforestation'. It beggars belief, but the first task undertaken on a typical project to 'green the Sahel' is to chop down the trees. Sometimes, given the prevailing chaos, it is also the last thing that is done.

The Maga Dam takes much of the flow of the River Logone, one of two main sources of water for Lake Chad. Most of the water goes to irrigate rice. The abstractions are one reason why the shores of Lake Chad are retreating. But, more important, they steal water that until recently watered the river's natural floodplain, which is fast drying out, and replenished groundwaters. The dam has lowered water-tables across 1,500 square kilometres of Logone floodplain. More even than 20 years of poor rains, the Maga Dam explains why pastures downstream that once supported 20,000 head of cattle now support only half that number.

It is the Maga Dam that is drying out the once-teeming Waza National Park, destroying habitats for the numerous local species of antelope and undermining the chances of survival for elephants sheltering in the park. Worst affected of all is the Grand Yaeres, an area of wetland twice the size of

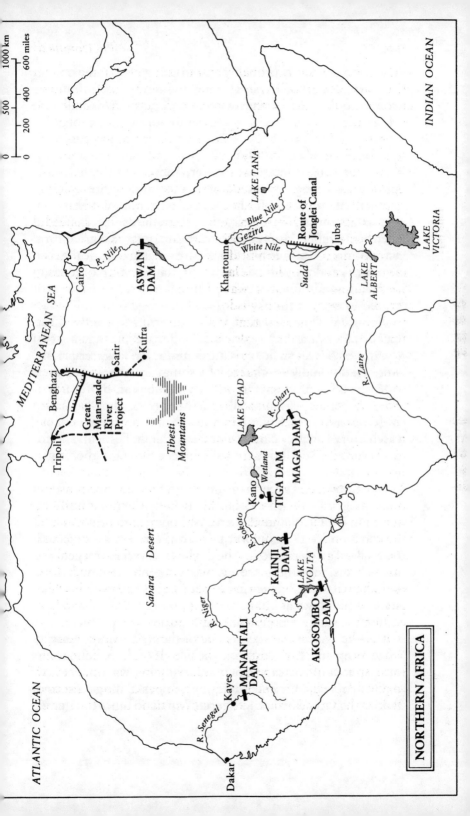

NORTHERN AFRICA

ATLANTIC OCEAN

MEDITERRANEAN SEA

INDIAN OCEAN

Cairo

R. Nile

ASWAN DAM

Benghazi

Sarir

Kufra

Tripoli

Great Man-made River Project

Tibesti Mountains

Khartoum

Blue Nile

LAKE TANA

Gezira

White Nile

Route of Jonglei Canal

Sudd

Juba

LAKE ALBERT

LAKE VICTORIA

R. Zaire

R. Chari

LAKE CHAD

Wetland

Kano

TIGA DAM

MAGA DAM

R. Sokoto

KAINJI DAM

R. Niger

LAKE VOLTA

AKOSOMBO DAM

MANANTALI DAM

Kayes

R. Senegal

Dakar

Sahara Desert

0   200   400   600 miles

0   500   1000 km

Luxembourg that is probably the largest haven in the central Sahel for fisheries, livestock and recession agriculture. Far from helping the region grow more crops, says Warshall, 'the Maga Dam has created a permanent hydrological drought'.

This should have been clear when the dam was designed. But, says Warshall, 'the Yaeres were considered a loss of billions of cubic metres of water, rather than a naturally fertilised and irrigated system of pasture, agriculture, fisheries and wildlife tourism.' In their enthusiasm to build their dam and irrigation canals, to green the desert, the engineers and aid agencies simply ignored the vast amount of agricultural activity already taking place in the area. Being outside the cash economy, and part of the old world that Chadian officials in their air-conditioned offices wanted to escape, it almost ceased to exist in their eyes.

As in the Thar Desert of India, governments in the Chad basin undermine old systems of collective management of natural resources such as pastures and rivers. 'Water priests' were traditionally in charge of fishing. In some areas their rules are still enforced. On one day in the year, thousands of north Nigerian peasants still rush into the receding fish-laden floodwaters of the River Rima near Sokoto with nets. They catch every fish they can during the Argungu Festival, and for the rest of the year leave the fish alone, ensuring a good catch next year.

But along rivers such as the Logone and Chari, the power of the water priests has been undermined by the rickety administrations of Chad and Cameroon. Today in the Sahel, states rather than local communities own the rivers and the pastures. But having destroyed the old law, ministers and generals in their distant offices are too weak to enforce new law. In Chad, civil strife has ensured there has been no policing of state fishing laws at all.

Sometimes, however, policing is part of the problem. The repressive arm of the state is one of the less savoury features of government efforts to bring the people of the Sahel into the mainstream of African society. Nobody knows for sure how many people died one April day in 1980 when the governor of Sokoto state in northern Nigeria, Alhaji Shehu Mohammed

Kangiwa, ordered police to retake the Bakolori irrigation project by force. The governor put the death toll at 14. Then 23. Local newspapers said 386, and published long lists of names of the dead.

By international standards the Bakolori Dam, a 50-metre high plug on the Sokoto River, is not big. Its reservoir covers only 80 square kilometres. But in the heavily populated and fertile Sokoto valley, a green ribbon on the fringes of the Sahel, that was enough to flood the homes and farms of 13,000 people. They were not pleased when they were offered dusty acacia scrub as replacement for their land. But the 40,000 families whose land was to be irrigated by canals filled at the dam were not much happier.

They had farmed their valley in time-honoured fashion, planting sorghum as the river floodwaters retreated and herding cattle on to the fields during the winter to graze the stubble. But now the government intended to bulldoze the fields into a table-flat prairie, then put roads, pumping stations, canals and a large sugar plantation across perhaps a third of it, divide the remainder into small parcels and hand it back – on condition that the farmers planted wheat.

The old system, known as recession farming or *fadama*, after the pools in which the farmers planted their crops, had worked well for perhaps 3,000 years. It was probably the first method of settled farming developed in West Africa and had fed several great civilisations in the region. It was versatile enough to keep the population alive in a drought-prone land now grown notorious for famine and refugee camps.

But the Sokoto River Development Authority knew better. Fields irrigated from the Bakolori Dam, it said, could grow high-yielding wheat varieties and provide bumper harvests. How could the farmers object? But they did, as they had objected in decades past when British imperial engineers had set up abortive irrigation projects to grow wheat across northern Nigeria. All had failed.

By late 1979, many disgruntled farmers had been kept off their land for three growing seasons in succession. Joined by angry compatriots flooded out by the dam, they armed themselves with hoes, and launched a peasant uprising. Five thousand blockaded the newly completed dam, threatening to cut off water supplies to the state capital, Sokoto City, 150 kilometres downstream.

The rebellion lasted seven months and ended in pitched battles with the police, and massive bloodshed at Birnin Tudu, headquarters of the construction company. Over the corpses of the dead, the peasants won many of their demands. Land was returned without restrictions on what they could grow. The sugar estate was abandoned. But in economic terms the result was the worst of all worlds. The floodplain farming system was destroyed at great cost, but there was no high-tech high-productivity system to replace it.

The only winner in this farrago was the Italian company Fiat, which had built the dam and canals, and supplied most of the equipment, from tractors and trucks to the advanced laser technology for levelling the fields. The real loser, apart from the Nigerian exchequer, has been the floodplain of the River Sokoto and the people who once depended on it for their livelihoods.

The impact of the dam has been felt downstream all the way to Sokoto City. Half of the *fadamas* once flooded each year by the river are now dry. Local varieties of corn and rice, selectively cultivated by local farmers over many generations to fit the river's natural flooding cycle, are now frequently useless.

Fishing was once almost as important an occupation as farming in the valley. But with the fish cut off from their feeding areas on the floodplain, it is in drastic decline. The British geographer, Bill Adams, in a detailed study of the impact of the Bakolori Dam, concluded that, if the loss of the *fadamas* and fishing had been taken into account in the assessment of the project, 'it should have been enough to prevent development of the project'.

The whiff of corruption, intrigue and incompetence surrounding development projects is stronger in Nigeria, Africa's most populous nation, than almost anywhere else on Earth. It pervades all of the nation's three major efforts to hold back the advancing desert in northern Nigeria in the past two decades: the Bakolori scheme, and the South Chad and Kano irrigation projects. Each probably helped the desert's advance. And each shows how large amounts of cash can cause untold damage to the environment and the lives of farmers, when the ostensible purpose is to benefit them.

South of Kano, the country's new northern metropolis, Nigeria has built the Tiga Dam. The dam captures the head-waters of the River Hadejia, which winds across the desert margins for almost a thousand kilometres to the shores of Lake Chad. Between them, the Hadejia and Sokoto drew a green line across most of northern Nigeria. But the Tiga Dam now dries out the Hadejia valley, just as Bakolori empties the Sokoto.

Tiga delivers its waters to Kano city taps and to the nearby Kano Irrigation Project. This Dutch-designed and British-financed project yielded its first water in 1981 and supplies farmers across 150 square kilometres with water for rice, maize and cowpeas in the wet season, and wheat in the dry season. It has not been a great success, with vast cost overruns and wheat yields on the finished farms typically of around two tonnes per hectare, less than half those anticipated.

Meanwhile, on the Hadejia floodplain huge areas of once-productive *fadamas* have dried out. More than 2,000 square kilometres of the floodplain were inundated in the 1960s. That has halved since 1983. Computer modelling shows that the Tiga Dam has been at least as responsible as drought for this decline. 'The floodplain is a vast natural irrigation scheme,' says Adams, who has studied the area with Ted Hollis, another leading British geographer. 'This natural irrigation required very little government money, yields large amounts of produce and supports a large population. It is obviously of great importance and should be preserved.'

Yet it is being wantonly destroyed. Water diverted from the Hadejia irrigates only around half as much land on the state irrigation project as it would have if left in the river to inundate the floodplain. Moreover, since the completion of the dam, fish catches on the floodplain have fallen, especially around Nguru, a railhead from which fish were once transported round the country. Wells sunk into local aquifers are also failing. In places, thanks to Tiga, the water-table has dropped by more than 25 metres.

The river floods once made the plains east of Kano one of the richest and most productive areas of northern Nigeria, a haven for migrants in times of drought. Their crops supported the lavish Hausa kingdoms of the region for many centuries. Any rational view of the economics and hydrology of the region must conclude that it is the water diverted by the Tiga Dam and others on to the white-elephant irrigation projects that is 'running to waste'.

In Nigeria, high-cost projects acquire an importance out of all proportion to their actual value, while any activity not classified by the government as part of a 'project' is treated as if it did not exist. That is why state irrigation schemes soaked up three-quarters of Nigeria's considerable capital expenditure on agriculture during the early 1980s, while at the end of the decade 94 per cent of Nigeria's irrigation was still done by small projects, none of which received a penny from the government's irrigation agency.

The World Bank says that in Nigeria during the 1970s and 1980s, irrigation projects were costing a staggering $100,000 per hectare to develop. While far less successful than traditional systems, the large projects continued to win government support because 'powerful incentives exist [including] the distribution of patronage ... to pursue the large-scale route'.

The World Bank has withdrawn its support for such projects, but the Nigerian government in 1992 completed a new dam on the River Hadejia at Challawa Gorge and began work on the 12,500-hectare Hadejia Valley irrigation project, which will further dry up the wetlands downstream. There are also plans to turn a long stretch of the River Hadejia into 380 kilometres of canal. This will ensure that the water left after the dams have taken their fill will be kept off the wetland, away from peasant farmers and their *fadamas*, away from the aquifers beneath, and away downstream. It will allow, said the EC's Nigerian agriculture adviser Geoff Rudd in a note to the European Development Fund in 1987, 'an agricultural heartland to be created between Gashua [a town on the river] and Lake Chad, based on irrigated agriculture production'.

Hollis says that instead, it 'will prove vastly expensive, ineffective hydraulically and highly damaging to existing systems. Instead of the cultivation benefiting from the free service of nature, a substantial sum of money will have to be spent each year on maintaining the whole system.' More than that, it is theft of water from the people who make best use of it.

For the most extraordinary failure of water planning in northern Nigeria we need to look to the shores of Lake Chad itself. There the Nigerians in the 1960s began to plan their most audacious attempt to green the desert margins. The South Chad Irrigation Project (SCIP), one of the largest irrigation schemes in all Africa, was to take water from the lake and irrigate 670 square kilometres of empty scrub along the lake shore to grow rice, wheat and cotton.

The scrub wasn't so empty, it turned out. Some 55,000 farming families were eventually removed to make way for SCIP. Most grew *masakwa* sorghum, a drought-resistant crop particularly suited to the soils around the lake, in fields around which they built bunds to collect rainwater. Today, three decades and almost a billion dollars later, the former *masakwa* fields are criss-crossed by 4,000 kilometres of canals and drains and are permanently dry and largely barren.

The SCIP was conceived in 1962, the last year before the Sahel's rainfall began a steady and ultimately catastrophic decline. That year, Lake Chad reached its highest level this century, covering an area the size of Wales. Coastal villages close to the future SCIP site flooded. Since then, flows in the rivers Logone and Chari that feed the lake have halved. And the lake itself, which loses two metres of water across its entire surface to evaporation each year, has never made good its losses. By the late 1980s it was a tenth of its former size. Villages that flooded in 1962 were almost 100 kilometres from the shore.

The decline of the lake is even greater than that of the Aral Sea. But the reason for the decline of Lake Chad, while partly the result of abstractions of water from rivers that feed into it, is also climatic.

Mott MacDonald, the British firm of consulting engineers,

told its clients that a 30-kilometre-long intake channel would 'operate at all stages of lake water level'. It didn't work out like that. At the beginning of the 1990s, the intake sat as useless as the ships' hulks that dot the lake bed. At times it was more than 60 kilometres from the lake shore, which had by then retreated over the border to Cameroon.

The company, though it knew that lake levels fluctuated widely, appears to have misjudged its hydrology. A project report written in 1973 confirms that in the feasibility studies then being done 'hydrology was considered to play a minor role . . . water of good quality was available in large quantities in the vast natural reservoir of Lake Chad'. That was written only months after the lowest lake level ever recorded, when the lake had retreated 22 kilometres from the site of the scheme's main pumping station. Even so the firm felt able to continue: 'The preoccupation with low lake levels is in some ways unfortunate; the present phase should be looked at in the context of a temporary short period within a long series of years.'

But some researchers have contested this view. One study claims that the lake has shrunk drastically before, between 1903 and 1908, and again in the 1940s. The author, Are Kolawole, a Nigerian geographer who has studied the SCIP project over more than a decade, maintains that: 'Irrigation at SCIP . . . would have been possible in only 41 of the first 88 years of this century.'

Terry Evans, a senior partner at Mott MacDonald and one of the men who designed the SCIP, today blames the greenhouse effect for the debacle. The implication is that the protracted Sahel drought is an unnatural phenomenon brought on by human activity, and that it could not have been predicted by his company. Even if the waters do eventually return, however, Warshall's team from the University of Arizona warn that lake water reaching the intake channel will be so salty as to 'cause severe soil damage', and prevent many crops from growing. This, they say, is a consideration that 'was not included in the irrigation design of the SCIP'.

Moreover, the execution of the project ensured that the entire area designated was virtually stripped of trees at the start, increasing wind speeds and raising the risk of erosion, especially of dry unirrigated soils. 'Gullying and earth heaving are occurring on the embankments of irrigation canals,' says Warshall. 'This is a common problem that should have been foreseen.'

The SCIP is an unhappy episode for water engineers. But local farmers, more mindful of the ways of the lake than their masters and foreign advisers, responded to its retreat as they have always done – by following it. By the early 1980s, across 225,000 square kilometres of exposed lake bed, traditional farming has sprung up. Farmers planted maize in the path of the advancing shore during the wet season, and cowpeas as the lake retreated. Some sank wells in the lake bed. Whole villages appeared. The soils turned out to be fertile and, even without fertiliser, yields were higher than on government irrigation projects.

The bumbling factotums of Nigeria's Chad Basin Rural Development Authority soon joined in. By 1984, the authority had assumed control of 4,000 hectares of lake floor. It gave the land to staff members and political friends, and began assigning spare resources originally allocated to the SCIP. They brought on to the lake bed tractors, pesticides, fertiliser, high-yield seeds and even lasers to level the ground. It was a flop. Kolawole, who followed the saga, says that the heavy farm equipment destroyed the fertility of the soil and the 'improved' varieties of cowpea did not grow because there was not enough water for them.

The SCIP saga underlines the prevalence in Nigeria of what Kolawole calls 'project fever'. It confirms his thesis that: 'The motive for irrigation development in Nigeria is more political than economic, commercial or technical.'

Besides illustrating the power of patronage, it is also a lesson in the folly of grand inflexible projects in a region of great climatic uncertainty, and in ignoring the superiority of local knowledge in farming the desert margins of the Sahel. Far from greening the desert at a time of drought, the SCIP canals and pumps sit useless in the desert. Far from being the conservative, unenterprising peasants of colonial myth, the farmers of the Sahel seized their chance to make the best of the drying out of the region.

One of the great tyrannies of European colonialists and modern university-trained technocrats alike has been to assume that their theoretical expertise and technology can substitute for local knowledge. But their rainfall gauges, in place for a handful of years, cannot compete with the depth of knowledge about past climates that is frequently still held by local villagers. Their satellite images tell nothing of the complexity of the landscape as understood by people who work on it every day. No computer model can yet touch the sophistication of the village elder who has seen it all.

Says Adams, who is author of several studies of traditional and modern African farming systems: 'The more we learn about agriculture in the pre-colonial period ... the more humble and cautious we are likely to be about advocating new initiatives and sweeping socio-economic transformations.'

Too often throughout Africa, tried and tested farming methods have been uprooted to make way for Western irrigation projects. Kenya's Bura Irrigation Project, and the Masinga Dam built on the River Tana in the late 1970s, flooded 45 kilometres of the valley, one of the most fertile in Kenya. The aim was to settle 5,000 families from all over Kenya in Bura New Town, and President Daniel arap Moi heralded the $100-million project as a major step towards national self-sufficiency. But, nearly a decade later, construction costs doubled, water supply to fields was poor, crop yields were low, settlers failed to arrive and dust storms whipped up loose soil on land that had been cleared but never farmed, clogging irrigation canals. Completion of the scheme was cancelled after a disgruntled World Bank pulled out.

Washing its hands of the affair, the Bank concluded that 'Kenya has promoted large-scale irrigation, but with very limited success, the worst case being Bura.' The cost of the scheme had reached $32,000 per hectare, enough to create a 'negative rate of return'. The experience 'discredited development of irrigation as a tool to achieve agricultural growth and employment', said the Bank.

But the real tragedy is that the valley was already being

irrigated long before the experts from Washington and Nairobi ever set foot there. Says Adams: 'The planning of the Bura was based on the assumption that the project area was uninhabited; it was in fact used by pastoralists', who grazed their cattle and irrigated river banks and terraces.

What goes wrong that such projects are built? Size is undoubtedly an important issue. In irrigation schemes of all kinds, Schumacher's famous dictum that 'small is beautiful' is winning the argument. Even the World Bank, which deals almost exclusively in large projects, says that Africa's large irrigation schemes have typically had rates of return only a half or a third those of small-scale projects. 'Economies of scale' turn out mostly to be diseconomies. Corruption, the consequences of design mistakes, cost overruns, social conflict, all seem to grow exponentially with project size.

Adams goes further. Size is not the essence of the argument, he says. Indigenous farmers will successfully use new technologies, big or small, provided they fit local perceptions about their needs and the local environment – and provided the farmers are in control.

Examples of small successful projects inspired by outsiders abound. David Gilbertson of the Department of Archaeology at the University of Sheffield is the author of a lengthy study of traditional water-gathering methods. He recounts the story of the resettlement of the Bellas, former slaves of the Tuareg in the Sahara. The Bellas moved to their new land in Niger on the edge of the desert after the drought years of the early 1970s. They were encouraged to build tiny water-collecting structures, known as microcatchments, for their sorghum by piling up soil round each plant. 'The size and shape of the plot enables construction by one man, who can reach half a circle round him with his arm to shovel earth,' said Gilbertson. When he wrote, 15,000 had been built.

Oxfam can claim another success for introducing the people of the Yatenga province in the West African state of Burkina Faso to the idea of using low stone walls to harvest scarce rains. The idea is credited at Oxfam to Bill Hereford, their local field director in the late 1970s, who spent a year's leave in Israel looking at how researchers there had harvested rainfall from the hills of the Negev by copying the Nabatean method of building stone walls across the land.

His inspiration came only just in time. Drought was stripping the vegetation from the fields of Yatenga. The soil was forming a crust which rains could not penetrate. Local farmers had no answer to their plight. The European Development Fund had stepped in twice to help. The first time its workers drove bulldozers across the land to create earth dykes to hold the rain on the fields, but the fields became waterlogged. Then they sank hundreds of wells, but the water-table also sank and the wells dried up. Meanwhile local acacia trees, one of the last and hardiest barriers to the desert, succumbed to the drought. The desert was taking over in Yatenga.

Hereford's low stone walls follow the contours, which prevents waterlogging, but hold the occasional rains on the fields long enough for it to sink in and reach the roots of crops. It turned out that stone walls were an old local technique of capturing rainfall that had died out in recent decades. Even so, it required results before most farmers were interested. Jean-Marie, the first farmer to build a wall in the village of Kalsaka, began work in the drought year of 1983 on a field that had not yielded a crop for ten years. He told Oxfam writer Paul Harrison: 'Everybody laughed at me at first. They said it was useless. I was wasting my time. When they saw my millet, they stopped laughing and started building lines.'

Soon the entire village was building long snaking walls across their fields and yields were up 50 per cent. Oxfam is now training hundreds of farmers a year in the simple technique – at a cost of roughly the same as creating two hectares of irrigated fields on the ill-fated Bura irrigation project in Kenya. By the late 1980s, there were walls in more than 300 villages. The idea spread to neighbouring Ghana, but by then back home it was becoming a victim of its own success. 'The basic material, the rocks that cover the plateau, are now in short supply in some areas and transporting them is becoming a serious problem,' says Oxfam, which produced £33,000 for a tipper truck to fetch stone.

Yatenga's stone walls won't save the world. Nor should

they. They are a locally developed response to a local problem and to try and transplant them elsewhere could be as destructive as any other imposed technology. The lesson seems obvious, but is rarely taken to heart. Says Gilbertson: 'The importance of an eye for the country, for detailed local knowledge, locally adapted plant varieties and local water management practices does not seem to have appealed to the major European colonists and engineers who subsequently acquired authority.'

The world may be accumulating millions of satellite photographs of the planet. But it is wilfully haemorrhaging large amounts of invaluable information about local environments, whether in the rainforests or the desert margins, and how humans can live in them. 'The wisdom of the ancients in managing these harsh landscapes', says Gilbertson, 'was more substantive than our own.'

15

FEED THE WORLD

For the first time, we may have the technical capacity to free mankind from the scourge of hunger ... within a decade no child will go to bed hungry.

Henry Kissinger, World Food Conference, 1974

The failure of large irrigation projects to green the deserts illustrates in an extreme form a much wider failure of large state water schemes, in harness with the new high-yield 'green revolution' crops, to banish hunger. In wetter lands, on good soils and away from Africa, the new farming has undoubtedly raised national farm outputs, sometimes remarkably. Irrigation, as much as fertilisers and pesticides, has been the feedstock of a revolution that has doubled crop yields throughout much of Asia in the past 40 years. But it has failed to solve the basic causes of hunger in the world, which have to do with access of rural communities to resources such as land and water with which to grow food. Round the world today there is hunger, and occasional famine, amidst plenty. And, if anything, state-run irrigation projects have made the disparities worse.

Three-quarters of the water put into service by humans today goes to irrigate crops. The amount of irrigated land increased tenfold between 1800 and 1950 and has tripled again since, during the years of the green revolution. Today, irrigated fields cover approaching three million square kilometres of the planet, mostly in the dry Middle East and the monsoon lands of Asia. On the face of it, this is not a huge amount: it is roughly the land area of Argentina. But irrigation reaches 18 per cent of all the fields in the world. And more than a third of the global harvest is grown on those fields.

By the mid-1980s, public schemes to extend irrigation in the developing world had soaked up $250 billion, with another $100 million of projects in the pipeline. As a result, these nations now have three-quarters of the world's irrigated farmland, a third of it in two countries, China and India. The arid lands of Pakistan and Egypt rely on irrigation for more than 80 per cent of their output.

For some, such statistics are proof of the success of the large publicly funded projects that have dominated irrigation investment. But, despite investment costs typically between $2,000 and $10,000 per hectare, and sometimes many times higher, virtually none of these projects have met their production targets or lived up to financial expectations.

The common image of irrigation making barren land fertile is wrong. Most land taken over for irrigation projects was cultivated before the engineers arrived – even on the desert margins, as we have seen in India and the Sahel. The irrigators usually take the best land in order to secure the best financial returns on their substantial investments. Frequently, too, as in northern Nigeria, water diversions for large state irrigation schemes dry up productive land downstream. So statistics showing how much greater crop yields are on irrigated land may be highly misleading as a measure of irrigation's success.

There were alarming signs through the 1980s that yields were falling on many schemes. It appears that some farmers could not afford the expensive fertilisers required to make irrigation water swell grain; that pests took increasing advantage of the susceptibilities of large monoculture plantations of high-yield seeds; and the quality of soils declined under the constant assault from chemicals, water and salt. It may be that the best the green revolution can produce is already past.

'It is now widely recognised that irrigation and drainage projects are not producing the benefits expected,' concluded staff from the World Bank's agriculture department in 1991, at the end of one of the best documented studies of the irrigated world that the Bank had done much to create. The study looked at 11 schemes from Mexico, Morocco, Sudan, Colombia, the Philippines and Thailand. In every case, the amount of water delivered to crops was well below expectations. On average only 40 per cent of the water, so expensively collected behind giant dams and distributed along thousands of kilometres of canals, reached the root zone of plants. The rest of the water seeped from unlined canals, evaporated in the sun or collected in waterlogged fields. More than one irrigated field in ten was 'seriously affected' by waterlogging and the build-up of salt.

A review of nine of the largest projects in Asia, Africa and Latin America by the World Resources Institute, a think tank with strong links to the World Bank, found that the projects cost three times as much as anticipated; that the amount of land irrigated was typically a third less than anticipated; and that projects were completed on average five years late. 'Operation and maintenance of completed systems have been deficient, and farmers have not responded as hoped ... many current projects cannot be justified,' said the report's author, Roger Repetto.

In India, one of the most irrigated countries in the world, the scale of the failure was brought home in the Sixth Five-Year Plan, published by the country's Planning Commission in 1985. It revealed that projected yields of grain on newly irrigated fields were not the 4 to 5 tonnes per year predicted but, more typically, 1.7 tonnes. A year later, the prime minister Rajiv Gandhi complained that:

> Since 1951, 246 large surface irrigation projects have been begun in India; only 65 have been completed. Perhaps we can safely say that almost no benefit has come to the people from these projects. For 16 years, we have poured money out. The people have got nothing back, no irrigation, no water, no increase in production, no help in their daily life.

Gandhi echoed a past warning by Robert McNamara, former president of the World Bank, that: 'The drama of harnessing a major river may be more exciting than the prosaic task of getting a steady trickle of water to a parched hectare, but to millions of smallholders that is what is going to make the difference between success and failure.' And he called on the Indian states to give priority to completing existing schemes. But within two years, they were lobbying

An aerial photograph of the English Fens shows the ghostly mark of a former meandering river, which lives on as a trail of light soil across the grid of modern fields. (*Cambridge University Collection of Air Photographs*)

Time-honoured tradition: irrigation of rice paddies on ancient hill terraces in southeast Asia. *(Paul Harrison)*

Pulleys and muscle power bring water from a well on the edge of India's Thar Desert. (© *Phillip Jones Griffiths/Magnum*)

The dying Aral Sea: as irrigation engineers divert the rivers that once filled the sea, these fishing boats now lie 40 kilometres from the shoreline on the exposed seabed. (© G. Pinkhassov/Magnum)

Varanasi, India: the Ganges breaks its banks and floods the city. While flooding irrigates and fertilises fields, it paralyses urban life. (© *Steve McCurry/Magnum*)

Construction works at Itaipu Dam in Brazil, the world's largest hydroelectric dam. (© *J. R. Salgado/Magnum*)

On Punjuma Lake, northern Nigeria. The new dams downstream threaten to dry out a vital resource for this parched scrubland on the edge of the desert. (*Eugene Richards*)

The $3-billion aqueduct, the Central Arizona Project, crosses the desert to fill the swimming pools and fountains of Phoenix. (*Bureau of Reclamation*)

New Delhi for permission to proceed with the largest projects yet, in the Narmada valley.

The green revolution began as a worldwide scientific effort to raise global food production. It was initiated in the years after the Second World War, as predictions that the world population was set to double within a generation conjured up spectres of widespread famine. The revolution began with a dwarf wheat variety developed in Mexico, and continued with the creation at the International Rice Research Institute in the Philippines of a hybrid variety of rice that could, given enough water and fertiliser, double traditional yields. These successes enabled Henry Kissinger to make his declaration to the World Food Conference in 1974 that: 'Within a decade no child will go to bed hungry.'

But, in reality, the crisis in world food was never wholly a technical problem, nor a matter of national production. And the leaders of the green revolution failed to distinguish between the desire to raise world food production, which they have done, and the need to buttress the rights and resources of the most vulnerable people. As a result, the revolution began to take food production out of the hands of the rural poor – the people who needed to grow food to live.

The drive to raise production produced bumper crops in some areas, indeed in some whole countries. India, Pakistan and Indonesia becoming self-sufficient in their staple grain crops for the first time in many years. Wheat yields in India and Pakistan doubled within a decade of the introduction of the new varieties in 1965. There were similar gains after the new rice varieties arrived in the late 1960s. Average grain production in India tripled to 150 million tonnes per year between 1950 and the late 1980s, keeping well ahead of the rise in population and making India self-sufficient in grain.

To make these new varieties grow required good, well-irrigated soils, and large inputs of water, fertiliser, pesticides and labour. Of these, most poor farmers only had the labour, and it is clear that the most important contribution to raised food production was the greater number of people available to till the fields. The problem was that poorer people, living on poorer soils without adequate irrigation, and without

access to the credit needed to buy chemicals and farm equipment, found themselves unable to join the bonanza. They
were pushed even further to the margins of society – often
becoming more rather than less vulnerable to drought and
famine.

In Mexico, where the wheat revolution began in the late
1940s, 80 per cent of the extra production from new wheat
varieties came from just 3 per cent of the farms. Mechani-
sation on large farms meant that, according to one study, the
number of days worked each year by Mexican landless
labourers dropped by half. The green revolution there
brought poverty and destitution to the Mexican countryside,
and was a prime reason why during the 1970s and 1980s a
thousand peasant migrants arrived each day at Mexico City's
bus stations, turning the city into the world's largest, with
approaching 20 million people.

In India, most of the increased production was concentrated in a few regions, such as the heavily irrigated Punjab.
This can be seen as the final vindication of the British irrigation projects here in the mid-nineteenth century. But,
according to the Indian ecologist Vandana Shiva, 'The introduction of high-yield varieties has led to increased rural
inequalities and landlessness, and has contributed to ethnic
violence which has claimed thousands of lives in the province.'

She criticises the statistics used to demonstrate the success
of the green revolution. 'In a country like India, crops have
traditionally been bred to produce not just food for humans,
but fodder for animals and organic fertiliser for soils. In the
[crop] breeding strategy for the green revolution, these multi-
ple uses of plants seem to have been consciously sacrificed.' So
while grain production has soared, output of stems and leaves
has fallen. There is less straw for animal fodder, for fertilising
fields or for thatching houses. The statistics also fail to assess
properly the inputs – and especially water. The single largest
investment in the green revolution has been the massive state
subsidies at the heart of the irrigation drive. Virtually nowhere
do farmers pay anything like the real cost of abstracting and
distributing their water. In one year, Pakistan spent two
billion rupees on irrigation projects, paid out another six

billion in interest charges on old projects – and received revenues on the sale of water of just one billion rupees. A sample of projects funded by the World Bank found that only 7 per cent of costs were recovered through revenues. This is not a phenomenon of third world or socialist countries alone: the equivalent figure for the state-funded irrigation schemes in the US is 17 per cent.

Who gains from this investment? In practice, says Repetto, 'the subsidies, borne by tax payers, go predominantly to better-off farmers'. You might put it another way. Most irrigation projects help the rich get richer and leave the poor to fend for themselves. This may be contrary to the aims of the green revolution, but the drive to irrigate has a life of its own.

The green revolution has massively increased the dependence of world food production on the supply of water – a resource in increasingly short supply. In the Punjab, until recently, farmers did not need irrigation to grow wheat, except during a drought. Now, for the new improved varieties, it is essential.

Some types of wheat can produce yields 40 per cent or more greater than traditional varieties, but only by consuming up to three times more water. In fact, they usually produce far less grain per unit of water than traditional varieties. They are, in other words, only high-yielding varieties when measured against the land they require on which to grow. Measured against water demand, they are extremely low-yield varieties. So wherever it is water rather than land that is in short supply, green revolution varieties of wheat make no sense. This is why, on desert fringes such as the Sahel, the great irrigation projects often produce less food than the *fadamas*, for instance.

The UN's Food and Agriculture Organisation, the chief international planning agency for the green revolution, notes in its main strategy document, *Towards 2000*, that: 'It is water rather than land which is the binding constraint for almost 600 million hectares of potentially suitable arable land.' In other words, for at least a third of the world's farmland, the real measure of yield for crops should not be in tonnes per hectare, but rather in tonnes per thousand cubic metres of water.

If so, then why does the FAO not publish data in this form? Why is its top priority not developing crops that make the most efficient rather than the least efficient use of water? The answer is that the prime day-to-day motivation behind the green revolution is making money, not food. Individuals own land from which they want to make money. Water is not owned, but allocated and expropriated. And its delivery is highly subsidised.

The next great challenge for the green revolution is to feed Africa, where much of the continent is untouched by either irrigation or the green revolution. Traditional African crops such as sorghum and millet have not yet been subjected to the laboratory scanning of their genetic potential to create a super-seed. And state-financed attempts to irrigate high-yielding varieties of wheat and rice imported from Asia have often turned into expensive fiascos. This, conventional wisdom has it, is why Africa has become chronically unable to keep the bellies of its citizens full.

But for an African green revolution to succeed, it will have to be very different, for Africa faces a profound water crisis. This is a result partly of absolute shortages and partly of the appropriation of water by elites. Malin Falkenmark, a Swedish professor of international hydrology, says that absolute water scarcity 'now threatens two-thirds of the African population'. She predicts permanent water crises in Tunisia, Kenya and Malawi by the end of the century, with Ethiopia, Somalia, Uganda and Nigeria in the same state by 2025. The failure of water distribution and allocation, of course, mean that many people in these countries suffer permanent water crises already. For them, a green revolution devoted to growing water-hungry varieties of their traditional crops would be a disaster.

There are three scourges that afflict hundreds of large irrigation projects round the world: the schistosome, corruption, and salt. The schistosome is a flatworm – a parasite about a centimetre long that lives inside humans, sometimes for up to

35 years. It lives either in the liver or in the veins of the abdomen. Males and females are permanently intertwined, producing eggs every day, which travel to other organs of the human host, such as brain, spinal cord, lung and uterus. The eggs inflame organs, causing myriad illnesses, including headaches, nausea, blood in the urine and, in more serious cases, cirrhosis of the liver. Many victims die. Infestation with schistosomes is called schistosomiasis or bilharzia. An estimated 200 million people suffer from the disease round the world – double the number of 50 years ago. It is one of the few infectious diseases growing more prevalent in the tropics, and particularly in Africa. It may be killing more people than AIDS.

Schistosomiasis is the dark shadow that follows irrigation projects across the continent. Children who play in water are its most numerous victims. They catch the disease by bathing in water containing snails, the host of the schistosome larvae. The larvae leave the snail, bore through human skin and enter the bloodstream. The snails love irrigation canals, and cling to weeds in the shallow, still waters. In modern year-round irrigation, the canals never dry out, allowing the snails and their worm larvae to proliferate.

The worm's life cycle is completed when their human hosts defecate in the water. In countries where flush toilets are rare and people relieve themselves in the open, a canal can be the only private place around. On farms where contact with irrigation water in ditches is a daily occurrence for almost everyone, for washing and doing laundry as well as operating the canals and sluices, almost everyone becomes contaminated.

Several other important infectious diseases, notably river blindness and malaria, are encouraged by the presence of standing water in irrigation projects. But schistosomiasis is the only one that has drastically increased its prevalence as a result of such projects.

In Sudan's Blue Nile province, schistosomiasis was once rare, for the fast-flowing Nile washed snails away from the banks. In the 1920s, aware of the dangers of snails migrating into the canals of the Gezira irrigation scheme, the British surveyed the new canals soon after flooding. They found no snails. But within 18 months the snails had arrived.

The British managers tried everything. They introduced ducks to eat the snails. They quarantined migrant workers from West Africa, who were accused of carrying the schistosome eggs. They appointed snail catchers to patrol the 2,000 kilometres of canals. Later, they poured a molluscicide developed by Shell into the canals. But all efforts failed. Today, more than half of the million or so people living on the world's largest farm at Gezira are infected. Among children, the figure is more than 80 per cent.

Muhamad Amin, a member of the London-Khartoum Bilharzia Project, a relic of colonial health care, surveyed Gezira in the 1970s. The spread of weeds through the project during that time turned it into a near-perfect system for infecting the maximum number of people. The small field canals had the most snails and the most contact between humans and water, he said. He estimated that on a typical day, one in eleven of the workforce was off sick because of the disease.

On other irrigation projects in Africa engineers have tried to combat the disease by spraying chemicals to rid the canals of weeds, by installing latrines beside canal banks, and by changing canal system design to eliminate standing water where possible. But in most places the battle is still being lost. Egypt is no newcomer to the disease: the ova of schistosomes have been found in 3,000-year-old Egyptian mummies. But since the completion of the High Aswan Dam, it has soared, and between a third and a half of the population has been infected. Similar figures emerge from surveys of irrigated areas around Lake Victoria in Kenya and in Zimbabwe, where 80 per cent of children in many rural areas are infected.

Schistosomiasis is most prevalent in Africa, where the host snails are most frequently found. But it is spreading and is now widespread on irrigation projects in the Philippines, parts of southeast Asia and China, in Iraq along the Tigris and Euphrates canal systems and in South America.

A study for the British consultants, Hydraulics Research, in the late 1980s noted: 'The vast amount of money that has been spent over the years in trying to control schistosomiasis has met with relatively little success.' It held out hope for a new range of drugs, but the basic problem is that the engineers' desire to stabilise flows in rivers and canals and ensure year-round availability of water is precisely what encourages colonisation by snails in farm irrigation canals and the spread of the disease. The scandal is that no irrigation project has ever been substantially redesigned to reduce the risks.

A second scourge of large irrigation schemes is corruption. Not just the gold-plated corruption that frequently surrounds their construction, but also the grinding day-to-day corruption that can cripple the operation of even the best designed scheme. One international study concluded brusquely: 'It is the general rule that the strong, the powerful, the well-connected, the local bullies, dominate the use of irrigation water. They get water first and tend to take as much as they please. Only after they are satisfied do they permit the masses of ordinary, unimportant, petty cultivators to have access to it.'

Robert Wade of the University of Sussex has studied corruption in Indian irrigation and concludes: 'Irrigation engineers raise vast amounts of illicit revenue from the distribution of water and contracts, and redistribute part to superior officers and politicians.' Managers take bribes to ensure that the right sluice-gates are opened and water reaches farmers' fields. He argues that this is not a petty matter, but 'is an important reason for the poor performance of canal-irrigated agriculture'.

Large irrigation systems are designed to provide assured supplies of water. Farmers need to know that, come rain or drought, their crops will be watered. If not, they might as well wait for it to rain. Yet, says Wade, 'While the purpose of the system is to make supplies secure, officials do best when water supplies are insecure. Merely by rumouring a shortage, money can be raised.' They have a vested interest in keeping farmers guessing about when their water is coming.

The third, and in the longer run most destructive, scourge of large irrigation projects is salt. A third of all the world's agricultural production comes from irrigated fields. Almost a third of these fields are suffering from a potentially terminal condition, a kind of cancer that could make them unfit for cultivation.

All natural waters contain some salt. Much of it is common table salt, sodium chloride. But there are many others: the carbonates, chlorides and sulphates of magnesium and sodium, as well as calcium. A clear bubbling stream high in the mountains may contain only fifty parts per million of salt. But it gradually dissolves more from the rocks over which it passes until it contains hundreds or even thousands of parts per million, by which time it will be unfit to drink or even to water crops.

Normally a river, even a dammed river, will convey the salt to the sea. But if the river peters out in a hot desert, or forms evaporation ponds along the way, then nature creates salt flats on which little or nothing will grow. Many irrigation systems can do in a few decades or centuries what it took nature millions of years to perform. They bring salt to the fields and then leave it there as the water is absorbed by plants or evaporated in the sun.

Badly designed or operated irrigation works create waterlogged soils, which speed up the process further. If the watertable rises close to the surface, a physical process called capillary action sucks the moisture to the surface, where the sun burns it off, creating a white, salty crust. If that happens, the soil is dead. From the American West to the Volga, from Australia to Pakistan, from former Soviet central Asia to Argentina, this is happening on a massive scale. Salt plus waterlogging is destroying fields overnight and creating deserts.

According to the UN Environment Programme, salt significantly reduces crop yields in perhaps 30 per cent of the world's irrigated fields. In 7 per cent there are drastic crop reductions. An area of land the size of Northern Ireland is lost to salt each year, as much as the size of England in a decade. A quarter of all Pakistan's fields are seriously damaged. In Egypt, thanks largely to modern canal irrigation which prevents floods flushing the soils clean, the figure is 30 per cent. In India, it is 25 per cent. In the New World, Argentina and Mexico both suffer extensively. In Australia, some 2,000 square kilometres of fields in the country's irrigated heartland of the Murray-Darling basin have been abandoned to salt. Fields covered in white salt crystals are going out of use almost as fast as irrigation canals reach new fields. As banks and aid agencies understand the salt problem better, they grow reluctant to fund irrigation projects. So the pace of new irrigation falters and salt gains the upper hand.

The accumulation of salt in irrigated soils is in the long run inevitable. The only question is how fast it is allowed to happen. In the past, salt has overthrown great civilisations as surely as any army, and with much greater permanency. In southern Iraq, the land that was once ancient Sumer, a world of green fields and the world's first cities, is now shimmering desert fit for little more than tank battles. Modern Iraq has not learnt the lesson. Half its currently irrigated fields are salt-infested, according to the UN Environment Programme.

There are technological 'fixes' that can extend the lifetime of irrigation projects. In Australia and India, they planted a deep-rooted and salt-tolerant tree, which lowered the water-table by taking up water through its roots. More typically, plastic drains tap the brine and convey it back into the river. The cost of a network of drainage pipes is usually greater than irrigating the fields in the first place. But in most places, it will have to be done, sooner or later, or the fields will be doomed.

Sometimes, even successful flushing and drainage of salts can be a disaster. In the American Colorado basin so much salt returns to the river that the river-water itself is barely fit for use on farms with intakes downstream. When they drained the fields of the Wellton-Mohawk irrigation project near Yuma for the first time, so much salt returned to the river that its water became toxic to plants and crops died over the border in Mexico. The US government dug a canal – a second River Colorado – to take the brine a hundred kilometres to the sea.

On the Colorado the best solution, says Jim Rhoades of the US government's Salinity Laboratory, may be to keep the salt in the soil and to prevent salty water reaching the root zone by using high-tech control systems to reduce irrigation. But on irrigated fields from central Asia to Africa, farmers more usually become caught in a vicious circle, pouring ever more irrigation water on to their fields in an effort to maintain yields and flush out salt. Ultimately they find themselves farming in a saline swamp.

Undoubtedly the best technical solution to salt and water-logging on irrigated fields is to pour on less water. There are massive increases in the efficiency of water use that can be made on almost every project. Rather than flooding fields, farmers may operate sprinklers or drip-irrigation systems – essentially long lines of hoses with tiny holes in them which are trailed along plant rows and trickle water on to the ground beside the roots.

Rhoades has pioneered the introduction of salt-tolerant crops and the tailoring of crop rotations to accommodate salt. But, in the long run, he agrees that the floodplain of the Colorado will turn into a desolate salt pan on which nothing will grow. The trick is to keep the show on the road as long as possible. 'There is going to be less water for agriculture. It will be more saline. We will have to use it more efficiently,' he says.

But can such lessons be learned in time for Pakistan? Pakistan has been transformed by irrigation – first when the British created its canal colonies across the Punjab and Sind, and later by the massive intensification of irrigation of the past 30 years. But the country is running out of water, and salt is beginning to take a terrible toll on its fields. For a nation where 80 per cent of its fields are irrigated the stakes are high. And the world should be watching. Here, as nowhere else, the success or failure of the green revolution and the ability of the Third World to fight salt will be decided.

16

THE UNHAPPY VALLEY

Their country's physical resources are not equal to the capability of the people to exploit them.

General Emerson C. Itschner, chief technical adviser
on the River Indus in the 1950s

General Itschner, an engineer from the US Army's Corps of Engineers, made the intriguing remark above in the 1950s, at the height of negotiations to secure a treaty between India and Pakistan on the future of the River Indus. Perhaps it was a compliment to his hosts. Perhaps it was a polite way of saying they were destroying their natural resources, of which the greatest is water. Either way, if any country epitomises the perils of the overuse of water resources, and the law of diminishing returns that follows, it is Pakistan.

The British took a while to extend their great Indus valley irrigation project from the Punjab south to the Sind. It was 1932, very late in their tenure of the Indian subcontinent, before they finally trekked into what they called 'the unhappy valley' and built the Sukkur barrage. The barrage with its 66 arches was the centrepiece of the new Sind irrigation system, which was intended to turn the desert province into a giant cotton farm, a Gezira for Pakistan.

Before the construction of the barrage, irrigation here was often fitful and there were famines. But after the completion of the barrage and seven irrigation canals – some of them the renovated and extended remnants of ancient canals – almost the entire Indus valley had been turned into the largest continuous system of irrigated land in the world. It was an engineering triumph, and the basis for the country's embracing of the green revolution. But it set in train a sequence of events that leaves the country permanently up to its ears in debt, attempting to sustain a system that many regard as unsustainable.

The dams and barrages diverted so much water into the Sind that the land soon became waterlogged. 'Before engineers installed the barrages,' wrote Roy Stoner, former head of Mott MacDonald, in *New Scientist* in 1988, 'the water-table in the vast sandy aquifers underlying the alluvial valley was 15 metres or more deep. With perennial irrigation, the water-table rose rapidly to about one metre below the surface.'

After the partition of India at independence in 1947, the new government of Pakistan was more concerned about preserving its supplies of water than about salt or waterlogging. Within months of independence, Pakistan's half of the Punjab irrigation system faced partial collapse when India cut off rivers that fed Pakistani canals. The rivers passed through the disputed territory of Kashmir en route from the Himalayas to the Pakistani lowlands. 'At a stroke, all the pre-independence agreements were made null and void, and there arose a bitter dispute,' says the British colonial engineer Henry Olivier. Water, even more than the glaciers of Kashmir, took the two nations to the brink of war.

A decade later, the two nations reached an accord, brokered by the World Bank and based on an offer from the Bank and Western governments of massive aid to re-engineer the system. In effect, the US government bought peace in the region with aid dollars. Under the Indus Treaty of 1960, India took water from the easterly tributaries of the Indus, and Pakistan took the westerly tributaries. Aid agencies provided Pakistan with $1.2 billion to build the Mangla Dam on one of its tributaries, the Jhelum, plus 50 barrages and more than a thousand kilometres of canals, to divert water across the Punjab to fill irrigation canals cut off by India. It was at the time the largest water development scheme in the world. The one obvious flaw was that it greatly increased Pakistan's dependence for its economic development on the Indus.

The Pakistani President, the Sandhurst-trained Field

Marshal Ayub Khan, drove a tough bargain. He persuaded the
Bank to help fund a second dam, the Tarbela Dam, on the
River Indus itself. Its purpose was to provide extra water for
the Sind. Engineers said the dam would be uneconomic. But,
recalls Olivier, after years of badgering, Khan won. The best
that Itschner, the American adviser to the Pakistani water
authorities, could say was that: 'It is definitely not a good dam
site, but it is the best site available on the Indus.'

In an effort to make it profitable, Khan built the dam far
larger than originally intended. It is 140 metres tall, almost
three kilometres long and contains more than 100,000 cubic
metres of earth and rock, and was at the time the largest dam
ever constructed. The billion-dollar dam also proved one of
the most technically flawed. There was a $25 million repair
bill before it opened for business, after its diversion gate
jammed during filling and the force of water emptying from
the dam ripped out tunnels. Tarbela is plagued by huge silt
banks washing through the reservoir towards the turbines, by
seepage through its foundations, and by the erosion of thousands of sinkholes in the dam's surface. There are seismic
worries, too. Engineers call it the most monitored dam in the
world.

On the face of it, human ascendancy on the Indus appears
complete. The engineers at the Pakistani Water and Power
Development Authority, the country's largest civilian organisation, can hold the monsoon floods in the upriver reservoirs
for power generation, and divert virtually the entire dry-
season flow into the canals. Irrigated land has grown from
15,000 square kilometres in 1900 and 82,000 in 1934 to
approaching 140,000 today. However, soils are waterlogged
and the salt is rising. According to government figures, the
water-table is within 30 centimetres of the surface across 80
per cent of the cotton fields of Sind. At that level, capillary
action comes into operation and salt can take a swift hold
unless constantly washed away with new water. In some parts
of the Sind, more than half the land is barren and covered in
salt and only a few clumps of grass and stubby scrub can
grow. Each year, according to the UN Environment Programme, farmers abandon another 40,000 hectares of land (an

area the size of the Isle of Wight), and eerie salt lakes dot the white landscape.

Each year, 22 million tonnes of salt are brought on to the flat plains of the Indus Valley, but only 11 million tonnes reach the Arabian Sea. The rest, almost one tonne for every irrigated hectare, stays in the fields of Punjab and, especially, Sind.

Farmers respond in the only way they can, by pouring more and more water on to their land. In the short term, this can maintain yields and flush out the salt. But they dare not let their land lie fallow, because one year left uncropped will almost certainly allow the salt to reach the surface and kill the land. According to Ghulan Rasool Sandhu of the Pakistan Agriculture Research Council, a quarter of the country's irrigated fields require permanent irrigation to prevent salt reaching the surface.

The sheer scale of the irrigation scheme has made it vulnerable. The British were anxious to levy taxes on as much irrigated land as possible, so they distributed the waters of the Indus across a wide area. The effect was to maximise revenues, but greatly to increase the waste of water, especially from evaporation under the clear skies of the Sind and seepage from the 60,000 kilometres of canals. It would have made more sense to concentrate irrigation where drains can channel the brine back into the river.

Today, arguably, the Pakistani government should be taking much of the Sind out of production before salt puts on its deadly embrace. That option, says Stoner, 'would be more productive than trying to keep marginal land in use. But the social and political implications are quite unacceptable to the government. It would force smallholders to leave their farms, joining the stream of homeless and jobless people in the cities.' It would also create ferment in the Sind, a volatile region dominated by the Bhutto family. So the government is committed to the near-impossible task of improving all the land, while running the serious risk of destroying much of it for ever.

Everybody knew that drains would ultimately be needed on this land to remove the salt. The British engineers knew it, and said they would pay for the drains out of taxes levied on the crops grown on the new fields – a promise never kept. The Pakistanis knew it after independence, but would not act until the Indus Treaty was signed in 1960. After that, they had other priorities, building dams and canals to replace the water ceded to India.

In the mid-1980s, Pakistan finally acted, borrowing $600 million to complete the first stage of the Left Bank outfall drain. The drain is a second, brine-filled River Indus, reaching the Arabian Sea across the flat marshes of the Rann of Kutch, 50 kilometres east of the main river. It will carry salty water from drains installed beneath the cotton fields of the lower 300 kilometres of the river's left bank.

The Pakistani government must also drain the right bank, where rice is the main crop. This project could take 25 years, according to a study by Mott MacDonald. Then, upstream, are a further 700 kilometres of river valley awaiting drainage. In recent years, Pakistan has spent $140 million annually on reclaiming saline and waterlogged land, doubling its spending on new irrigation schemes. Nobody can see an end to the task. The country already has 64,000 kilometres of canals and irrigation ditches – more canals than roads. Now it must dig an almost equal length of drainage ditches.

Far from being intimidated by the task, Pakistan is determined to increase irrigation yet further. Where the state cannot provide more water, it is helping farmers to install new tube-wells to pump groundwater on to their fields. Much of the groundwater is leakage from fields and irrigation ditches – and much of it is saline. In the 1980s, the government helped fund 12,000 tube-wells with the aim of lowering the water-table, irrigating crops and flushing out salt. The strategy worked for a while, but water-tables soon began to rise again. And however much you recycle salt it doesn't go away unless there are drains to remove it. To provide electricity to power these tube-wells, the government has spent large sums providing almost every village in the Punjab with electricity. Now it is short of electricity and must turn to the Indus to provide hydroelectric power.

Pakistan's whole economic future has now been made

dependent on the Indus, and in particular on the success of the two huge dams at Mangla and Tarbela. Between them, they provide 40 per cent of the nation's electricity and 50 per cent of its water. But this dependency is dangerous. Both reservoirs are silting up fast. Mangla, which flooded the historic town of Mirpur and forced the relocation of 110,000 people on its completion in 1967, may be of little use for storing water or generating hydroelectric power much beyond the turn of the century. The Tarbela loses 2 per cent of its capacity to silt each year and is plagued by technical problems which could force its premature abandonment.

Earthquakes are a constant threat to the integrity of the dams. Also, high in the headwaters of the Indus and its tributaries are giant lakes held back by walls of ice. Every century or so, one of these lakes bursts, bringing devastation downstream. Kenneth Hewitt, a Canadian geographer, says that in the past, 'The bursting of glacial lakes has caused devastation hundreds of kilometres downstream. Such floods are a threat to new water and power installations.'

In the 1980s, partly to replace the storage lost to silt, Pakistan proposed building a third major dam – at Kalabagh, downstream of Tarbela. The World Bank agreed to fund it, but disputes between the Punjab and Sind provinces over who should receive its water have since held up the project. If Tarbela was 'not a good site' for a dam, Kalabagh is worse. In order to capture only two-thirds as much water as Tarbela, Kalabagh will flood twice as much land. It will displace at least 120,000 people in the Punjab and North West Frontier provinces, as well as numerous bridges, roads and stretches of railway line and prime farmland in the Peshawar valley. Depending on the precise height of the dam, which is likely to exceed 250 metres, it could also inundate the town of Nowshera, which has a population of over 100,000. The law of diminishing returns is taking hold with a vengeance in Pakistani water development.

Such talk cuts little ice with Asif Kazi, chief engineering adviser to the Pakistani power authorities. He says: 'There is a strong feeling in developing countries that most rivers in developed countries are saturated with dams. But now our turn comes, now our nations are free from colonial rule and can start building our own dams, suddenly environmentalists are so aggressive to stop us.' He sees a new generation of 'green imperialists' bent on stopping his country's economic development. The dams, he says,

> allow us to export rice, be self-sufficient in wheat and have plenty of cotton and sugar cane. In Pakistan nobody is hungry, nobody is without shoes. This is due to the irrigation network, the biggest in the world. I cannot imagine Pakistan remaining on its own two feet without these two reservoirs. God made Pakistan a desert. Sometimes when people say that deserts and swamps should be protected, they don't know what that means to a country like ours. I don't ever want to see a swamp, whatever rare species live there.

No one would disagree that the Indus and its tributaries have become the lifeblood of modern Pakistan. But while Kazi celebrates his country's dependence on its two great dams, others fear it. The risk today is that modern agriculture is in the process of creating a vast salt pan across the Sind. The questions are whether the natural beneficence of the Indus is being so overused that its future is at risk, and whether the nation will bankrupt itself attempting to maintain the insupportable.

Nasir Gazdar, a Pakistani academic teaching in the USA, is one of the 'green imperialists' to whom Kazi objects. In 1990, he wrote an assessment of the Kalabagh project, which he subtitled 'Promising a rose garden, but delivering dust'. For him the proposed new dam 'is a domino in the continuing saga of the destruction of the Indus basin's resource base in the twentieth century'. There are alternatives, he insists. Pakistan would not have to revert to desert primitivism if it attempted to rely less on its creaking and corroded Indus plumbing system. It should spend the money earmarked for the next dam on ending its addiction to cultivating water-hungry export crops such as cotton and sugar cane and on making radical improvements in the efficiency of its use of both water and electricity.

One long-time expert on Asian irrigation problems, Robert Chambers, estimates that in Pakistan: 'Improved management of existing irrigation could save three times more water than is supplied by the Tarbela Dam.' The task would cost roughly a quarter as much as providing the same amount of water from a new dam such as the Kalabagh.

Five thousand years ago, one of the great early civilisations of the world flourished in the heat of the Sind desert. The great city-state of Mohenjodharo cultivated the land, irrigating wheat, cotton and vegetables with water taken from the Indus. Archaeologists believe that the great city fell around 4,000 years ago when waterlogging caused a build-up of salt in the soils and crops failed.

Now the same process is taking hold again in the same valley. Efforts to excavate the ancient city during the 1960s had to be abandoned because canals delivering water to fields had waterlogged the site. Today, the Pakistanis are attempting to drain this same soil in order that excavations can resume. If the country can drain its land and keep the salt at bay, then it may have a prosperous future. If not, then it may ultimately share the fate of its predecessor in this valley.

17

THE PULL OF
THE PERIPHERY

If I had my way, this disgusting water would soon know its
place! The place for water is behind dams and in pipes – all
under control.

Mr Galvanic in 'Headlong Down The Years' by Clough
and Amabel Williams-Ellis, 1951

Wheels that lift water from rivers or ditches are almost as old
as irrigation itself. But the use of water-wheels for grinding
corn is far more recent. The Romans may have been the first
to build water-powered mills. At Barbegal in southern France,
a mill with eight water-wheels, arranged in a long cascade and
fed from above with water from an aqueduct, drove eight
horizontal millstones. The mill ground flour to feed 80,000
soldiers, government officials and their families at nearby
Arles.

Archaeologists have uncovered a profusion of Roman
water-mills in northern Europe, particularly in Britain. The
mills survived the Romans' departure to become one of the
most distinctive technological features of northern Europe.
The Domesday Book recorded 5,624 water-mills in Britain at
the end of the eleventh century, one for every fifty households.
Most of them ground grain to make flour, but, as their power
and versatility grew, some began to drive tools such as lathes,
pumps and crushers.

At first all mills in England were 'undershoot' wheels,
which were dipped into a stream. But in the twelfth and
thirteenth centuries came the 'overshoot' wheel, for which
water was captured by a weir and poured into the blades at

the top of the wheel. The undershoot wheel used the impact of water alone on its blades to turn its axle. In a small stream it generated little power. But the overshoot wheel could also utilise the weight of the water to turn it. There were other advantages: the wheel need no longer sit on the bank of the stream itself, because water could be taken to it. And water could be stored, behind a dam perhaps, for later use.

The Cistercian monasteries were among the first to build overshoot wheels. They were also the first to attach a cam to the wheel's axle. This could lift and release a wooden hammer to pound newly woven wool, cleaning and thickening it – a process called fulling. This was the first aspect of the textile industry to be industrialised and boosted the Cistercians' export trade in wool, which generated the wealth for such buildings as Fountains Abbey in North Yorkshire.

Water power was soon spinning silk, too. Industrial centres included Chester, a former Roman garrison which recovered some of its glory after building a weir, which provided water for mills that ground corn, fulled cloth and later powered paper and snuff mills. By the thirteenth century the streams of the Weald in southeast England were driving the bellows and hammers of the fast-growing iron industry. William Camden wrote of the Weald in the 1590s: 'Divers brooks in many places are brought to run in one channel, and sundry meadows turned into pools and waters, that they might be of power sufficient to drive hammer mills, which beating upon the iron, resounded all over the place adjoining.'

These mills in the midst of Kentish woodland continued their din until the eighteenth century, when coal replaced charcoal as the fuel for iron forges and the industry moved to the coalfields. Most of the scars on the landscape of the Weald have now healed. Millponds in sought-after commuter villages such as Biddenden and Crowborough have silted up and returned to pasture or woodland. But archaeologists have located the remains of about a hundred old dams, some as much as 7 metres high and 200 metres long.

Similar developments were taking place elsewhere in Europe. The Harz Mountains of Germany rang to the sound of furnaces and forges powered by water from the sixteenth century on. One dam fed water into 190 kilometres of canals that powered 225 water-wheels. Total production from this single dam was around a thousand horse-power, enough to power more than 700 one-kilowatt electric fires.

The start of the Industrial Revolution is conventionally dated to the 1770s on the Pennine hillsides of Lancashire. Here, a series of inventions in the cotton industry allowed most of the industry's tasks, once done by villagers in their cottages, to be accomplished in water-powered factories. By the 1790s, there were 122 cotton spinning mills, driven by water and each with its own weir diverting water from the Pennine streams.

Within three decades the factory owners had been made rich by water and moved on, investing in steam-power and building mills lower down the valleys. By then coal and steam were kings, though there were some valiant efforts to revive water power, notably in Scotland. In 1827, a water-power enthusiast, Robert Thom, completed a large waterworks at Greenock to supply 31 mills and the town's taps. In defence of his effort to hold back the tide of history, he made one of the earliest claims for the cleanliness of water power. As coal-burning mills began to cover the towns of central Scotland in black soot, he wrote: 'Here you have no steam engines vomiting forth smoke and polluting the earth and air for miles around, but, on the contrary the pure "stream of the mountain" flowing past in ceaseless profusion, carrying along with it freshness, health and vigour.'

The French, who had little coal to generate steam, also persisted with water power, which to this day they call 'huile blanche', or white oil. Their engineers by degrees turned the water-wheel into the water-turbine, an innovation sometimes compared to transforming the humble paddle into the propeller. Rather than relying on water falling directly on to blades, they enclosed the turbine so that water reached it through pipes under pressure from the 'head' of water behind it.

It was a small step from the water-turbine to the generation of hydroelectricity. Rather than being hooked to millstones, bellows or hammers, the turbine shaft was connected to an

electricity generator. There is a continuing debate about who
first demonstrated hydroelectricity. Americans claim it was
first achieved in Wisconsin in 1882. But Europeans point to
the Munich Exhibition of the same year, where a little-known
engineer called Schukert demonstrated an electric motor that
ran without batteries. He had installed a water-wheel on the
River Isar ten kilometres away and linked it to a motor on the
exhibition stand by copper cable.

It is a long way from the experiments of the 1880s to the
Hoover Dam of half a century later. But the evolution of
hydroelectricity is frequently glossed over, not least because it
calls into question the assumptions of modern hydro-
engineers that there was something inevitable about the drive
to build the largest possible dams driving the largest possible
turbines.

For a while, small hydroelectric plants generating less than
a megawatt of power (which is sufficient to run 1,000 single-
watt electric fires, or 10,000 light bulbs) were a common
source of power in both Europe and North America. In
Switzerland in 1914, there were 7,000 such plants on the
streams of the Alps.

Wherever they are built they are both popular and successful, and in the past 20 years there has been a modest revival of
small hydro-plants. Since 1970, China has built approaching
100,000 such plants, using local labour and materials. Individually, many provide only a few dozen kilowatts of assured
electricity. But they supply a third of rural China with around
10,000 megawatts of power, as much as Grand Coulee.
Chinese engineers say that the small hydro capacity could be
raised eventually to 70,000 megawatts.

In Sri Lanka, scene of the construction of the massive
Mahaweli hydroelectric scheme in the 1980s, there were 600
small hydro-plants in the 1950s. Nepal too installed hundreds
of small hydro-plants to serve its villages, while at the same
time contemplating giant dams to generate power for sale to
India.

However, the invention of high-voltage transmission lines
and the creation of regional and then national grids, coupled
with the growing electricity demands of industry, switched

attention to ever larger hydroelectric dam projects. In densely populated industrial countries and for large cities, the change of scale made sense. But that was not always the case with efforts to electrify sparsely populated rural areas from central generating points. As the energy analyst Amory Lovins remarked, under such circumstances using electricity from a central grid to boil a kettle or lift water could be 'like cutting butter with a chainsaw'.

Uganda is a case in point. The century was not a decade old when Winston Churchill wrote in *My African Journey*: 'What fun to make the immemorial Nile begin its journey by passing through a turbine.' He identified the best spot as Owens Falls, a couple of kilometres downstream of the White Nile's exit from Lake Victoria, saying: 'It is possible that nowhere else in the world could so enormous a mass of water be held up by so little masonry.' There one cubic metre of dam could hold back a million cubic metres of water. Engineering enthusiasm for such a site brooked no caution, and Churchill finally had his fun in 1954, a year before leaving office as prime minister for the last time, when Queen Elizabeth II opened the dam at Owens Falls. She spoke optimistically of how its power

> will serve industries which are already in being and which will be established in the future. It will help you, the people of Uganda, to reach the higher level of health and prosperity towards which you so rightly aspire. I confidently believe that your children and grandchildren will look upon this scheme as one of the greatest landmarks in the forward march of their land.

The ambition was stillborn. The hope then, as Henry Olivier, the British engineer who completed the project, put it, was that 'the power project will create the market' for its electricity. But it didn't. Uganda failed to prosper and a generation later, the Owens Falls hydroelectric station still had a generating capacity of only 150 megawatts. And what market there was didn't want to pay. A reported 90 per cent of its customers were illegally connected to Uganda's ramshackle grid.

Owens Falls was but a hiccup in the remarkable post-war

spread of hydroelectric power generation. A century after first being demonstrated, it today produces more than a fifth of the world's electricity from plant with a combined capacity of more than 360,000 megawatts, the great majority attached to large dams. So attractive has this new source of power appeared, that many dams have been built as speculative ventures. More insidiously, once dams are built, the apparent abundance of their supply encourages nations to become extraordinarily profligate with their water-generated electricity. The four nations with the highest per capita consumption of electricity – above even the US – are Norway, Iceland, Canada and Sweden, each of which relies on hydroelectricity for the majority of its power.

Elsewhere, and particularly in the Third World, governments are building hydroelectric dams specifically to attract electricity-hungry industries, such as metal smelters. This is usually the case with 'wilderness dams', the ones that excite the most overweening ambition among politicians and hydrologists – and the most anger among environmentalists and human rights groups.

So it was in Tasmania, where a famous environmental dispute over a hydroelectric dam project erupted in the early 1980s. This island off the southern coast of Australia is both wet and mountainous. In 1895, the Tasmanian town of Launceston became the second town, after Niagara in the USA, to be connected to hydroelectric power. The first metal smelter was built in 1920. An aluminium smelter arrived in the 1950s and by the 1980s, 70 per cent of the island's power went to a few such industrial plants.

The entire state was in thrall to the Hydro-Electric Commission, run for 30 years by an uncompromising engineer called Sir Allan Knight. It was said that he generated as much political as electrical power. In the early 1970s, he amazed outsiders by browbeating the Tasmanian parliament into approving a plan to inundate the Lake Pedder National Park and fill one of Australia's national treasures, Lake Pedder, to 25 times its natural size. His high-handed treatment of parliament led a government commission from the mainland afterwards to accuse Knight of 'exhibiting a level of professional arrogance that is totally out of place in a modern democratic community'.

The inundation of Lake Pedder, described in a UNESCO report as 'the greatest ecological tragedy since the European settlement of Tasmania', brought a fierce backlash. A decade later, when Knight's successors attempted to flood a large slice of rare temperate rainforest in the wilderness of the Franklin River valley, they faced a coruscating campaign. Environmental campaigners from round the world came to lie in front of the bulldozers, and won eventual victory in the Australian courts.

The thrall appeared to have been broken, but in the early 1990s, battle could be resumed once more, Despite the hydrocommission's past demands for more power, the state now has surplus hydroelectric capacity. Environmentalists have suggested taking advantage of this to drain Lake Pedder to its former size. But the state government is instead discussing plans to connect the island to the mainland by underground electricity cable across the Bass Strait. It wants to sell the surplus to the state of Victoria.

In many countries of the Third World, the dream of cheap, clean hydroelectric power and its ability to transform a wilderness into an industrial heartland remains strong. Some of the world's greatest rivers are in the tropical rainforests and the Arctic tundras. Hydrologists eye the Yukon and the Mekong, the Great Whale and the Amazon, the Zaire and the Ob, with awe – and an itch to tame them. The tribal people of those regions look on with a mixture of fear at the destruction of their ways of life and expectation at the wealth they are promised the dams could bring. Geographers, meanwhile, wonder at a process they call 'the shift to the periphery'.

The main economic force behind large-dam construction in the world's wildernesses is the metals industry, and especially aluminium smelting. The aluminium companies need huge amounts of cheap power and will go anywhere to obtain it. A precious metal in the nineteenth century, when it was worth more than gold, aluminium has been the wonder-material of the past 60 years. It is light, resistant to corrosion and capable of combining with a range of other metals to create alloys

with other valuable properties. Aluminium is refined from the
rock bauxite, and extracted in an electrolytic process at high
temperatures that require vast amounts of electricity. During
the 1930s, Germany became the world's leading manufacturer
of the metal, and it was the basis of the awesome strength of
the Luftwaffe.

In 1941, when the USA entered the war, it had the good
fortune to have the Hoover Dam in operation and to be
completing Grand Coulee, easily the world's largest dam at
the time, on the Columbia River in the northwestern state of
Washington. Along with the nearby Bonneville Dam, Grand
Coulee provided unrivalled amounts of hydroelectric power
capacity. The US government turned both dams over to the
war effort, first to manufacture aluminium for American
planes (60,000 aircraft were built in four years) and from 1943
on, to provide the huge amounts of power needed for the
manufacture at nearby Hanford of plutonium 239, the key
ingredient in the atomic bomb. These two hydroelectric dams
were, it can be argued, the difference between victory and
defeat in 1942 and 1943.

After the war, aluminium manufacturers, faced with a
slump in military demand, unveiled the first aluminium can in
1963. Today cans are the largest single use for the metal,
ahead of cooking foil, frozen-food trays, window frames and
so on. World aluminium production soared from 4 million
tonnes in 1959 to more than 15 million tonnes per annum in
the late 1980s – 3 kilograms for every person on the plant.

The energy used in aluminium manufacture is staggering.
The power to smelt one beer can will operate a television set
for three hours. Most smelters are sited close to the cheapest
sources of large amounts of power – hydroelectric dams.
Besides Hoover and Grand Coulee, early aluminium factories
were built near sources of hydropower at the Niagara Falls, in
Norway and Tasmania, in the French and Swiss Alps and in
the Scottish highlands. Now the rest of the water-rich world
wants to join in.

In 1986, the world's then largest hydroelectric project was
completed on time and within budget by American engineers
in the Venezuelan rainforest. The $5-billion Guri Dam on the

River Caroni has a capacity of 10,000 megawatts and was the latest stage in Venezuela's attempt to convert the profits generated by its oil reserves into a more permanent source of energy. The government has plans eventually to install 20,000 megawatts of generating capacity on the Caroni from a line of dams that will flood the entire valley. The power will help the expansion of the country's aluminium industry, which is the second largest source of foreign exchange after oil.

When a Japanese aluminium manufacturer had a plan for a smelter at home vetoed in the mid-1970s, it fell into the open arms of the Indonesian government, which offered it cheap power from a hydroelectric plant at the mouth of the Asahan River on the remote northern shores of the island of Sumatra. The $2-billion smelting complex, completed in 1982, was Asia's largest, manufacturing 225,000 tonnes of aluminium a year.

With the factory taking 80 per cent of the dam's electricity, most of the aluminium shipped straight from the shore, and few jobs on offer, local Indonesians benefit little from the giant factory in their midst. Instead, thousands of people were bundled off their land to make way for the dam and smelter, and dredgers on the river destroyed local fisheries and rice paddies.

Across the straits, the Malaysian government had similar plans in the 1980s. Reynolds Aluminium wanted to move one of its largest plants from near Hamburg on the Elbe River in Germany, where it had been forced to cut production because of widespread pollution, and agreed to move to the Malaysian port of Bintulu on the island of Borneo. It set one condition. The Malaysian government must provide cheap power from a 200-metre-high German-designed dam to be built inland on the Rejan River in the heart of one of the largest stretches of virgin rainforest in the world. It would have been the largest dam in southeast Asia, and threatened to drown 700 square kilometres of forest and many traditional longhouses occupied by Penan and other forest tribespeople.

A combination of economic downturn and a virulent international campaign by environmentalists caused the cancellation of the scheme in 1988. But two years later, the

Malaysians proposed building instead a series of small dams on the Rejan River basin to power the aluminium smelter. While the idea of a series of small dams sounded tempting to environmentalists, the new scheme would probably involve drowning a greater area of forest, and many more longhouses, to obtain the same amount of power.

All this is small fry compared to what is happening in the Amazon basin. Here nobody has attempted to dam the main channel of the river, which discharges through its mouth one-fifth of all the water that flows from land to the sea on the planet. But the dam-builders are at work on its tributaries, many of them giant rivers in themselves.

The Tucurui Dam on the River Tocantins, for instance, is a 100-metre high plug of earth holding back 46 cubic kilometres of water deep in the heart of the rainforest. Completed in 1984, it flooded 2,400 square kilometres, the size of a large English county. More than 20,000 people were 'relocated' to make way for it. Rotting vegetation in the reservoir gives off fumes, kills fish and creates plagues of mosquitoes that make life unbearable in villages up to 30 kilometres away. There were big protests about the mosquitoes there in 1991.

Tucurui is the tenth largest hydroelectric station in the world. It was the first, and so far largest, of 77 dams that the Brazilian government wants to build in the Amazonian region to electrify the jungle. During long years of military rule, Brazil went heavily into debt in order to finance the construction of large dams such as Tucurui.

From Tucurui's turbines, power lines swing out across the rainforest, like great unending metallic creepers. Pylons higher than the tallest trees stride through Indian reservations all the way to aluminium smelters at Vila do Conde and the port of São Luis. The raw metal for the smelters comes from bauxite mines dug in the jungle floor of the Grand Carajas mining region to the southwest.

Most of the eastern half of the Amazon basin lies within the state of Para, home of Tucurui, Grand Carajas and most of the destructive enterprises built in the forest in the past two decades. The state was earmarked in 1966 by President Castello Branco as a 'development pole' for his grand plan,

Operation Amazonia, to people the rainforest. Since then, wide areas of virgin forest have been carved up by roads and power lines, mining complexes and plantations. Natural wealth is being ripped up to create a probably transitory man-made wealth.

This was no inevitable process. It required political commitment and a mass of tax breaks, blank development cheques and heavy government subsidies on almost every aspect of daily life. The ranch hands, gold panners and land speculators pouring along the roads from the south are driving out the remnants of the great Indian communities that once thrived on the forest's wealth. And they know that, however far they go, their petrol will cost not a penny more at the roadside pump than it did in São Paulo.

It can hardly be said either that Tucurui is a necessary or inevitable product of this colonisation. Its market is the aluminium smelters owned by Albras, a partly Japanese-owned company, which uses half of all the electricity consumed in Para and yet employs, according to one recent estimate, just 1,200 people. Albras has plans to triple its output, and that means more dams. So once Tucurui is fully utilised, the government-owned electricity utility for the Amazon will tackle the next major Amazon tributary to the west. This is the Xingu, which also pours out of the grasslands to the south and flows through more than a thousand kilometres of rainforest before joining the Amazon close to its mouth. It is a nutrient-rich 'clear water' river, which contains one of the most prolific fisheries in all the Amazon. But that won't save it.

The Brazilian government's planners have earmarked six dam sites on the Xingu. They would flood an area of the valley the size of Wales, including part of Altamira, the largest of a series of boom towns which have grown up along the frontier of the rainforest. According to *Plan 2010*, the main planning document for development of electricity in the Amazon region: 'The use of the Xingu will possibly constitute the major national project of the end of this century and the beginning of the next.'

The first dam, under proposals current in 1991, would inundate the town of Belo Monte. The two largest would come later – at Jurua and Babaquara on the great Xingu Bend, where the river plunges more than a hundred metres to meet the Amazon. These projects, known together as the Altamira Complex, would create one of the largest hydroelectric complexes in the world. Babaquara alone would flood 6,000 square kilometres – more than two English counties – and join the world's top ten power generators.

The construction of the Altamira complex may not happen just yet because the World Bank, under pressure from green-minded American legislators, has refused to fund it. Instead the government has pushed ahead with the Cachoeira Porteira Dam on the Trombetas, another Amazon tributary. It should be generating power by 1995 for the oldest and biggest Amazon boom town, Manaus, the city in the heart of the jungle. A second declared purpose of this dam is to provide subsidised electricity to help mining companies exploit the local, largely untapped reserves of bauxite – probably Brazil's largest.

Little of the bauxite in the Amazon basin would be mined, and even less smelted, without government guarantees of low electricity prices. In 1979 the government issued a decree guaranteeing that for the next 20 years, government hydro-electric dams would sell electricity to smelters at prices tied to the international price of aluminium. As a result, when Tucurui was completed, it sold electricity to Albras at roughly a third of the cost of its generation. When in 1989 a reformist, democratically elected administration took over a government almost bankrupted by such behaviour, President Collor declared an end to all government subsidies that contributed to the destruction of the rainforests. But he left intact the decree on electricity prices.

Brazil's hydroelectric energy programme was conceived at a time of national energy shortage and sold to its people as a means to keep the nation's lights on. But the billions of dollars were spent instead on persuading the aluminium industry to invade the rainforest. This misguided investment contributed greatly to the financial crisis now facing the nation in the 1990s.

The most ugly and pointless legacy of Brazil's hydroelectric binge in the Amazon rainforest is the billion-dollar Balbinas Dam. The dam is 50 metres high, but much of the stagnant reservoir, which flooded an area the size of an English county, is far shallower. Says Philip Fearnside, a veteran Amazon researcher based near the dam in Manaus, 'From the air, you can see brown trees beneath the water across huge areas. A third of the reservoir is less than four metres deep; 1,500 islands break its surface. There are so many bays and inlets that it looks rather like a cross-section of a human lung.' On the islands, tiny groups of animals that were isolated when the reservoir filled gradually die.

It is hard to see what possessed the government to build a dam here. It has a catchment that is only eight times larger than the reservoir itself. The flow of water through the reservoir is so sluggish that water hangs around for years. The bays and backwaters fill with floating weeds, many of which can root in the reservoir bottom. The introduction of a herd of grazing manatee, and of teams of workers to cut and remove 80 tonnes of weed every day, has no impact. Water stripped of oxygen by the mass of rotting vegetation pours from the dam's turbines and kills fish downstream. Mosquitoes breed in the stagnant waters and invade a nearby town.

The reservoir covers an area roughly that of Tucurui (almost double it, if you include the islands), but produces only one-thirtieth as much electricity. It generates on average only 110 megawatts, flooding forest equivalent to more than two football pitches to generate enough power to run a one-kilowatt electric fire. Much of this land was once the territory of the Waimiri-Atroari tribe.

The dam is no early folly of an innocent industry in the rainforest. Balbinas was commissioned in the early 1980s and completed in 1987. It is such a disaster that Electronorte, the electricity utility, now denies that it ever wanted to build it. Says Fearnside:

Electronorte officials have unofficially stated that they received the order to build the dam directly from Brazil's presidential office – it was not a proposal developed on technical grounds. The government was eager to have

something to give to the state of Amazonia. The military
political party (PDS) was in power at both the national level
and in the state of Amazonia. In the 1982 state elections,
Balbinas was presented to the public as an example of the
governor's ability to extract benefits from Brasilia.

Balbinas and Tucurui now join a growing tradition of
rainforest dams built in South America without bothering to
cut down the timber first. The continent's first big jungle dam
was built at Brokopondo in the former Dutch colony of
Surinam in the early 1960s. It flooded around 1,300 square
kilometres of dense virgin forest to provide power for an
aluminium processing industry to be based on the country's
large bauxite reserves.

As the trees decomposed, they generated hydrogen sulphide
gas. It could be smelt miles downstream of the dam and for
two years workers at the site had to wear gas masks. The
decomposing vegetation also made the water in the reservoir
acid. It corroded parts of the turbines, and fed a mat of water
hyacinth that spread most of the way across the giant reservoir. Rotting vegetation removed most of the oxygen from the
reservoir water. When water was released through the turbines, fish died tens of kilometres downstream.

The lessons went unlearned at Tucurui and Balbinas. And
in 1989, engineers from Electricité de France began work in
French Guyana on the Petit Saut hydroelectric plant. It will
inundate 310 square kilometres of dense rainforest to provide
power for the European space launch pad which is run by the
French firm Arianespace at Kourou just 50 kilometres away.
Ironically, in 1991, a European scientific satellite, ERS-1, was
launched from Kourou to help monitor the destruction of the
world's rainforests. The engineers behind the project report
that decomposition of the drowned forest behind the dam
'will very significantly affect the water quality', producing
hydrogen sulphide, ammonia and carbon dioxide. It will
consume all the oxygen in the lower layers of the reservoir for
several years and kill fish up to ten kilometres downstream.

The saga of South America's rainforest dams is a major
component of the environmental and social tragedy unfolding

in the Amazon rainforest. But it is evidence of a wider brutality that overtakes nations seeking to generate wealth in the world's wildernesses. It finds a strong echo in the treeless Arctic wastes of northern Canada. Here the Cree Indians, like their counterparts in the jungle, fear the long arm of the aluminium companies with their promises of instant industrial development and the greed of those who respond to 'the pull of the periphery'.

18

HEWERS OF INGOTS AND DRAWERS OF WATER

The world must realise that environmental disasters don't happen only in the Brazilian rainforest.

Grand Chief Coon-Come, 1991

Matthew Coon-Come, head of the Cree nation, is a thin, wiry man in his mid-thirties. He wears glasses, a blue short-sleeved shirt and black suit trousers, and is quiet-spoken with a light Canadian accent. You might take him for a small-town computer programmer. But on stage he packs a punch, grasping the microphone and speaking with a directness peculiar to American Indians. This is his story:

We are the indigenous people of Canada. Around the Hudson Bay, where we live, everything abounds: rivers, lakes, marshes, wetlands. It's where the geese come to nest, where whales end their migration; we have caribou, sturgeon and trout, the mighty moose and the beaver. The land provides everything that we need. We have always looked after this land, which we have inhabited for at least 5,000 years.

Let me tell you what Canada did to us. I am thirty-five now. Until I was sixteen, we lived in tents. I went to the lake to get a pail of water. Our people were scattered all across the land, fishing and tending our trap-lines. Then one of our people, Philip Awashish, went to Montreal and read in a newspaper about a plan to dam 11,000 square kilometres of our land. They had built a road, airstrips, gravel pits. Soon they were destroying our trap-lines. They did anything they wanted. They didn't even write us a letter. We spent nine months in court trying to stop them, but construction continued. When the court found for us it was overturned by an appeal court in four days. They said it was in the interests of six million Quebecois, even though when the land had been given to Quebec in 1912 it had been on condition that all the claims of indigenous people would be met. Discouraged and with our funds spent, we were advised to negotiate a settlement.

The settlement was worth $225 million, plus permanent entitlement to a much smaller area of land. The scheme that needed the Cree land was the James Bay hydroelectric project. A twinkle in the eye of Robert Bourassa when he became the new premier of Quebec in 1970, a year later he had transformed it into 'the project of the century – the key to the economic progress of Quebec'. His instrument was the state-owned company Hydro-Quebec.

For Bourassa, the Arctic north of Quebec, where the northern spruce and pine forests give way to the frozen taiga of lichen and moss, was not a native homeland. It was a wasteland awaiting the imprint of man. 'Quebec is a mighty hydroelectric plant in the bud,' he wrote later, 'and every day millions of potential kilowatt-hours flow downhill and out to sea. What a waste.' The Cree's claim that 'only beavers have a right to build dams on our territory' cut little ice with Bourassa. His dream was to 'conquer and tame the north'. And it felt like it.

Says Coon-Come: 'The project went ahead like a desperate military campaign.' The booty from Bourassa's war against the northern wilderness is carried south for more than 1,000 kilometres on five great lines of high-energy transmission cables. The pylons bring the power which pops toasters in Montreal, runs air-conditioners as far away as New York – and supplies even more electricity, at rock bottom prices, to the state's large collection of aluminium smelters. The Cree for their part, having mostly moved from their tents into permanent communities, feel as if they are living in a prisoner of war camp. Now Bourassa, like some movie mogul who has stumbled on a winning formula in James Bay I, is promoting for his latest term in office a sequel – James Bay II. It will be his monument, but the Cree fear it will be their tomb.

The 'project of the century', James Bay I and II, is intended to divert and dam nine violent, free-flowing rivers – including the Great Whale, the Eastman, La Grande, the Rupert and the Nottaway. The rivers hurtle off the Arctic north of Quebec state, an area the size of France, into the eastern side of Hudson Bay and its southern offshoot, James Bay. The reservoirs behind the dams, those that have been built and those that await Bourassa's hand, are huge. 'Our country is very flat,' says Chief Coon-Come. 'The dams aren't built in canyons like in the US. They flood huge areas; dykes extend for hundreds of miles to divert the rivers.'

James Bay I tamed the Eastman and La Grande rivers, capturing and diverting 90 per cent of the Eastman and pouring it into La Grande. Its five reservoirs cover 11,000 square kilometres. Its four giant hydroelectric plants, by the time add-ons are completed in 1994, will have a capacity of almost 15,000 megawatts, a powerhouse matched only by the US's efforts on the Columbia. The 170-metre-high dam known as La Grande 2 contains an immense underground generating station twice the size of Notre-Dame, cut into the hard rock of the Canadian Shield. Outside there is a spillway that climbs down from the dam in a series of giants' steps, like some Aztec monument for human sacrifices to the Gods. It is as high as the Niagara Falls and can carry twice the flow of the St Lawrence Seaway.

Work on the first phase of James Bay II is set to be completed by the end of the century. The Great Whale Project will dam the Great and Little Whale rivers, turning 80 per cent of the former into a reservoir in order to create 3,000 megawatts of generating capacity. Finally will come the 'NBR project', damming the rivers Nottaway, Broadback and Rupert, to generate another, 9,000 megawatts.

When completed sometime early next century, the entire James Bay project is intended to have a capacity of 27,000 megawatts. It will have cost an estimated $63 billion and will have drowned an area the size of Belgium. Doing rather better than the Amazon dams, each football pitch of flooded land will provide enough power for ten single-kilowatt electric fires.

La Grande, the first river to be tamed by Bourassa, is now twice the river it once was, but with none of the personality. Bloated by the Eastman's waters it is forced to flood in winter, when humans want its power, rather than as nature intended, following the spring thaw. It has washed away the small island at its mouth where the Cree village of Fort George once stood. The Cree spent much of their compensation from James Bay I on building a new settlement. Chisasibi has a shopping mall where former hunters go to stock their freezers, a motel, electricity and a sewage system. But half the small town is unemployed and alcoholism and suicide are rife.

Everyone, it seems, has lost their way. The geese, say the locals, cannot find their old nesting grounds. The breeding places for thousands of pairs of waterfowl disappeared beneath the reservoirs on La Grande. In 1984, around 10,000 disorientated caribou drowned just downstream of the Cania-piscau dam when the sluice-gates opened. It was an 'accident of nature' said Hydro-Quebec. It was an act of man, came the reply.

Will they say the same when the endangered Beluga whales that use the estuaries of the Great and Little Whale in summer, finding their waters narrowed and unusually cold, react by beaching themselves? And what of North America's only population of freshwater seals, which live in the head-waters of the Great Whale River? Will their widely predicted extinction also be an accident of nature?

There were plenty of dire predictions about the impact of the project back in 1972. Many have not happened. The climate has not changed. And while some caribou migrating routes were blocked, overall their numbers have continued to grow. But the biggest mistake made by scientists beforehand was not so much to exaggerate certain risks as to overlook the potential impact of mercury.

The soils of the Canadian Shield contain mercury. It is normally insoluble and harmless. But where large areas of soil and vegetation have been covered by reservoirs, bacteria that convert the mercury into soluble methyl mercury have flourished. The methyl mercury accumulates in water, in fish and in fish-eating animals such as beavers – and humans.

It was fish laden with methyl mercury that caused gross deformations among children at Minamata in Japan in the 1960s, though on that occasion the source of the mercury was industrial pollution. Now, to prevent natural methyl mercury unleashed by the James Bay reservoirs doing the same to the Cree, health authorities are forbidding them to eat fish from the waters of La Grande. Pike in that river now contain two parts per million of mercury, and many other species have levels above safety limits. The Cree must put away their fishing-lines and head for their shopping malls to buy TV dinners.

The problem was entirely unexpected and remains unresolved. 'First they said it would disappear, and they simply advised pregnant women not to eat the fish,' says Chief Coon-Come. 'Then they said it would take twenty-five years and that nobody should eat the fish. Now most independent scientists think it will last for a hundred years. But fish is our food; we don't fish for sport. And international law says that indigenous people must not be denied their own source of sustenance.'

The mercury will not go away. Jean-François Rougerie, environment coordinator for the Great Whale Project at Hydro-Quebec, admitted in a long article in *Canadian Water Watch* in 1990 that: 'The creation of new reservoirs will add considerably to mercury concentrations, entailing temporary restrictions for the commercial and subsistence fishing practised by native populations.' The NBR project in particular, because of 'the large surface area of the reservoirs planned, as well as the extent of the subsistence fishing practised by the Cree population', will make the problem 'more acute', says Rougerie.

The Great Whale Project will for the first time discharge methyl mercury directly into the Hudson Bay. With 80 per cent of the Great Whale River set to be turned into reservoir, the potential for mercury creation is high. It's yet another hazard for the beleaguered Beluga whales in the Bay, admits

Rougerie. 'Marine mammals, an important component of the Inuit [Eskimo] diet, may accumulate high concentrations of mercury.'

The Inuit live on the Belcher Islands, 150 kilometres out in the Hudson Bay, and travel on sea-ice to hunt for seals and fish. If Bourassa's bulldozers get the go-ahead to remake the valley of the Great Whale, the Inuit seem set to be receiving government health warnings with their daily diet before the end of the decade.

What of the benefits to Quebec from the 'project of the century'? In February 1991, the Quebec Superior Court ruled that these were state secrets. A large proportion of the electricity culled from the wilderness is earmarked for 13 multinational companies, mostly aluminium smelting firms, under long-term contracts struck with Bourassa's cabinet and Hydro-Quebec. The courts refused the Cree Grand Council's application under the Canadian Freedom of Information Act to see copies of the contracts. The price agreed was commercially sensitive information.

During 1989, Quebec had offered deals to aluminium smelters to establish more plants in the state. The aim was to ease bankers' fears about loaning up to $40 billion for James Bay II at a time when half of Hydro-Quebec's income was being paid out in interest bills on its debts, mostly incurred in building James Bay I. That year Quebec approved plans for three new smelters and expansions to existing plant. Altogether the extra annual electricity consumption tied up by the deals for Hydro-Quebec amounted to business worth more than $3 billion.

The outlook appeared promising. But opponents alleged that the multinationals had been able to strike ludicrously good deals by agreeing to take a stake in the project through 'risk-sharing' agreements. They had, it was claimed, played on Bourassa's determination to proceed with the project at whatever cost.

Within weeks of the courts' secrecy ruling, Norsk Hydro, one of the metal-smelting companies involved in the deals, broke ranks. It revealed that its new smelter in Quebec would receive electricity at roughly half the going rate for

Hydro-Quebec's regular industrial customers over the life of its 24-year contract.

Prising open the door of secrecy further, the *Montreal Gazette* pieced together a list of power prices for aluminium companies round the world. The New York Power Authority charged Alcoa, the world's largest aluminium manufacturer, about $18 per megawatt-hour. The power company that has harnessed Grand Coulee to eight aluminium plants charged $23. World average prices, as revealed by Alcoa itself in 1986, were Japan $46, US $21, Europe $20, South Africa $14, Australia $12, and, bringing up the rear, Latin America at $12 and Canada at $4. 'Well, well, we are quite a bargain,' commented the paper's columnist.

He went on to point out that there was little to be gained from attracting aluminium smelters to Quebec's shores. The real money was in milling the aluminium ingots into sheets, bars and other products. Unlike many of its rivals, Quebec did little milling and thus missed out on most of the jobs and most of the profits in the aluminium business. In other words, Bourassa's province looked more like a short-changed Third World nation – Brazil, for instance, or Ghana – than a thrusting go-ahead industrial nation investing in the future. 'Are we forever condemned to be hewers of ingots and drawers of water?' the paper asked.

The Canadian secrecy about the contracts with aluminium companies made a strong contrast with the attitude of state governments in New York and New England. These states were, at the same time as the Canadian court action, holding public hearings about the terms of their own proposed 20-year contracts to take electricity from James Bay. In the USA, the public right to know was fuelling a debate about whether it would not be cheaper for the states' electricity utilities to invest in energy-saving measures at home.

A similar, though less official, debate was beginning in Quebec. Experts commissioned by environmentalists argued that if the state switched its investment out of the Great Whale Project and into energy conservation measures, it could save twice as much energy as the project was designed to produce. Canada, it was pointed out, was one of the four least energy-efficient nations on Earth. And Quebec was the least efficient province within Canada. In early 1992, with the prospects bleak for electricity sales to the US and a worldwide glut in aluminium causing the closure of smelters, Quebec postponed work on the Great Whale project for at least a year.

All over the world, the debate about how to save energy rather than attempting to generate ever more is taking off. And nowhere have the statistics been more stark than in countries with plans to develop hydroelectricity. In India and China the inefficiency of heavy industry is notorious. So is their reluctance to stagger working hours to prevent the need for 'peak load' power, such as that to be demanded by the Indians from the Tehri Dam.

In Brazil, a study by Jose Goldemberg, before he became President Collor's secretary for science and technology, concluded that a billion-dollar worth investment in more efficient refrigerators, street lighting and industrial motors could defer the construction of $4 billion of hydroelectric power plant. He cited subsidised electricity prices as a major barrier to progress on energy conservation that could reduce the nation's projected energy needs for the year 2000 by 20%.

The evidence is plain that cheap power leads to a wastage of resources – and cheap hydroelectricity is among the worst offenders, largely because of the impression of unlimited and infinitely renewable power conjured up by the hydroelectric dam. But, as we shall see in the next chapter, the notion that hydroelectricity is a renewable source of energy is one of the most pernicious illusions of all.

19

THE MYTH OF
RENEWABLE ENERGY

Who knows what sedimentation will be in 30 years' time?
Certainly the engineer will long since have been paid.

Ernest Razvan, Delft Hydraulics Institute, at ICOLD conference,
1991

One of the great public relations coups of dam-builders has
been to claim that the energy produced by their structures is
'renewable'. As long as the rivers flow, they say, dams will
generate energy. But the real world is not like that. Many of
the largest hydroelectric dams in the world today, occupying
the best sites for power generation, will have lifetimes shorter
than the average coal mine. And when they are shut down,
their magnificent gorges will be as useless for creating energy
as an empty oil well.

The most spectacular example of why this is so sits on the
Yellow River in China. They finished building the Sanmenxia
Gorge Dam in 1960. Two years later, its reservoir had been
filled with a layer of silt more than 20 metres thick and the
dam was taken out of action to be rebuilt. The Yellow River
isn't called 'yellow' for nothing: it carries a greater concentra-
tion of silt than any other major river on Earth. Its flow
through Sanmenxia includes around 1.7 billion tonnes of silt a
year, most of it washing from the fine 'loess' soils of central
northern China. And when the 106-metre-high dam held back
the river, most of the silt settled out on to the bottom of the
reservoir.

The Chinese blamed Soviet engineers, who had predicted
that the dam would have a lifetime of 50 years before silt filled

the reservoir. But they admit today that this calculation was based on Chinese data, provided with more revolutionary zeal than scientific wisdom at the height of Chairman Mao's Great Leap Forward. Li Rui worked with the Ministry of Fuel Industries in the 1950s and visited Moscow to collaborate with his Soviet counterparts. In a book published in 1989, he said: 'Hot-headed and over-optimistic, we believed that the mass campaign of soil and water conservation carried out in the upper reaches would surely turn the Yellow River into a clean stream.' Fervour must have been intense indeed for them to have forgotten an old Chinese phrase, 'When the river runs clear', meaning never.

But amnesia was essential for survival during the Great Leap Forward. Says Peng De, former vice-minister of communications and transportation: 'During those days this project [Sanmenxia] was a criterion for one's political stand. Those who supported the project were for the Party, while those who had different opinions were against the Party.' Then, officially, the reservoir promised everything. Mao's Party revolutionaries boasted that it would prevent floods, irrigate fields, generate hydroelectric power and even halt damage from sheets of ice pouring down the river in spring. They moved 300,000 people off the land, sending many as pioneers to the arid far west of the country, in order to make way for the reservoir.

The Sanmenxia Dam is back in action now, having been dynamited and rebuilt twice. The reservoir today has less than one-third of its original storage capacity of 35 cubic kilometres. It has to be emptied each winter and scoured of its encrusted silt. All this for just 250 megawatts of generating capacity, less than a quarter of that planned.

The Chinese are unabashed. Li Rui says the old misguided optimism is still evident. They intend, eventually, to build 15 dams in a cascade down the Yellow River to generate power and hold back floods. According to Chinese engineers, writing in a Western trade journal in the late 1980s: 'The government is seeking to expand demand in this northwest region by building up energy-intensive industry such as aluminium smelters, and/or transmitting a considerable amount of hydroelectric power to coastal cities.'

The reservoir at Liujia Gorge, completed in 1974, is already a fifth full with silt, despite attempts to flush it clean each year. Another began generating power in 1990, and three more are on the way. This time, the Chinese say they are allowing for silt. The new Xiaolangdi Dam, immediately downstream of Sanmenxia, will eventually hold seven cubic kilometres of silt and five of water.

Chinese engineers have lived with silt for thousands of years. Only with their conversion to the construction of large dams does their wisdom appear to have deserted them. The very size of these structures appears to have convinced them that nature can be set aside. But outside the Middle Kingdom, too, silt often still seems to come as a surprise.

India has built more large dams than any other nation on Earth. British engineers finished one of its first, the Nizam-sagar Dam, on the scrublands of the Deccan Plateau of central India, in 1931. The rate of siltation behind the dam was 16 times that predicted by its designers and 30 years later two-thirds of the reservoir's capacity had been lost to silt. Less than half the fields connected to the reservoir by canal receive any irrigation water.

Far from learning from this early disaster, India has replicated it many times. The nearby Sriramsagar was completed in 1970 and lost a third of its storage capacity within two years. In the Himalayas, Indian engineers predicted the rate of siltation of reservoirs in its steep valleys would be only a half to a fifth of the rate recorded in practice. And there is little evidence that their skill has improved. An Indian engineer reported in 1987 on two Himalayan dams completed in the 1970s: 'The 60-metre-high Ichari Dam and 39-metre Maneri Dam became silted to the crest of the spillway within two years of operation.'

The first large dams were built in the temperate lands of Europe and North America, where the weathering of rocks, the first step in the creation of silt, is slow. But in the tropics, high temperatures and heavy rains make natural rates of weathering much higher. Chemical weathering, in which water dissolves salts in rock, is typically 20 to 50 times faster in the tropics than in temperate lands. Chemical weathering leaves behind a crust on rocks, which is vulnerable to mechanical erosion by wind or water, and frequently ends up on the floor of reservoirs downstream.

The Tarbela on the Indus in Pakistan, one of the world's largest dams, traps more than 200 million cubic metres of silt (the equivalent of 80 Great Pyramids) each year, and has filled its reservoir at a rate approaching 2 per cent per annum since its completion in 1974. A delta of silt, deposited as the Indus enters the reservoir, is advancing down the reservoir towards the dam itself. According to Khalid Mahmood, a Pakistani from the George Washington University in the USA writing in a report for the World Bank, which financed the dam, the designers 'grossly under-estimated the delta's streamwise progression . . . The actual delta crest after nine years of operation [of the dam] was located about 18 kilometres upstream of the dam instead of 45 kilometres.' Engineers are working to prevent the delta of silt from inundating the turbines. Even if they succeed, it will remain a very visible harbinger of the dam's ultimate fate.

Each year, more than a billion tonnes of silt, about 10 per cent of the entire annual discharge in the world's rivers, ends up on the bottom of reservoirs. Dozens of major dams are likely to become useless by early in the twenty-first century. But only now, after several decades of headlong construction, are engineers beginning to realise the extent of the problem. Dams such as Tarbela now have a predicted lifetime of 40 years or less.

Some of the ignorance about silt has been wilful. Ernest Razvan of the International Hydraulics Institute at Delft told delegates to the ICOLD conference in Vienna in 1991 that engineers have no interest in warning their clients about such long-term threats. 'Who knows what sedimentation will be in 30 years' time? Certainly the engineer will long since have been paid.'

Data collection on siltation is a low priority. Indian government engineers insist against all the evidence in nearby valleys that the Tehri Dam, being built high in the Himalayas in a valley made of crumbly shales, will have a lifetime of at least a hundred years. Critics claim that silt sampling points along the river have been placed where silt levels are least, and that the data ignores the 'bedload', the rocks and other debris that roll along the bottom of a riverbed during high monsoon flows. Bedload never becomes suspended in the water itself, but will certainly accumulate in the bottom of a reservoir. Independent investigations by the Wadia Institute of Himalayan Geology at Dehra Dun calculate that this bedload could more than double the rate at which the Tehri reservoir fills, bringing the dam's life down to only 30 or 40 years.

At the mouths of rivers, the impact of dams is obvious. The Indus used to carry 440 million tonnes into the Arabian Sea. Now it carries 100 million tonnes. The silt discharge of the Mississippi into the Gulf of Mexico has been cut in half by dams on its tributaries, that of the Rio Grande by 95 per cent. The Zambezi leaves two-thirds of its silt in reservoirs, and the Colorado takes only one grain in a thousand all the way to the sea.

Mahmood completed a wide-ranging study of dam siltation in the mid-1980s for the World Bank, which has loaned more money than anybody else for dam construction in the tropics in the past four decades. He estimates that about 1 per cent of the combined storage capacity of the world's reservoirs is being consumed by silt every year, making a loss of a staggering 60 cubic kilometres each year, almost twice the capacity of the reservoir behind the Hoover Dam. Even with conservative estimates of construction costs, Mahmood puts the value of this lost capacity at $6 billion each year, with a total loss to date of $130 billion.

The loss is not merely a matter of wasted cash. It is also about wasted dam sites. 'In many basins, additional sites [for reservoirs] are hard to find, and in general, remaining sites for storage reservoirs are more difficult and, hence, more expensive to develop,' says Mahmood. Pakistan, for instance, is already planning a replacement for the capacity lost behind its Tarbela and Mangla dams. Its choice is Kalabagh. A dam here will flood twice as much land as Tarbela, at several times the cost, but produce only two-thirds as much power.

Silt is a most pervasive menace in Asia, home today of 20 of the world's 30 tallest dams. The erosion of the continent's young rocks provides around two-thirds of the sediment in the world's rivers. Erosion here yields more than 380 tonnes per square kilometre of land each year, more than twice the global average. The basins of the Yellow, Ganges and Brahmaputra rivers yield more than a thousand tonnes. In the loess plateau of central China, where the Yellow River rises, the figure reaches 10,000 tonnes. Thanks to dams, an increasing amount of this silt never reaches the sea.

Latin America also suffers badly. The Anchicaya reservoir in the Colombian Amazon silted up within 12 years of coming into operation. Particularly in central America, hydroelectric power is the dominant source of electricity, and studies during the 1980s for the US government showed that many reservoirs have serious siltation problems. The destruction of forests in the catchment areas of dams is widely blamed for causing soil erosion that silts up reservoirs. In consequence, Guatemala is to spend $100 million on tree planting to reduce the silt load that threatens the central dam in its Pueblo Viejo Quixal project.

But Mahmood warns that such initiatives frequently do not work, especially in larger river basins. 'High concentrations of sediment [in reservoirs] are largely associated with climatic, tectonic and geological factors,' and 'Sediment yields are largely unaffected by watershed management.' Certainly, as Mao discovered at Sanmenxia, it would be foolish to believe that soil conservation can save reservoirs from silt. The Yellow River has always been yellow.

Engineers have developed a simple statistical formula, the Sediment Delivery Ratio, which predicts that only 10 per cent of the sediment in a river system is delivered in a short period to the mouth of a river or reservoir. The rest gets caught up on sandbanks, floodplains and elsewhere in the basin, where it may remain for decades or even centuries. In small catchments, the ratio will be higher, so soil conservation measures could have an impact on siltation behind dams. But in large catchments it may be much less.

The best documented instance of the failure of tree planting to halt siltation is in the catchment of the Mangla Dam, where Pakistan planted trees and protected soils across almost

8,000 square kilometres between 1959, five years before the dam was completed, and 1989. 'It was anticipated', says Mahmood, 'that sediment load at Mangla would reduce by about 30 per cent. [But there was] no discernible difference in the sediment loads,' even in the areas of most intense and earliest activity. It may be that, measured over many decades, the efforts to keep soil on the land will reduce sediment load in the river – but by then the Mangla reservoir will be abandoned, clogged to its turbines with silt.

The world's stock of large reservoirs – once gleaming and brand new – is starting to age. While the oldest are mostly in temperate lands, where siltation problems are least, half the world's 270 largest dams were completed before 1974. Many will be approaching halfway through their useful lives, unless engineers can find methods to prevent the remorseless build-up of silt.

As the need to give dams a new lease of life grows, new techniques to help clean them out will no doubt be devised. But there is no sign of a quick fix. Those techniques currently on offer include flushing the reservoir with river-water, dredging, and even building small dams upstream to catch the sediment before it reaches the main dam. But, says Mahmood, debris dams can end up costing more than the main dam. Sediment flushing has been tried on Pakistan's Warsak Dam on the River Kabul, which lost 18 per cent of its capacity in the first year of operation, though only about 6 per cent of the annual silt deposition was ever removed. Dredging currently costs about 20 times the price of building a reservoir of equivalent capacity. None the less, says Mahmood, it may be the only way to save irreplaceable dam sites. His own country may be among the first to attempt to use them.

If dredging is the only way, it will cost $2,600 billion to clear out the mountains of silt already sitting on reservoir bottoms. And it would cost more than $100 billion each year to keep the reservoirs clear of fresh silt, which is accumulating at a rate of 1,600 cubic metres every second – enough to fill three standard swimming pools. The truth is that if hydro-electricity is to be genuinely renewable, it will rarely be cheap. If it is to be cheap, it is not renewable.

PART IV

River Basin Mismanagement

20

CHINA'S SWORD
OF DAMOCLES

The consequences of failure at Three Gorges would rank as
history's worst man-made disaster.

Philip Williams, hydrologist, 1990

China is on the verge of building the biggest, most expensive,
dam project in the world. It will dam the main stem of the
third largest river in the world. If it is built, the Three Gorges
Dam on the Yangtze River will cost $20 billion, take 20 years
and flood a million people from their homes. It will create a
reservoir stretching 500 kilometres into the remote western
interior of China and, on paper at least, generate as much
power as eight Aswan Dams. But its main declared purpose is
to prevent the kind of floods that have killed 300,000 people
on the river this century and struck most recently, killing more
than 2,000, in the summer of 1991. The problem is that it
could make the risk of floods much worse.

'I'm sure there will be a correct decision,' Wei Tingzheng,
head of the Yangtze Valley Planning Office, told journalists as
floods rampaged down the Yangtze in June 1991. 'The future
of this project is very bright.' With the Chinese government in
the final stages of considering plans for the Three Gorges
Dam, the floodwaters surging through the country's premier
farming region and threatening the dykes round Nanjing
could not have come at a better time. Premier Li Peng, an
enthusiast of the long-planned project, would be sure to win
approval this time.

The dam will plug the most downstream of the three gorges
through which the Yangtze pours on its way out on to the low

fertile floodplains of the east. Dam construction will obliterate Sandouping, a community of rickety wooden houses and soggy fields of orange trees, and its reservoir will inundate hundreds of towns including the city of Wanzian, currently home to 140,000 people.

The floodplain of the Yangtze supports more than a third of China's population. One person in 13 on the planet lives beside its waters. But its floods have devastated the people of southern China throughout their history, just as those of the Yellow Rivers have in the north. More than two millennia ago, Chinese philosophers debated how to manage these rivers. The Taoists believed that they should flow freely. If there were dykes, they should be low and set far back. The Confucians wanted to tame rivers with large dykes set close to the main channel to dictate its course.

By and large, the Confucians won. China built dykes that stretch for thousands of kilometres and tower up to 16 metres above the Yangtze. They are every bit as impressive as the Great Wall. But, as an extra insurance, the Chinese set aside flood basins, areas of land to be kept as pasture and deliberately flooded in times of danger. They provided the river with a safety valve.

Dykes require constant repair. At the height of the 1991 floods, a million people were shovelling and bulldozing earth to prevent breaches. But for day-to-day repairs there are increasing signs that, in the words of one peasant quoted by John Gittings in the *Guardian*: 'The peasants won't take orders any longer, and dams and dykes don't get properly repaired.'

The last vestiges of China's 'hydraulic civilisation', sustained in recent years by the Communist Party, may be about to crumble. China's response is increasingly to fall back on engineering to make unnecessary the back-breaking work the peasants no longer wish to do. That means large dams to control floods before they reach the floodplain.

The country's experience so far with superdams has been unhappy. The fiasco of the silting of Sanmenxia was only the worst of many engineering disasters. The Gezhou Dam on the Yangtze has been regarded as a test run for the Three Gorges, but was completed six years late and at four times the budgeted cost. In its first seven years of operation it lost 44 per cent of its capacity to silt. But there have been social disasters, too. Approaching 3 million people have been flooded from their homes and fields by dams since 1950. An estimated 140 people were ousted for each megawatt of generating capacity built. Cheng Xuemin, an adviser to the China Electricity Council, admits that: 'Many oustees still live in poverty, despite the power stations having been on line for many years. Such situations have been causing much public concern.' But, like most engineers, he believes that this time, at Three Gorges, they will get it right.

It was Sun Yet-Sen, the Chinese revolutionary of the first two decades of the century and founder of the first Chinese republic, who first proposed damming the Yangtze at Three Gorges. Later, after floods on the river killed 200,000 people during the 1930s, Nationalist leaders surveyed the area with American engineers from the Bureau of Reclamation. Then, after floods in 1954 which left 30,000 dead, Soviet engineers produced their own plans for the new Communist ruler of China, Mao Tse Tung.

After swimming in the Yangtze in 1956, Mao wrote in a poem, *The Lake Among the Gorges*, that: 'Great plans are afoot. The mountain goddess, if she is still there, will marvel at a world so changed.' During the late 1950s, the Yangtze Valley Planning Office had some 10,000 technicians drawing blueprints. But after 1960, the project was dropped in favour of irrigation and drainage projects, notably the Red Flag Canal, a 'march to conquer nature' by bringing water through the mountains to half a million farmers in Hunan.

Through the turbulent politics of the next three decades, Three Gorges came in and out of favour. Finally the ascent of Li Peng, a long-time enthusiast, as Chinese premier brought the plan back to centre-stage. But Three Gorges has also become a focus for dissent. Among those arrested after the massacre at Tiananmen Square in 1989 were public opponents of the dam such as the journalist Dai Qing. That year, she had interviewed Chinese engineers sceptical about the plan and published their views in a book, *Yangtze, Yangtze*. After the

Communist clampdown, opponents of the dam were den-
ounced as 'bourgeois liberals', and she served 11 months in
gaol, before being granted a passport to leave for the US in
late 1991.

Three Gorges has three declared aims: to protect some 10
million of the people along the banks of the Yangtze from
floods, to generate hydroelectricity for industry and to 'open
up' the Chinese interior above the gorges by improved navigation along the Yangtze. But can it fulfil all these objectives?
American engineers who visited the site in the early 1980s flew
home unconvinced. It would not prevent flooding, said the
former chief of the US Army Corps of Engineers, Lieutenant-
General John Morris. Landslides, earthquakes or military
attack could all breach the dam and kill millions. And construction work would disrupt navigation for two decades.

But scepticism was soon drowned by the lure of big contracts. Within a couple of years a consortium of the USA's
dam-builders was bidding for the project. So too were Canadian companies, who spent $14 million of their government's
money on a feasibility study. When Canadian environmentalists (after a Freedom of Information claim) read the study,
they declared that it was riddled with errors and amounted to
'expert prostitution'. They filed formal complaints with the
engineers' professional bodies.

The study's estimates of the financial benefits of flood
protection, for instance, largely involved totting up the value
of protecting buildings on the floodplain that had not been
built, but which might be built if the dam were constructed.
And it turned out that, to reduce the billion-dollar bill for
resettlement, the Canadian study team had accepted the
Chinese plan that people living on the margins of the reservoir, whose homes would be drowned if the reservoir were
completely filled, would not be moved away. So if the reservoir were ever used for its primary purpose, to prevent a
major flood downstream, it would flood land occupied by
nearly 500,000 people.

Says Philip Williams, a British hydrologist who has examined the flood-control plans: 'The dam operators would have
to choose between flooding out large numbers of people living

in the reservoir, or large numbers of people living downstream adjacent to the river.' It is not clear, he says, which option would flood the fewer people.

Williams believes that large flood-protection dams have an inbuilt tendency to create precisely the kinds of disasters that they are designed to prevent. He has a 'nightmare scenario' for the tens of millions of Chinese living downstream of Three Gorges. A dam completed in say, 2010 would hold back small floods for a number of years. The authorities downstream would soon feel confident enough to build in flood-prone areas and old flood basins. By about 2030, when a really dangerous flood came hurtling out of the west, the dam's managers would keep the floodgates closed, expecting to see off the flood and prevent downstream destruction. When they finally realised that the flood was too strong, it would be too late for a controlled release of water. They would be forced to release huge amounts of water in one go in order to save the dam itself from destruction.

'Inevitably, the loss of life in such circumstances would be greater than if the dam had never been built,' says Williams. He's seen it happen before on a small scale, in India in the late 1970s and even in the USA during the 1980s. Confidence in a dam's ability to hold back a flood, he says, is a very dangerous thing. And the bigger the dam, the greater the confidence and the greater the danger.

Many Chinese engineers have braved political repression to speak out against the Three Gorges project. It would only protect against floods along a relatively small stretch of the river immediately below the dam, they say. It could not stop floods emanating from the great tributaries that join the main river on the floodplain. Lu Qingkan, a hydroelectric engineer for 40 years, told Dai Qing that if the floods of 1954 were repeated with the dam in place, the 6 million inhabitants of Wuhan, a city only 300 kilometres downstream of Three Gorges, would fare no better than in 1954, when it was surrounded by floodwaters for 40 days.

In many ways, the Yangtze would be a more dangerous beast if the dam were built. With much of its burden of silt left behind on the bottom of the reservoir, the river's currents would have greater power to destroy dykes. Official estimates put the likely death toll from a breach of the main JingJiang dyke at 100,000.

Also, the region of the Three Gorges is seismically active and landslides are frequent. In 1985, a chunk of cliff face the size of the Great Pyramid in Egypt slid into the Yangtze in the zone of the proposed reservoir. It created a wave said to have been 36 metres high. An earthquake or a landslide overtopping or breaking the dam could submerge downstream cities such as Wuhan. China has its precedent. In 1975, the Banqiao reservoir in Hunan province, which held a mere half-billion cubic kilometres of water, collapsed, submerging a city and four towns and killing 10,000 people.

'The consequences of failure at Three Gorges would rank as history's worst man-made disaster,' says Williams. He believes that the risk of such a failure is greater than the risk of a once-in-a-thousand-years natural flood that the dam is designed to hold back.

Finally there is the risk of sabotage. Any nation could threaten a military strike against Three Gorges. The threat alone could cause panic among the 350 million people downstream. If the reservoir were emptied to neutralise the threat, the nation's war-machine would be crippled by the loss of electricity. No existing dam anywhere in the world carries such a risk from its destruction. 'War is the key fact that determines whether or not we should construct the Three Gorges project,' said one military expert interviewed in *Yangtze, Yangtze.* 'Are we going to make a Sword of Damocles that will hang over the heads of future generations for decades to come?'

Despite the fears, Three Gorges may ultimately be built to provide power. China, like India, has projections for its future energy demands that make environmentalists blanch. If it concentrated on exploiting coal reserves, China could on its own double the worldwide greenhouse effect within 50 years. From this perspective, the attractions of pollution-free hydro-electric power are obvious. But the mountain gorges that can generate the most electricity for China are in the west of the country, while the large factories that consume most energy are along the eastern coast. Three Gorges is the nearest thing to a solution to that problem. It is the largest and most easterly gorge site in China. There is, say the authorities, no alternative.

Many Chinese engineers quoted in *Yangtze, Yangtze* argue that more power could be created more quickly by building smaller hydroelectric dams on the tributaries of the Yangtze. If that involves moving industry west, they say, then so be it. They also believe that the construction of Three Gorges would drain the nation of cash and expertise for other projects. Far from leading China into a bright new future, it could place a log-jam across national economic development until well into the next century.

Many environmentalists resist the idea that China needs such megaprojects at all. The country is grossly inefficient in its use of power. Chinese factories, many built by Russian advisers in the 1950s, consume an average of two to six times more power than their Western rivals, and seven times more than the Japanese. If China has $20 billion to spend, they say it should invest half in making factories more efficient and the other half on furthering its already remarkable programme of constructing small run-of-river hydroelectric plants.

21

BANKING ON A FLOOD-FREE FUTURE

It is engineering hubris likely to lead to a massive waste of scarce resources.

Peter Rogers, Harvard University, on the Bangladesh Flood Action Plan, 1989

Only one nation in the world runs greater risks from catastrophic floods than China. That is Bangladesh. Plans drawn up in 1989 after the inundation of half the country by the Ganges and Brahmaputra in both the previous two years aim to banish that threat. New embankments are to be built to keep the mighty rivers on the straight and narrow. But, as in China, there is a growing fear that more people will be at greater risk after the billions of dollars have been spent than there were before.

To travel by boat on the great rivers that cross Bangladesh is to be overwhelmed by the domination of the huge forces of nature over the puny efforts of man to tame them. Almost the entire country is built on the delta where two of the greatest and most ferocious rivers on Earth, the Ganges and Brahmaputra, reach the Indian Ocean.

Floods are routine. Every year, roughly a quarter of the country is covered in a thin sheen of water as the rivers are swollen by monsoon rains. Disasters happen when exceptional monsoons swell the rivers, or when cyclones ravage the long flat coastline, setting up tidal surges. The cyclones are the great killers, and unstoppable. But in the capital Dhaka, built on a branch of the Brahmaputra, they are just as concerned about river floods, such as those of 1987 and 1988, which they think they can prevent.

The Ganges and Brahmaputra, and the scarcely less fierce Meghna, can permanently move their channels by a hundred metres or more within a few days, destroying land at will. During my visit, the Brahmaputra devoured more than 10 square kilometres in Pabna and made 5,000 families homeless. It merited two paragraphs in the *Bangladesh Observer*. The rivers create as they destroy. Huge beds of silt of up to a kilometre long move downstream at rates of 600 metres a day during floods, forming new islands and river banks that are swiftly populated by farmers.

The constant transformation of the delta landscape is bad news for those who want to transform Bangladesh into a modern Western-style economy. It cost billions of dollars to repair Dhaka after the floods ripped through its heart in 1988. The same floods played havoc with farms planted with modern high-yield varieties of rice. These varieties require tightly controlled conditions, with regular irrigation and no sudden inundations. They are quite unlike the traditional, more hardy, floating rice, which can respond to rising waters by swiftly lengthening its stem. So the government has persuaded the international community to prepare plans to spend billions of dollars to hold back the rivers behind giant embankments. It wants to control the floods, and preferably to banish them altogether.

It sounds a forlorn task. But what few realise is that the 'taming' of the great rivers of the delta has been achieved before. Indeed, its structures were largely intact when the British arrived in the area in 1757. 'We've lived with floods for centuries,' says Ainun Nishat, professor of hydrology at the Bangladesh University of Engineering and Technology. 'Before the British took charge there was full flood protection.'

By the mid-eighteenth century, the Bengalis had extensively engineered the delta, both to protect against floods and to ensure that the silt-bearing river-waters could fertilise and irrigate fields. The first Britons to travel across the delta reported seeing thousands of kilometres of canals and embankments. In West Bengal, the Mogul kings had dug seven long canals to relieve one important branch of the River

Ganges, the Damodar, by distributing its waters eastwards through such outlets as the Gorai. Much of the delta is in fact man-made, according to William Willcocks, the imperial water engineer who first made sense of the structures in a report published in 1930.

The British at first thought the canals were only for navigation and ignored them. Later, they noticed that the canals appeared to prevent floods. What they never realised, says Willcocks, was that the primary purpose of the canals was to irrigate and fertilise the land of the delta. They could not understand that the floodwaters of the delta brought life as well as death to Bengal, just as those of the Yangtze and Yellow rivers brought 'joy and sorrow' to China.

The Bengalis irrigated 30,000 square kilometres of fields with diverted Ganges waters, says Willcocks. They did it by making cuts in the banks of the canals to divert silt-laden river-water to the fields in times of flood. Rainwater falling directly on to fields normally provided all the moisture that crops needed to grow. But the river-water 'was used to manure the fields and to kill the mosquitoes', which it did by preventing the formation of stagnant pools.

The British oversaw the gradual destruction of the ancient feudal system under which landlords forced peasants to maintain the dykes and clear the canals. Colonial administrators took no steps to find replacement labour. As the canals silted up, they began to overflow and became, for the British, 'a menace to the country'. Inspectors were appalled to see that the peasant farmers continued to cut holes in the canal banks during the flood season. Ignorant of the fact that the breaches fertilised fields, they banned this practice. For many years, there were running battles between gangs of peasants who set out each night to cut holes in the canals, and the British police, who tried to stop them.

Without a regular flushing with silty water, the fields of West Bengal became stagnant ponds of rainwater in which malaria-carrying mosquitoes proliferated. Malaria fever killed a million people, about a third of the population, in the Burdwan district of the Damodar between 1862 and 1872. The prime cause of the scale of the epidemic, according to an official at the local public works department quoted by Will-cocks, was the closing of a large dyke in 1863.

By 1930, when Willcocks wrote, traditional overflow irri-gation served a mere 80,000 hectares of West Bengal. Else-where, he said, 'the poverty of soils, congestion of rivers and malaria have stalked rivers and canals ... the country is strewn today with the wrecks of useless and harmful works'. Today, river branches such as the Gorai are silting up, with more and more of the Ganges staying in the main channel.

Willcocks concluded with proposals for the restoration of the ancient works, in order to 'bring in again the health and wealth which central and west Bengal once enjoyed'.

The lessons of the past give Bangladesh cause to believe that it can bring under control the great forces of the rivers that made the country. But this may be a false impression. The ancient works took many centuries to construct. They were built, moreover, in small steps, bending to the will of the rivers at each stage. It was a training, rather than a taming, of the rivers. The Bangladeshi authorities and their foreign advisers today show neither the patience nor the contrition to adopt such an approach. They want to mould the rivers to their designs, rather than vice versa.

For the Bangladeshi authorities, river floods are things to be prevented. The agriculture department, I was told, had warned that much of Bangladeshi farming is dependent on the floods. They fertilise soils and replenish the groundwaters beneath the delta. Even the exceptional floods of the late 1980s, which undoubtedly did great damage to summer crops, spread so much silt on to the land that there were bumper crops the following winter. Warnings of famine made by politicians as the waters rose over the gardens of the Presi-dent's palace in Dhaka, failed to materialise.

But the hydraulics engineers are in charge, and city-based politicians have their own priorities. Within days of the floods of 1988, the French President François Mitterrand, reaching for a triumphalist language rarely heard today, addressed the UN General Assembly with a call for a new generation of grand development projects aimed at taming nature. 'Devel-opment is achieved through the launching of major projects of world interest which are capable of mobilising energies to help regions devastated by natural causes,' he declared. 'I will take as an example the stabilisation of the major rivers which flood Bangladesh; such an action would provide a perfect opportunity for the first project of this type.'

A year later, French engineers delivered to the Bangladeshi government and the World Bank proposals for the construction of 3,500 kilometres of embankments along the main rivers of Bangladesh, using more than 400 million cubic metres of earth. The project was 'indispensable to the economic development' of Bangladesh, they said. The grandiose scheme was too much even for many civil engineers. But it was what the Bangladeshis wanted to hear and, in a moderated form, was adopted in the Flood Action Plan, a document signed by the Bangladeshi government and the World Bank and backed by aid money from Western governments.

The plan calls for the gradual construction of embankments, beginning on the Brahmaputra in the north of the country and moving south. It is likely to cost $5 billion to implement. Among donor governments contributing to the plan only the US government, advised by hydrologists, opposed the embankments plan on the grounds that it would not work.

One image recurs in discussions about the proposal. Somewhere in the distant future, said the French engineers, is 'the dream that the waters of Bangladesh be tamed like those of the Netherlands'. And one of the chief foreign advisers for the Flood Action Plan is a Dutchman, Wybrand van Ellen. He agrees. 'In future, Bangladesh will look more like our country. The only question is when it will happen.'

A trip on the rivers reveals, as nothing else can, the extent, and probably foolhardiness, of such a vision. These rivers are many times more ferocious than the Rhine. In places they are as wide as the English Channel. Out here, nobody banks on living in one place for too long. The fragile villages that nestle beside the rivers are made of light shacks that can be packed up and removed within minutes if the river rises.

Only the government builds to last in such places, with large pump houses and factories, civil servants' compounds and bridges. But such signs of permanence are mostly fantasy. At Chandpur, a sizeable river port on the Pabma (the name for the waterway created by the merged Ganges and Brahmaputra), the ferry station has constantly been moved in recent years as half the town has been ripped away by the river. In the space of a few days in 1988 the river shifted its course into the town by 500 metres. Mosques, shops and part of the railway station were submerged as the river cut a new channel 45 metres deep. What remains of the town today is perched on a series of dykes that are surrounded by water even in the dry season.

Could a new embankment save the town? Peter Rogers of Harvard University, who wrote a detailed criticism of the Flood Action Plan, doubts it. 'No embankments or river-training works in the world can control these forces if they are taken head on,' he wrote. Barry Dalal-Clayton of the International Institute for Environment and Development in London conducted a study of the plan at the request of Britain's Overseas Development Administration. He warned: 'It is difficult to be optimistic that man-made interventions will be able effectively to constrain the powerful and highly mobile rivers of Bangladesh.' Only the Bangladeshi government, which has built a large concrete compound for staff of the water development board behind a dyke at Chandpur, appears to disagree.

Upstream of Chandpur is the prestige Meghna-Dhanagoda irrigation project. Here $50 million has been spent on ditches, embankments and pumping stations to keep out monsoon floods and institute controlled irrigation of the kind essential for the growth of high-yield varieties of rice. Embankments tower high over the project's 200 square kilometres of fields. Inside, the land is marked out in neat rectangles and fed with fertilisers and pesticides. It is a tropical version of the Netherlands.

But there is no taming the rivers that swirl outside. The Meghna-Dhanagoda project is, in effect, an island, surrounded on all sides by rivers. Peer over its western bank and you are looking at the point where the merged Ganges and Brahmaputra join the Meghna. It appears the height of arrogance to invest so much money at the very point where the three great rivers of the delta meet. In 1988, the rivers washed away the project's banks and flooded 40 square kilometres of its fields, plastering them with a thick layer of infertile sand, and carving out a new channel 18 metres deep. Since then, engineers have rebuilt the banks three kilometres back from the new line of the river. But the river continues to encroach.

Everywhere in Bangladesh the story is the same. During the 1960s, an embankment was built along part of the right bank of the Brahmaputra to stop floodwaters from spilling across the northwest of the country. But the river took little notice, knocking away the embankment as it continued a westward shift in its course that has persisted for centuries. According to a study by the University Research Centre in Dhaka, the embankment encouraged the Brahmaputra to dump more of its silt on the bed of its main channel, so worsening flooding on the left bank. Under the first stages of the Flood Action Plan, the right bank is to be built higher still and a new left bank constructed. Now the river will be forced to dump its silt on its own bed. This will nullify the effect of heightening the embankments, and create new hazards downstream. As Rogers puts it: 'Embankments do not reduce floodwater, but merely move it; excess water that is confined in the stream bed higher on the river will increase the volume and velocity, and perhaps the depth, of the flow that has to be managed in the districts closer to the sea.'

This paints a dim future for towns such as Chandpur and its irrigation projects, where flooding is likely to worsen under the action plan. The story is reminiscent of the early days of the 'taming' of the Mississippi.

Van Ellen believes that the risk of devastation downstream can be reduced by the creation of 'compartments' behind the main banks – separately defended areas, rather like the large polders in his native Netherlands. 'If there were high discharges of water coming downstream, then the authorities can decide to flood a particular compartment to order to protect other areas,' says van Ellen. 'The Chinese do this, though of course Bangladesh is not such an organised society.' He agrees that it would be hard to justify flooding some areas to defend others. And who would make the decision?

It is clear to many engineers that banishing the floods is neither possible nor desirable. Says Rogers: 'Without the annual flood, Bangladesh would find itself in very serious economic and environmental straits.' The more realistic engineers now talk rather of controlling the floods. They believe they can prevent the most destructive ones, while preserving the lesser, beneficial flooding for the benefit of the farmers. Maybe they can. But in modern Bangladesh, there is another wrinkle to this story.

Many Bangladeshi farmers today irrigate their fields in winter with groundwater pumped to the surface by new cheap tube-wells. Van Ellen calls tube-wells one of the great success stories of modern Bangladesh, and credits them with allowing the country to escape famine at a time when its population has doubled within a generation. Yet it is a vulnerable success. Already water-tables are dropping. And the flood plan seems bound to jeopardise groundwaters further. The reason, apparently largely unnoticed by the plan's backers, is that it is the annual flood, spreading out across the fields of Bangladesh, that replenishes the underground water each summer. Take away the flood and the replenishment will diminish. Water-tables could plummet, says Dalal-Clayton.

Modernisation is turning Bangladesh from a water-based to a land-based economy. Everywhere, roads are being built. To get anywhere, the roads require hundreds of bridges, underlining the fact that the most obvious and direct means of transport is usually by boat. There are other signs of this blindness to water. In the economic equations used to justify flood prevention, fishing, which provides 80 per cent of the nation's animal protein and employs 5 million people, is largely ignored.

The floods are essential to the fisheries. While most fish and shrimps hatch in rivers and estuaries, they feed and grow in rivulets and marshes, known in Bangladesh as *beels*. In its drive to modernise farms, however, the government has helped farmers to drain the *beels* and, to create flood-free zones, has cut off the channels that link them to rivers. Result:

fewer fish. At Chandpur, one embankment reduced local fish production by a third within two years. The flood plan, by lowering water-tables and blocking channels, will destroy thousands of *beels* – and their fish.

At the launch of the Flood Action Plan in London in 1989, Britain's overseas development minister, Lynda Chalker, warned that: 'We must avoid setting up projects which effectively control flooding but which adversely affect the livelihood of the Bangladeshi people.' It was a pertinent warning, but one that the plan does little to address. Dalal-Clayton calls the plan 'a political response to the clamour for flood protection from wealthier, influential, urban-based groups'. Urban areas need flood protection most; rural areas the least. And in the countryside it is the richer landowners who will gain from flood control. They can invest in the modern methods of irrigated farming – to plant high-yield varieties of crops that require the flood protection banks the government is to provide. But the poor farmers and fishing communities will find their catches and crops dwindling if the annual flood is lost.

They will also find themselves more vulnerable to the dangerous floods the government says it wants to protect them from. Under the Flood Action Plan, says Dalal-Clayton, 'A great many people who presently live along the main rivers and on islands in the river channels will be exposed to increased risks from flooding.' Hugh Brammer, a British expert on Bangladesh and its rivers, believes 6 million people will fall into this category. Already the creation of large irrigation projects such as the Meghna-Dhanagoda is depriving hundreds of thousands of people of their land. The dispossessed are everywhere clustered beside the marauding rivers. The Flood Action Plan will recreate the blunders of Meghna-Dhanagoda on a grand scale. It will become a massive nationwide device for depriving the country's poorest people of the free natural resources of the rivers – its silt and fish and floodwaters – and for channelling the dangerous face of the rivers in their direction.

Look inside the towering banks of the Meghna-Dhanagoda irrigation project and this 'tropical Holland' seems remarkably empty of people. But look outside, between the embankment and the rivers, and there are people in their hundreds and thousands. I visited the village of Gazipur, which is home to a few hundred people whose land was taken for banks to protect the irrigation project or who were too poor to stay inside the embankments. The village, a collection of huts leading down to a makeshift wooden jetty, is just outside the embankment at one of the most dangerous points on the river. If the Pabma is swollen, its waters pour towards this spot.

To reach the shacks, you must clamber over huge piles of large round boulders. They look like a handy protection for the villagers against floods. But, says Nasirudin Khan, liaison officer with farmers on the safe side of the bank, 'the rocks are not to protect the village. If the floods rise, we will move the boulders to strengthen project embankments that are threatened.' He shrugs when I ask him what will happen to the people of Gazipur.

As our boat approaches another bankside community he tells me: 'Until two years ago, there were shops beneath where we are now. The villagers have to move back a hundred metres each year as the bank erodes. Soon they will be forced back against the embankment and they will have to go somewhere else. But that is not our responsibility.' He did not know whose responsibility it was.

22

TALES FROM
THE RIVER BANK

The primary effect to date of river basin development in
tropical Africa has been to transfer the resources of rural
riverine habitats to the urban, residential, commercial and
industrial sectors.

Thayer Scudder, unpublished manuscript, 1988

Wherever planners attempt to 'manage' river basins in a
rational manner, they seem to create irrationality. What
Thayer Scudder, an American development scientist who has
watched the progress of African rivers for 30 years, identifies
above as the basic flaw in that continent applies through much
of the world – as the following four sketches of river-basin
management in action in Africa, Europe and Asia underline.

The Manantali Dam in the hills of western Mali, the heart of
former French West Africa, is miles from anywhere. Its
remoteness has encouraged nations to conjure ludicrous
dreams around its shimmering form. As the dam rose across
the valley of the River Senegal during the 1980s, the dreams
were sustained by a bureaucracy called the OMVS, the
Organisation pour la Mise en Valeur de la Vallée du Fleuve
Senegal, set up by Mauritania, Mali and Senegal with a remit
to remake the valley.

The Senegal is like the Nile, but about a quarter of the size.
It begins in rainy highlands in the continent's interior, and
flows through more than a thousand kilometres of a flat desert
on the border between Senegal and Mauritania, before reaching the sea through a delta. The West Africans wanted to

build their version of the High Aswan to master the river, saving its summer floodwaters for growing a second or third crop in the long winter dry season.

The OMVS nurtured their dreams. It told Senegal that the dam would provide 800 gigawatt-hours of cheap hydro-electricity annually for its capital, Dakar, a thousand kilo-metres away. It told landlocked Mali that the dam would maintain levels in the river so that ocean-going ships could sail at any time of the year the 900 kilometres upstream to its tiny river port of Kayes which has been unreachable by boat since the drought year of 1974. It told Mauritania and Senegal of a bright new future growing cotton and sugar and rice on almost 4,000 square kilometres of irrigated farms along the Senegal's floodplain. Where once a million or more peasants and fishermen had eked out a subsistence livelihood, contri-buting nothing to the national export drive, soon there could be a dollar-making agricultural heartland. And it told the world that the spread of desert sands across the western Sahel would be halted.

To fulfil the dream, the OMVS borrowed $800 million, mostly petrodollars from Saudi Arabia, Abu Dhabi and Kuwait. The money went to European construction com-panies to build the dam. In the summer of 1987, the dam was complete and the reservoir behind it began to fill. Then the dreams began to fade.

There were neither turbines nor pylons to take electricity to Dakar or anywhere else. There was no money to carry out the huge amount of blasting and dredging needed before ships could reach Kayes. And the bottom had fallen out of the markets for sugar and cotton, so nobody was much inter-ested in new ventures in irrigated farms. The governments of the three nations had grown so poor while the dam was being built that they could afford none of the means to exploit it.

Everybody had lost interest in the project, except the bankers, who were owed $800 million, and the million or so people about to be deprived of their livelihoods when the dam halted the river's flow. The farmers lived by recession agri-culture, planting crops on the wet floodplain as the river re-treated each summer, and by catching the immense shoals of fish trapped in the pools that the receding waters left behind.

The OMVS responded to the crisis by agreeing, for the first decade of the dam's operation, to make releases of water that would mimic the natural flood. In this way, they would maintain a water supply for the farmers and fishermen of the floodplain, until such time as there was money to build the promised irrigation schemes. The plan offered, for the first time in Africa, a dam that controlled the flow of a river in the interests of peasant farmers on the floodplain. For a while, the plan was applauded as a new deal for peasants, and a model for the sensible management of dozens of other wayward dams across Africa. Scudder wrote that it could 'enhance existing production systems, hence increasing the productivity and living standards of local populations'.

The reality, at any rate in the first years of the experiment, proved different. Word of the new arrangement appeared not to have reached the operators of the dam in the hills of Mali. In 1987, they allowed no flow down the main stream of the Senegal. They explained that they were filling their reservoir. The farmers made do with some brief flooding from lesser tributaries that entered the Senegal below the dam. In 1988 there were, as elsewhere in the Sahel, massive late floods. The engineers released water from the dam for the first time – not at the time when it might have helped farmers, but to save their dam from possible destruction. In 1989 filling of the dam resumed, but luckily the tributaries produced a good flow for the farmers.

Then came 1990. The word went out that this year there would be an artificial flood for the farmers; the new farmer-friendly river regime was ready to roll. The British geographer Ted Hollis went to see the show. It never happened. He said later:

> The engineers at Manantali had decided that they want-
> ed to test their sluice gates with the reservoir full. But
> they didn't tell anyone. When I asked the engineers why
> the farmers had not been told, they said this was an agri-
> cultural question, which was up to the member govern-
> ments, not the OMVS. But the government of Senegal said

that even it had not been told.

Better luck next year? It turned out that in 1991 the dam engineers planned to provide their 'natural' flood at an unnatural time of year – the first two weeks of September. This is not much good for the sorghum farmers on the floodplain, says Hollis. 'To practise their recession agriculture, they need to plant seeds after an early flood. A late flood from Manantali is worse than useless. It washes away all their crops before they are ready for harvest.'

He asked the operators why they could not open the dam earlier, to coincide with the floods from the tributaries, which rise in neighbouring Guinea:

> They said they could not do this because they only get flood forecasts three days ahead. I pointed out that they could get more advanced warning by using data collected from rain gauges set up by American aid workers in Guinea. But it turns out that the OMVS doesn't acknowledge the existence of Guinea because there was a row back in the 1960s and it left the family of Francophone nations. So they won't acknowledge the data either.

Meanwhile, social unrest has been compounded by violent expulsion by the Mauritanian authorities of thousands of farmers from the floodplain to make way for intended irrigation projects. There is a lot of support for artificial flooding regimes in Africa, to help traditional farmers. It could be the belated making of river-basin management there. But, Hollis wonders, 'Will it work given these kinds of institutional constraints? Is this yet another technological cul de sac?'

Such exasperation is common among even the most saintly water scientists. An increasing number conclude that, whatever the environmental issues, most African states are not currently capable of handling large dams. The US government's Agency for International Development, and to a lesser extent Britain's Overseas Development Administration, have adopted something close to a no-dams policy in many parts of the world.

Europe does not have great rivers on the scale of the Yangtze
or the Ganges. Nor does it any longer have tens of millions of
people dependent for their daily survival on the natural
rhythms of floods. But it does have rivers that are greatly
loved, and which people will fight to defend. The Danube is
such a river, a fluvial artery rich in history, spanning east and
west in a continent which has suddenly become whole again.
The Danube pours out of the Alps across Bavaria and through
northern Austria until it drops on to its flat floodplain near
Vienna. Here, for perhaps a hundred kilometres, it forms an
inland delta. With its gradient suddenly reduced, the river
slows, drops much of its sediment and divides. Two branches
fan left and right. The main channel breaks up into myriad
channels that wind through the pristine flooded forests, reed
beds and rustic scenery of eastern Austria, Slovakia and
Hungary.

The Danube between Vienna and Budapest provides a rare,
and still remarkably unspoilt, example of what the forested
floodplains of many other major European rivers – from the
Thames to the Rhine, Rhône and Elbe – were like until the
engineers took them in hand. It is as if the engineers had
missed a piece of their jigsaw. When they tried to insert that
piece in the mid-1980s, Europeans from both east and west
discovered that they could get passionate in their opposition
to dams on their own rivers as well as in faraway lands.

The love affair between greens and dams lasted a long time
in central Europe. 'Even though we Austrians love our mountains, most environmentalists supported the construction of
dams in their valleys,' says Karl Wagner, the young President
of the World Wide Fund for Nature in Austria. But then the
Austrian electricity authorities decided they needed a dam on
the Danube floodplain, just downstream of Vienna.

The spot they chose would have flooded one of Europe's
largest surviving naturally-flooded river forests. The Hainburg
forest is no remote wilderness. It is filled at weekends with
BMW drivers unloading inflatable boats to test their nautical
skills on the backwaters and float beneath willow trees
up half-hidden creeks. But what it has lost in solitude, it
has gained in popularity. And when, in December 1984,

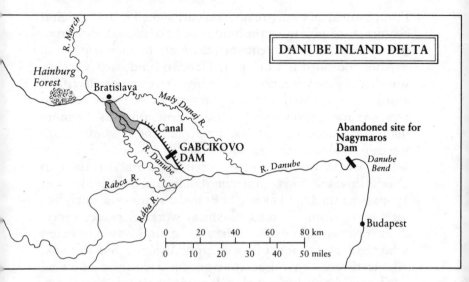

dam-builders suddenly began clearing the forest, angry greens from Vienna had the backing of millions when they decided to blockade the forest and prevent the destruction.

A week before Christmas, the police moved into the forest, and there was bloodshed. But by then the blockade was an international news story, and the media backed the greens. A demonstration through central Vienna attracted 40,000 people. Then a High Court action, brought by the protesters to test the legality of the dam, appeared to provide the government with cover for a climb-down. At any rate, the court halted construction, and it never restarted. The battle had been won. But the war to save the inner delta of the Danube merely moved downstream – and over the border into eastern Europe .

There had been talk of building dams along the Danube where it forms the border between Czechoslovakia and Hungary since the 1950s. The idea was to even out seasonal fluctuations in river flow, so that the shallow reaches could be made deep enough for ocean-going ships. In 1965, the nations along the river agreed to build a trans-European waterway, linking the Danube to the Rhine, so that ships could sail from the North Sea to the Black Sea. This idea had enthused

Europeans since Charlemagne first attempted it in the eighth century. But, until now, the muddy bed and meandering flows of the middle Danube remained the main impediment.

After the oil crisis of 1973, Hungary and then Czechoslovakia decided that they also wanted to generate electricity along the river. They drew up plans for a complex scheme to combine navigation and electricity generation along more than 200 kilometres of the river, from the border with Czechoslovakia almost to Budapest.

The works begin as the river flows from Austria into Czechoslovakia. This is a strange landscape. One minute you are passing the blighted city of Bratislava, where a smell like cat's urine from the huge chemical works pervades everything, raw sewage fills the river and chemical wastes have left a layer of oil on top of local groundwaters. But the next minute, the river has miraculously purified itself and is flowing in narrow channels through delightful forest.

Below Bratislava, the Czechs and Hungarians had agreed jointly to construct a large weir across the river, creating a reservoir about 15 kilometres long. Roughly 90 per cent of the water leaving the reservoir would pass into a wide canal on the Czech side of the old river. The canal would make a 20-kilometre journey to a dam at a village called Gabcikovo, where its water would drive turbines in the dam before plunging back into the main river.

The scheme would drown much of the riverine forests beneath the reservoir, and turn the canal into the new Danube. The two countries' Communist Party bosses duly signed an agreement and the engineers were put to work. By 1991 both the canal and the Gabcikovo dam were complete, but the Communists were no longer around to take delivery. Budapest was arguing with Prague, the Czechs with the Slovaks, and the Slovaks with the villages close to the canal.

The canal itself sat unfilled, a monstrous asphalt-lined channel 700 metres wide and with banks towering in places 17 metres above the countryside. From the bed of the canal, you could just see the spires of village churches over the top. Graffiti on it demanded 'Stop the water monster'.

The canal was built to carry up to 5,000 cubic metres of

water a second. Czech government engineers claimed that it would tame the Danube and prevent the floods that have inundated these low-lying villages in previous years. But for the villagers living with the raised canal passing above them, within a few metres of many homes, it would be a constant threat of a kind of flood of which they had no experience. The water would not rise slowly, as past floods had, over their river dyke, across their football field and on to the road. It would come from above, in a torrent, if the canal bank ever failed.

The villagers had no reason to trust the engineers. The worst recent floods here occurred in 1956, when 50,000 people were evacuated after two Czech dams collapsed. And it was an accident with lock-gates at Gabcikovo in late 1989 that roused the villagers to oppose the project. Two years and a revolution later, the Gabcikovo site engineer, Oto Kelemen, had to agree. Standing on top of his dam, he said: 'The people here have real fears. They have 17 metres of water above them. I can tell you we can understand their feelings. If something happens on this dam, it could be a catastrophe.'

Anti-dam campaigners from round the world took a day off from picketing the meeting of ICOLD, the International Committee on Large Dams over the border in Vienna, in order to walk the canal. They dug holes in the black asphalt and planted saplings in the canal bed. And they were taken to the land cleared for the reservoir at the head of the canal.

Local environmentalists had erected along one bank a series of artists' easels that held up to the skyline photographs of the land as it was a decade before. They showed a near-replica of the Hainburg forest, with abundant oak and ash, poplar and silver willow, mingling with thousands of waterways. But now, stretching as far as the eye could see behind the easels, there was a dried-up treeless landscape of scrub, sand and, in the distance, huge gravel workings. A hotel that must once have fronted on to the flooded forest was now trapped amid the desolation behind a high dyke.

Later, the campaigners addressed a meeting of villagers beside the Danube, with the canal looming in the background. Among them was Janos Vargha, a biologist and journalist, who in the early 1980s had taken on the Communist bosses in Budapest to oppose the re-engineering of the Danube. He formed a samizdat group called the Danube Circle which was for several years a banned organisation. But it grew in power and influence, partly with the help of strong links with Austrian greens. The first target of the Hungarian campaigners had been a second dam, known as the Nagymaros Dam, to be built downstream of Gabcikovo at a beauty spot called the Danube Bend, near Budapest. It was to generate electricity for Hungary and Austria, which had agreed to help build it after protesters had halted the Hainburg project. This unholy alliance between capitalist and Communist dam-builders had seemed a neat trick. Austria was in effect exporting its environmental problems to Hungary. What neither side had bargained for was that Austria also exported the germ of their environmentalists' anger.

By 1988, Hungarian opposition to both Nagymaros and Gabcikovo was rife. The first major public protests against the Communists on the streets of Budapest for thirty years came when tens of thousands of people defied the state authorities to protest against the dams. One of the first decisions of the new democratic government in 1989 was to abandon the Nagymaros Dam and Hungarian involvement at Gabcikovo.

In Czechoslovakia, however, there was little popular opposition to the Gabcikovo Dam. By the time the Communists were removed from power, the dam was almost complete. When he was a dissident playwright, Vaclav Havel had opposed the dams. But, as President, he announced in 1990: 'What has been built at Gabcikovo – that nightmare – cannot be destroyed. [We must] salvage what has already been built, so that the existing buildings have some use.' $600 million of investment could not simply be dismantled. But many agreed with Juraj Holcik from the Slovak Academy of Science, who complained bitterly: 'The tragedy is that by continuing with this megalomaniac scheme, our new democratic regime has proved a true successor to the Communists.'

By the end of 1991, there was an impasse. The half-completed weir that would divert the Danube into the canal was the responsibility of the Hungarians – who now vowed never to complete it. Miroslav Liska of Hydroconsultant Bratislava, a chief engineer on the project, revealed that if Hungary refused to complete the weir and divert the waters, then Czechoslovakia would extend the canal for 10 kilometres as far as Somorja, where both banks of the river are in Czech territory, and construct a new weir there.

With almost the entire flow of the Danube rushing through its inland delta, touching nothing more earth-like than asphalt, the changes to the character of the region will be profound. The river's vital link with its floodplain will be cut. Holcik predicts that the inland delta will dry out, destroying 50 per cent of the fish, 75 per cent of mammals and perhaps 95 per cent of reptiles. Three thousand hectares of forests will be lost, and a similar amount will dry out within five years – a massive loss to the forestry industry as well as nature. 'We know the nation needs electricity,' said Ladislav Nagy, the mayor of a village in the shadow of the new canal, 'but at what price? We can produce electricity by ten other methods. But we cannot reproduce nature.'

From here on, the script could have been written in Bangladesh or Nigeria. Engineers insist on treating rivers as plumbing systems, like a network of pipes conveying water from mountain to sea. But, especially in their floodplains, rivers are much more. While encasing the river in asphalt and concrete may help the navigation of large ships, and provide electricity for the chemical works of Bratislava, it will drastically reduce fisheries and other wildlife in the 'real' Danube. And by interrupting the river, it threatens to destroy the largest groundwater reservoir in central Europe.

The gravel beneath the inland delta contains 14 cubic kilometres of water, constantly replenished by the river. Almost half of all Hungary's water supplies come from the Danube – usually not from the river itself, but from wells sunk into the sand and gravel beds beneath the river's floodplain. Budapest alone obtains around a million cubic metres a day from such wells.

The engineers in Bratislava insist that the groundwaters will not be damaged. But Hungarians such as Vargha fear that the water-table in the gravels could fall by as much as four metres, drying out lush farmland and forests along with wells on which hundreds of communities depend, on both sides of the border. 'The devilry starts', says Heinz Loffler, a biology professor in Vienna, 'when you try to cut off a river from its plain.' It's an old lesson.

The Mekong rises amid the glaciers of the Tibetan Plateau and travels south through Burma, Laos, Thailand, Cambodia and, finally, Vietnam. There are schemes afoot for the 1990s to harness the Mekong, the eighth largest river in the world.

Land-locked Laos, high in the mountains of southeast Asia, hopes for a hydroelectric money-spinner. The power produced by a single modestly-sized dam, the Nam Ngum, exported to neighbouring Thailand, has in recent years made up more than 80 per cent of Laotian export earnings. It is a cash register sitting on a tributary of the Mekong River. And the country's government, emerging from years of political isolation from the West, would like another one – preferably on the main river.

Thailand is a willing buyer. While the countryside of its neighbours became battlegrounds, Thailand has spent the past 30 years in rapid industrialisation. Demand for electricity increased seventy-fold in that period. The country has used up most of its best sites for generating hydroelectric power. The ones left are mostly in national parks, which the country's environmentally-minded middle class want left alone, or are defended by peasant farmers, such as those who blockaded the construction site of the Pak Mun Dam on a tributary of the Mekong during 1991.

The agency for the transformation of the Mekong will be the Mekong Committee, which was established in the late 1950s by the governments of Laos, South Vietnam, Cambodia and Thailand, under the auspices of the UN Development Programme. The committee nurtured ambitious plans for transforming the region through giant dams, most of them the product of a three-week visit to the region by the USA's Bureau of Reclamation in 1956.

The programme inspired President Lyndon Johnson in the

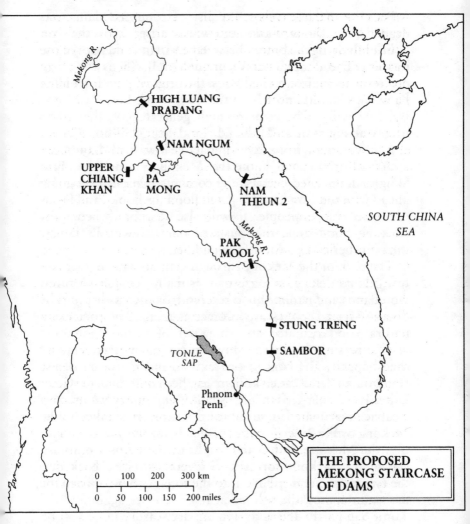

THE PROPOSED
MEKONG STAIRCASE
OF DAMS

mid-1960s, as the Vietnam War began to escalate. When he
wanted to 'cut a deal' with Ho Chi Minh, he offered US
finance and expertise to harness the Mekong in return for an
end to the war. 'The Mekong can provide water and power
that would dwarf even our own Tennessee Valley Authority,'
he said. But Ho turned him down. Only now are the plans
being dusted off once more.

Back in the late 1950s, the list of proposed dams was headed by Pa Mong, a kilometre-wide barrier across the river to be built along the border between Thailand and Laos, close to the Laotian capital of Vientiane. And so it is today. In deference to environmental fears, the original plan for a High Pa Mong dam has now been turned into the Low Pa Mong. But 'low' will still be 67 metres high, generate more than 2,000 megawatts for sale to Thailand – and cost $2 billion.

Nor will its environmental impact be low. In mid-1991, the senior environmentalist on the Mekong Committee, Erik Skoglund, resigned because the committee insisted on going ahead with the dam. Pa Mong will flood the homes and farms of up to 80,000 people. It will also disrupt the complex Mekong flood cycle that sustains one the world's largest inland fisheries and floods rice paddies.

The path of the Mekong through Cambodia and Vietnam towards its delta is a maze of seasonally flooded pastures, woodlands and natural flood reservoirs known as *bengs*. The *bengs* cover 20,000 square kilometres in all. They act like a natural flood regulator, absorbing part of the monsoon flood and increasing dry-season flows in the main river. Half of their capacity is found in one extraordinary feature of the Cambodian landscape, known as the Tonle Sap or Great Lake. The Tonle Sap is a large shallow expanse of water, with a capacity estimated at 80 cubic kilometres. It is linked to the Mekong by the River Tonle Sap, which normally drains south into the Mekong. But at the height of the monsoon floods, the mighty Mekong forces it to reverse, bursting back into the Great Lake and spilling into the forest around. When the monsoon abates, the fish-laden river reverses again and the Tonle Sap partly drains during the dry season.

The inhabitants of the Mekong valley have ordered their lives for many centuries to make the best use of the river's flood regime. The Cambodians, rather like their counterparts in Bengal centuries ago, make holes in the natural dykes of the *bengs* to let silty Mekong water on to their fields. The Viet-namese have turned the delta, which floods for up to six months each summer, into a marvellously productive environ-ment that provides 10 million tonnes of rice and 100,000 tonnes of fish, two-fifths of Vietnam's food. As a French colonial administrator put it early this century:

> The rhythmical movement of the waters, regular, like breathing, furnish much of what is needed to improve the land. High waters deposit on the soil a layer of rich silt and spare the farmer the drudgery of transporting fertiliser to the fields, and when the water recedes he finds the ground all ready to support rich and remunerative crops.

The secretariat of the Mekong Committee says that the Pa Mong and later dams will be operated for the benefit of river management downstream as well as customers for electricity. But there are competing interests, for power generation, traditional farming and fisheries and 'green revolution' agriculture each have different needs. The need to generate cash in the short-term to repay loans on large dams is certain to result in power and, to a lesser extent, modern farming gaining priority. The giant natural life-support system provided by the flooding river, which sustains 30 million people along the river, may shrivel and die.

The Committee says it will release more water to flow down the river in the winter dry season. This suits the needs of power generation. It will also allow farmers to remove more water from the delta river channels to irrigate rice paddies. But in the natural river system, this role of hoarding floodwaters for the dry season is already accomplished by the *bengs* and the Tonle Sap.

John Dennis, who has studied natural resources in the Mekong basin for the UN Development Programme, predicts that the operation of the Pa Mong dam to hold back monsoon waters will drain huge areas of the Tonle Sap. In effect, it will take over the role of the Tonle Sap and the other *bengs* as regulators of the river's flow. Swamp round Tonle Sap will cease to fill during the wet season and a similar amount of wetland along the Mekong floodplain will also dry out.

For hydrologists, this might not matter. But for the inhabitants of the floodplain, it makes all the difference in the world. If the *bengs* emptied, their fertile, silty waters could no longer provide free irrigation for Cambodian farms. And, according to the Mekong Committee's own fisheries experts, these threatened wetlands, and especially the Tonle Sap, are also the spawning grounds for 90 per cent of the fish in the river. According to Larry Lohmann, an environmentalist who has studied the Mekong:

> Between June and October, fish swim into the 30- or 40-kilometre wide band of flooded forest and shrub land around the edge of the Tonle Sap, where they can avoid predators and feast on the decaying vegetation of the shallow water. As the water recedes, the fattened fish return to the lake and into thousands of waiting fishing nets.

Some fish spawn not in the *bengs* but far upstream, beyond the Pa Mong. Smaller fish might be able to use fish ladders to by-pass the dam. But what about the giant local catfish, which grows up to two metres long and weighs twice as much as a man? If the dam were built, the catfish would become extinct. Likewise, the hilsa, one of the most widely eaten fish in south and southeast Asia, might disappear from the river. Fish caught in the Mekong are the main source of protein for tens of millions of people and their conservation should be the top priority of any management plan for the river.

All this is being lost sight of as development agencies pursue their goals of fermenting a green revolution in the delta region. And, because 'high yield' plant varieties are delicate, always vulnerable to too much or too little water, the developers are anxious to gain control over the flood in the delta as fast as possible. In fact, they don't want to wait for the upstream dams.

Consultants for the UN Development Programme and World Bank in 1990 embarked on a three-year project to create a 'master plan' for the development of the Vietnamese delta. Within weeks they were suggesting that it would be a good idea to 'discipline' the Mekong by building a barrage across the mouth of the Tonle Sap. They want to delay the flow of water out of the lake at the end of the monsoon season in order to provide a greater dry-season flow in the main river. What effect this might have on the fisheries on the lake and the already critically high rates of siltation there remains to be asserted.

The trouble is that the Mekong Committee and the governments represented on it increasingly want economic progress – the kind that can be measured in dollars in the bank rather than hilsa in a peasant fisherman's net. They want large plantations to take over from small farmers in the Mekong delta and, with no known large reserves of fossil fuels in the region, they see hydroelectricity as the route to industrialisation. If in the process they destroy the natural wealth of the Mekong, then the first sufferers will be peasants of the river banks and the delta. Tragically, these were the very people who suffered most during the decades of war.

No country has more plans for superdams than the mountain kingdom of Nepal. According to published lists it wants to build 11 dams, each taller than London's Post Office Tower. The first, if the World Bank and the Nepalese government get their way, will be in the Chisapani Gorge, high in the Himalayas on a tributary of the Ganges known as the River Karnali.

Chisapani could be the largest engineering project in the Indian subcontinent in the 1990s – a $6-billion hydroelectric behemoth, generating as much electricity as Grand Coulee. Nepal has no need for so much power. It has the lowest per-capita energy consumption of any nation on Earth. But Chisapani Gorge is only 45 kilometres from the Indian border. Nepal would sell the electricity to the giant industrial cities of northern India.

Much of the planning has been done. A 'pre-feasibility' study completed in 1989 but unpublished two years later proposed a swift go-ahead for a 270-metre-high dam, the highest in the world outside former Soviet central Asia, and six times the size of the dam first proposed for the gorge by Japanese engineers in the 1960s. With the World Bank's coffers open and both Japanese and Indian construction companies keen to bid, the dam could be looking back on 200 kilometres of flooded valley by the end of the century.

Over the border, the electricity authorities of India also

want the dam badly. They warn of a growing crisis in energy supply in northern India, a region of 300 million people where black-outs and brown-outs are a way of life. This will probably be enough to overcome Indian misgivings about tying part of its economic future to five high-voltage power lines crossing the border from Chisapani.

The pre-feasibility study for Chisapani conceded that there were 'major environmental effects requiring urgent review'. The dam would flood large areas of forests as well as farmland. More forests would be cut down to rehouse the evacuees. Reductions in river flow below the dam would destroy habitats for the rare Ganges river dolphin and the local Gharial crocodile.

Groups such as the World Wide Fund for Nature see the fight to preserve Chisapani Gorge as a possible repeat of the successful campaign to prevent construction of a dam in the forested Silent Valley in India in the 1980s. But their opponents are playing for high stakes. They see Chisapani as the first stage in realising a dream to turn the valleys of the Himalayas into a hydroelectric cornucopia. After Chisapani may come the 2,000-megawatt Pancheswar Dam, also on the Karnali and another scheme with long-standing support from the World Bank.

There is growing pressure among Nepal's urban middle-class community, the same people that forced the monarchy to cede power to democratic institutions in 1991, to realise the potential of one of the country's greatest economic assets, its sites for hydroelectric power stations. The nation's Water and Energy Commission in Kathmandu estimates the exploitable hydroelectric potential at more than 40,000 megawatts. Soon electricity may replace carpets and tourism as the country's chief earner.

In a small way, India is already tapping the hydroelectric resources of another Himalayan neighbour, tiny Bhutan. The first joint project, at Chukha on a tributary of the Brahmaputra, was completed in 1988. Two years later, officials in New Delhi signed up to build two more. They are relatively small run-of-river projects, which need no large reservoir and rely on the natural flow of the river. But, say Indian planners, Bhutan could eventually supply them with up to 20,000 megawatts of power.

Some of the best sites for large dams on the Brahmaputra – indeed some of the best sites for large hydroelectric projects anywhere in the world – are in India itself. In the far northeast of the country, there is one dam site, on the bend of the Brahmaputra as it passes through the Himalayas and turns into India, that could generate 25,000 megawatts of power. So great is its power that engineers estimate around 18,000 mega-watts could be generated by a run-of-river plant without a large reservoir. However, the whole area is claimed by China and without a resolution to the territorial dispute, its potential will go unrealised. The thought of China and India engaged in a 'dam war', with India threatening to bomb Three Gorges and China sending terrorists down the Brahmaputra, is too horrendous to contemplate.

Some enthusiasts claim that strings of great dams on the Himalayan rivers, besides unlocking vast stores of hydro-electric power, could hold back the kind of monsoon river surges that flooded half of Bangladesh in 1987 and 1988. But according to studies for the US government, to make any significant impact would require at least 60 cubic kilometres of storage space, cost a cool $60 billion and take 50 years – by which time the first reservoirs would probably be full of silt.

Bangladesh, meanwhile, has proposed the construction of dams on the Ganges for a second purpose – to hold back monsoon floodwaters for release at the end of the dry season to improve river flows. These low flows have been a constant source of tension between India and Bangladesh. In 1976, India completed a large barrage across the Ganges at Farakka, just before the river crosses the border into Bangladesh. While the barrage remains obstinately open when floodwaters rush down the delta, the Indians close it during April and May, the driest months of the year, to divert half the river's flow and keep it on Indian territory.

While not causing the ecological disaster predicted by Bang-ladeshi ministers at the time, the barrage has exacerbated spring water shortages in southwest Bangladesh, especially along the River Gorai, once one of the major routes of Ganges water to the sea. Mohammad Rahman of the World Conservation Union in Bangladesh says that: 'The flow of the Ganges is now too reduced to flush away the rotting vegetation, insecticides and industrial wastes which are dumped in the river. Many reaches are now stagnant and unable to support aquatic organisms. Stocks of hilsa, the mainstay of the country's fisheries, have declined since the building of the barrage.' As river flows fall, salty seawater penetrates even further inland, disrupting production of jute mills and a power station that need fresh water, as well as poisoning crops and threatening the long-term survival of the Sunderbans, Bangladesh's largest natural forest. Besides being a refuge for the Bengal tiger, the forest also acts as a barrier to the penetration inland of killer cyclones.

Meanwhile, India is anxious to find yet more water to put into the Ganges in the spring months. The purpose is to allow the country to divert more water out of the river, both in West Bengal and further upstream, to irrigate fields that have so far missed out on the green revolution. The plan is to capture behind dams some of the huge flows of the Brahmaputra as it rushes through northeast India towards Bangladesh, and divert the water by canal into the lower Ganges. India envisages constructing a 300-kilometre canal as wide as the River Thames through London, carrying 3,000 cubic metres of water a second from the northeast Indian state of Assam to the Farakka barrage.

There are two problems, both of which seriously exacerbate border tensions in a region where the politics of water are fraught. First, as we saw, the far northeast of India where the canal would begin is disputed territory: run by India, but claimed by China. Second, though the canal would begin and end in India, the odd configuration of national borders created at the partition of India means that most of its journey would be in Bangladesh. And Bangladesh sees the plan as another attempt at the theft of its water.

Dhaka's counter-proposal is for a series of large dams in the upper reaches of the Ganges in Nepal to hold back the river's monsoon flows and provide more water during the dry season. Either scheme was costed in the late 1970s at around $7 billion, a figure likely to have at least doubled since.

The stories of the four rivers discussed above all underline the failure of modern engineers and politicians to fulfil the dreams of fifty years and more ago to manage entire river basins for the good of their inhabitants. Each has, or will, instead create substantial ecological damage, anger local communities who feel their interests are being ignored and ferment international disputes.

Whether on the Senegal or the Ganges, the Danube or the Mekong, there has been a complete failure to balance the conflicting interests on the river. On the Ganges and the Danube, this has created a political stand-off. On the Senegal, desert dreams have turned to farce as engineers refuse to release 'their' water to farmers. On the Mekong, the signs are that once the engineers get busy and the dams start rising, all these problems will emerge there too.

At least, despite the conflicts, nations have not yet resorted to war over these rivers. But in the examples in the following chapter, the inability of natural systems to absorb the wounds inflicted by water projects and still deliver the water requirements of nations has set the war drums beating. In some instances, battle may not be far away.

23

PYLONS FOR PEACE
– OR WAR

Power and water, in abundance in Mozambique, will together
spark the industrialisation of the country.

Henry Olivier, 1990

Africa's first great dam was the Kariba on the River Zambezi,
the largest river in southern Africa. It was built by the British
colonial authorities where the river formed the border
between Northern and Southern Rhodesia (today's Zambia
and Zimbabwe). Colonialists had always looked with awe at
the great Victoria Falls on the Zambezi, the spine of Africa's
third largest river basin, and imagined harnessing its power to
generate electricity. By the early 1950s, the massive growth of
the copper mines run by the Anglo-American Corporation
and a Rhodesian syndicate had created the demand for such a
scheme. The Falls themselves were not, it turned out, a good
site because there was no gorge in which to store water. But
construction went ahead at the nearby Kariba Gorge.

The Kariba Dam attracted the biggest loan that the World
Bank had ever given at that time. It was higher than St Paul's
Cathedral and created a reservoir more than 280 kilometres
long, the largest in the world until the completion of the High
Aswan Dam more than a decade later. Kariba also captured
the world's imagination – nature had been tamed in the heart
of Africa. There was massive publicity for Operation Noah,
the rescue of wild animals flooded out by the dam, but rather
less for the 50,000 Batongans who, after pitched battles with
soldiers, also lost their homes.

There was no pretence about who the Kariba Dam was

designed to benefit. The authorities made no plans for rural electrification. Nor were there local irrigation projects. And while fish flourished for a few months in Lake Kariba as rotting vegetation created a surge of nutrients in the lake, stocks then declined drastically. The people of the newly flooded Middle Zambezi, whose rich alluvial soils had supported one of the highest densities of population in all of central Africa, gained nothing from the dam and lost large areas of their land. Downstream, the ending of the annual flood dried out large areas of the Zambezi floodplain, and caused widespread erosion of the banks.

The fecundity of the flooded land was underlined during the droughts of the 1980s, when Lake Kariba was drawn down for long periods, exposing wide mud-flats. Enterprising farmers returned and, from 1981 to 1984, the exposed mud-flats on the north bank of the reservoir became Zambia's main source of maize, before once again disappearing beneath the waters. A permanent arrangement of this sort, in which the dam operators guarantee their flooding schedules, could greatly benefit farmers, says Thayer Scudder, an American researcher into African river systems.

After gaining independence in 1964, a year after Lake Kariba had filled, Zambia's President Kaunda decided that he wanted his own source of hydroelectricity, independent of Ian Smith's rebel white regime in Salisbury, which declared UDI from Britain the following year. Zambia completed its own hydroelectric dam at Kafue Gorge in 1972, and followed up with a second dam upstream of the gorge in 1978. These two dams have flooded more of the fertile Zambezi valley and drained water from the wetlands of the Kafue Flats – 'the single most valuable agricultural entity in Zambia, probably in central Africa', according to one study completed before the dams. The rich fishing grounds had attracted migrants from neighbouring Malawi and Tanzania, and herdsmen who brought their animals there during the dry season were the wealthiest pastoralists in central Africa.

Today, the Kafue Flats are on the wane. While dam operators release some water each wet season to inundate the flats, the floods last only about four weeks, compared to six months

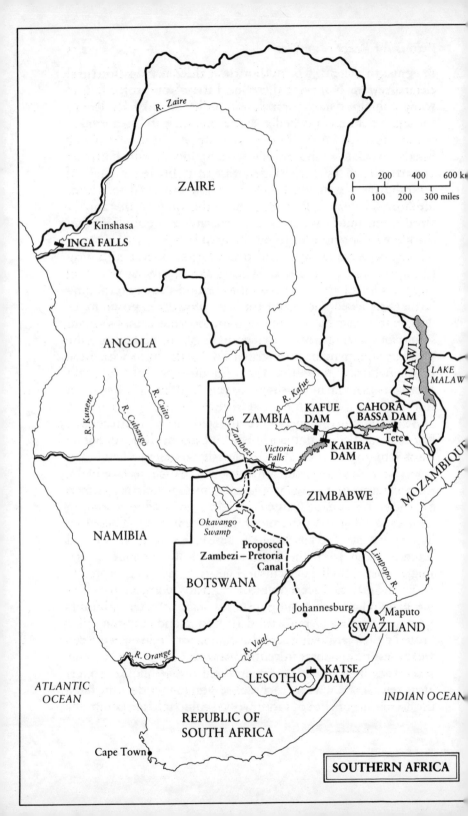

SOUTHERN AFRICA

under natural conditions. Meanwhile, the Zambian electricity company wants to install drainage channels across the flats to bring a larger, more reliable flow to the Kafue Gorge Dam.

Scudder retains his belief that dams such as these can be made to work in the interests of all. It is the urban and industrial bias in the politics of still largely rural African countries such as Zambia that prevents this happening. At least the dams at Kariba and Kafue Gorge provide reasonable amounts of electricity. That is more than can be said for the third and most expensive hydroelectric scheme on the Zambezi, the remote Cahora Bassa Dam in Mozambique. This is potentially the world's fifth largest source of hydroelectric power, capable of delivering up to 4,100 megawatts of electricity, more than 20 times the entire electricity consumption of Mozambique. Reality has been rather different.

Begun in the 1970s to keep the industrial engines of the Transvaal in South Africa humming, the dam construction site was soon in the front line of the battle for the future of southern Africa. As Frelimo guerrillas fought the Portuguese for independence in Mozambique, the dam site suffered direct military action. None the less, construction was completed, and in 1974 the reservoir began to fill – just six months before Mozambique's Independence Day. The new Frelimo government set about transforming Cahora Bassa from a symbol of oppression into a symbol of liberation. This was bad news, however, for the 25,000 people in the remote Lower Zambezi basin who had been removed from the reservoir zone to 'strategic villages' at the same time as the Portuguese were attempting to clear the area of rebels. There was to be no liberation for them. Their homeland was by then a reservoir the size of an English county.

The ironies proliferate. At independence, in order to secure a continuing flow of foreign capital, control of Mozambique's most prized asset was placed with a company in the expelled colonial power, Portugal. That company retains to this day full powers to operate the dam and sell its power, though since 1984, Mozambique has received a share of the meagre revenues. Secondly, far from seeing the power lines strung for 1,300 kilometres from Cahora Bassa to Johannesburg as a reason to reach an accord with its neighbour, the government in South Africa was soon arming and financing a guerrilla army, Renamo, that wanted to break the link as part of its campaign to usurp Frelimo. In late 1987, at the height of a long guerrilla war during which only fitful supplies of electricity ever reached South Africa, Renamo destroyed 500 pylons along the route.

While the pylons may be down, the dam continues to be opened and closed to provide a little local power. Operation is erratic, not least because there is no discussion between the Portuguese engineers and their counterparts at the Kariba Dam upstream about who releases what water when. This is inconvenient for the dam operators and disastrous for the river. 'Floods occur out of season, disrupting the whole natural cycle of flood and ebb,' says a recent study. A single regular natural flood in February or March has been replaced by a haphazard regime in which most years see two flood releases from Cahora Bassa and some years see three.

Biologists regard the Lower Zambezi valley as one of the least explored regions of the world. No studies have been carried out before or since dam construction. None the less, it is clear that, with most of the river's silt held behind the dams, the fertile Zambezi delta is receding and the shrimp fishery at its mouth has collapsed without the silt from which the shrimps gained the algae on which they feed.

One of the central problems on the Zambezi is the failure, because of the fractured politics of the region, to make the most efficient use of the reservoirs so expensively built. But, despite efforts by the UN Environment Programme to encourage agreements to manage the river more sensibly, governments seem determined to go it alone with more dam projects.

In 1991, Zambia asked consulting engineers from 11 countries to put forward proposals for a new 196-metre dam in the Batoka Gorge. It would flood 100 kilometres of the Zambezi valley, all the way from the top of the Kariba reservoir to the Victoria Falls. The dam might generate 1,200 megawatts of power, but what will it do to the operation of the Kariba Dam? Is it indeed an attempt to hijack the power of

Kariba, currently shared between Zimbabwe and Zambia, for Zambia's exclusive use?

The proposal seemed to be fulfilling the worst predictions made in a study of the Zambezi basin by the International Institute for Applied Systems Analysis, a UN-backed organisation currently looking at the operation of several major river basins. Its 1988 report warned Zambia that constructing a dam at Batoka Gorge would represent 'short-term expediency. It seems more reasonable, even from the hydroelectricity generating perspective, to try to optimise energy output from the already existing hydropower plants.'

The future of the Zambezi and several other rivers in southern Africa is likely to be increasingly bound up with that of the region's largest economic power. South Africa is the most industrialised country in Africa, with much the greatest demands for both water and power. For both of these it is likely to become increasingly reliant on its neighbours to the north. It is eyeing the prospects for constructing pipelines and pylons to link its often parched lands to the wetter world at the heart of the continent. The political implications could be immense. They already have been for its tiny neighbour, Lesotho.

The Orange and Vaal rivers dominate South African hydrology. Both have their headwaters in the highlands of the east and flow west to the Atlantic Ocean. The Vaal is the smaller of the two, but passes through the Transvaal and the key mining and industrial centres of Pretoria and Johannesburg, the heartland of the old Afrikaans republic. Its flow is all but consumed within the Transvaal. From the mid-1990s, it will be replenished by a massive dam and a 50-kilometre tunnel bored through the mountains from the headwaters of the Orange River, which are in nominally independent Lesotho.

Lesotho, whose main export is Basuto labourers to South African gold mines, will now have a second money-maker, water. Under the $2.5-billion Lesotho Highlands Water Project, the 180-metre Katse Dam, the highest dam in Africa, will capture the flow of the River Orange and send it beneath the mountains and into the Vaal. Eventually there will be five dams, each more than 150 metres high, and 240 kilometres of tunnels.

Money for the scheme comes from both South African finance houses and the World Bank. To get round formal embargoes on aid to South Africa then in place, the money passed through a trust fund set up in Britain. A report to the World Bank concluded that the project 'could well become a classic example of the economic advantages which can be obtained by international agreements on inter-basin transfers of water'.

But the economic advantages will mostly be with South Africa. Lesotho, one of the world's poorest countries, will gain little. Its government is expecting an annual royalty payment of $80 million, rising further once the scheme is completed in 2020. It will eventually make Lesotho self-sufficient in hydroelectric power. But there will be no water to spare to irrigate its fields, and the South Africans have insisted that herdsmen give up some grazing areas on hillsides to reduce soil erosion and so combat siltation in the reservoirs.

More worryingly still, the country lost its fragile political independence for the benefit of the scheme. Signature of the treaty approving the project was held up for two years, reportedly because the South Africans did not trust the Lesotho prime minister Chief Leabua Jonathon. In January 1986, South Africa imposed an economic blockade on the country and then saw its friend, General Metsing Lekhanya, stage a successful coup. Within six months Lekhanya suspended the constitution, banned all political activity, and signed the treaty for the water project.

Provided the impetus for economic development continues in South Africa beyond the end of white rule, demand for water in the republic seems certain to rise. And possible new sources of water to feed into the Vaal after the Lesotho project has exhausted its potential are already under discussion.

The first target is the waters of rivers that rise in the republic but flow into Swaziland and Mozambique. South Africa has already built a series of dams on east-flowing rivers. To the north, another east-flowing river, the Limpopo, is almost emptied for long periods as it runs along the border between South Africa and Botswana, en route for Mozambique. The flow only recovers after receiving 500 million cubic metres annually of sewage from Johannesburg and Pretoria.

A study of water strategy in southern Africa, completed by British and Portuguese consultants for the World Bank and the UN, concluded that both Swaziland and Mozambique need large reservoirs to promote economic development. But it warns that: 'Serious water development problems will arise ... unless there is close cooperation between South Africa, Swaziland and Mozambique.' The seeds of a future conflict are being sown.

South Africa is also looking further north. One proposal, first made in the late 1970s and revived in the drought of the mid-1980s, is to divert up to 3 cubic kilometres of water a year from the Zambezi above the Victoria Falls in Zambia and bring it south along a 1,300-kilometre canal through the sands of Botswana. The scheme, while taking only 1 per cent of the river's total annual flow, could leave the river's upper reaches empty in the dry season. And, whatever Zambia felt about the deal, it would be in direct conflict with a Zimbabwean plan, first mooted by the colonial authorities in the 1930s and revived in 1990, to divert the same water to a massive irrigation project for Matabeleland. South Africa might also consider tapping the Okavango, Botswana's great desert swamp, known as the 'jewel of the Kalahari'.

If water is important to South Africa, so too is electricity. And in southern Africa there is growing talk of an international trade in electricity derived from water power. One man who believes that the future of water development in southern Africa lies in such trade is Henry Olivier, the veteran British engineer who built the Kariba Dam on the Zambezi in the 1950s. Unperturbed by the farce at Cahora Bassa, he looks forward to a pan-African transmission grid linking South Africa to the great rivers of the north, which he believes will all soon be devoted to the cause of power generation.

Olivier's proposed new map of the Zambezi sees the entire river from the Victoria Falls to the Indian Ocean turned into a cascade of large dams. Zambia is already considering a dam to fill the 'gap' between the Victoria Falls and Lake Kariba. Olivier also proposes plugging the space below the dam at Kariba before the beginning of the lake behind Cahora Bassa with a new reservoir, Lake Feira. Its reservoir would be in Zimbabwe, but its dam would be just inside Mozambique – a politically blighted but naturally bountiful country for which white South Africans have great ambitions. Downstream of Cahora Bassa, he proposes two more dams to create a total hydroelectric capacity on the river of 11,000 megawatts, nine times that of Kariba.

In Olivier's world, there is little ecological or agricultural sacrifice in this. Turning the Zambezi into a long staircase of reservoirs will 'mitigate the annual floods', he says, as if they had no worth in themselves. Instead, the water could make possible the realisation of old Portuguese plans to irrigate the Lower Zambezi valley, and especially the delta, for plantations of sugar, rice and cotton. 'Power and water, in abundance in Mozambique, will together spark the industrialisation of the country,' predicts Olivier, and 'the backbone of industrialisation will be mining.' At the town of Tete, just downstream of Cahora Bassa, lies a 'shallow, 175-kilometre long, 9-kilometre wide seam of cokable coal'. There could be 200 million tonnes of vanadium ores nearby, plus copper fluorspar, manganese, nickel, chromium and asbestos. In Olivier's imaginings, Tete is to become a great mining and iron and steel centre.

Looking further north, Olivier sees ever greater hydroelectric potential, for example at the exit to Lake Malawi, and on the Kunene River between Namibia and Angola. The vision stretches to the Inga Falls on the River Zaire, the world's second largest river and a potentially vast source of hydroelectricity.

The Zaire could hardly have been better designed for power generation. Unlike most other rivers in Africa, it runs almost undiminished through the seasons. Its flow is ten times that of the Zambezi. Moreover, after flowing for almost 2,000 kilometres along a flat saucer-like plain, it descends to sea level through a series of rapids – the most impressive of which, the Inga Falls, drops by 98 metres within a few kilometres. The extraordinary power behind the great river in these falls makes Inga 'one of the greatest single natural sources of hydroelectric power in the world', says Olivier.

The potential annual production of electricity here equals the combined consumption of France and Italy. Zaire has so far tapped a small fraction of this power. Inga I, built by the Americans in the 1970s, and Inga II, being extended in 1991, take perhaps a twentieth of the potential energy at the site. Most of the power generated here, close to the capital, Kinshasa, travels by pylon overland for 1,700 kilometres to the Katanga mines in the far south of Zaire. The rebellious province is tied literally and figuratively to the capital of the sprawling jungle state.

Now South Africa is proposing the construction of the Grand Inga Project – a scheme of staggering dimensions that, by stages, could include 52 electricity generating units, each as large as a big conventional power station and with a combined capacity of 39,000 megawatts. This would make its generating capacity 30 times that of Kariba, almost 20 times that of Cahora Bassa or the US's Hoover Dam, 2.6 times larger than Brazil's Itaipu, the largest hydroelectric plant on Earth, and more than twice the size of the proposed Three Gorges Dam in China. At the end of the 1980s, the newly privatised South African electricity company, Eskom, began talks with the Zaire government about collaborating on the Grand Inga project.

Just as South Africa dreams of transforming the bottom half of Africa with dams and pylons, so Egypt still yearns to reorder the top half. Stage one is finally taming the Sudd. Despite dredging of the main channels, water still takes months to pass through the swamp, losing a large part of its flow to evaporation. Egypt returned in the 1970s to the idea of reducing this loss by digging a new channel for the White Nile to by-pass the Sudd. To dig the new channel, called the Jonglei Canal, they bought the bucket-wheel.

Nothing, in all their days of watching foreigners chasing back and forth along the upper Nile, can quite have prepared the Dinka herdsmen of the Sudd for the arrival of the bucket-wheel, the canal diggers' answer to the combine harvester. On to the plains of southern Sudan in the late 1970s crawled a great digging wheel, five storeys high, a fearsome parody of the ancient Persian water wheel with 12 buckets attached to grab earth rather than water. The bucket-wheel weighed 2,300 tonnes and consumed 40,000 litres of fuel a day – more than all the buildings in Juba, the regional capital.

The wheel rotated once every minute, night and day, its trajectory fixed by laser beam. At each revolution its buckets ate up and threw aside enough soil to fill a full-size swimming pool. The entire machine was second-hand, constructed in the early 1960s by a German firm to dig a canal across the Punjab in Pakistan. It took 30 months to dismantle and carry by truck, train, steamer and camel across the Indian Ocean and up the Nile to the Sudd, and began excavation of the Jonglei Canal in June 1978.

This was not a good moment to dig a canal through the backwoods of southern Sudan. The region was in turmoil as the Muslim north of the country attempted to impose its will on the Christian south. But the politicians in Cairo and Khartoum had agreed that now, with the High Aswan Dam almost full, was the time to undertake the long-planned canal project that would end the huge evaporation losses suffered by the White Nile as it meandered through the Sudd.

The Jonglei Canal would be up to 50 metres across and divert up to a quarter of the White Nile before it entered the swamp. The extra flow would be sufficient to increase the water reaching Khartoum, Aswan and eventually the Nile delta by about 5 cubic kilometres. The joint project between Egypt and Sudan would divide this water 50:50, though in practice Egypt was the only country able to make use of extra water.

To help sell the project to the locals, Abel Alier, president of Sudan's High Executive Council, announced: 'If we have to drive our people to paradise with sticks, we will do so for their own good and the good of those who come after us.' The herding metaphor was especially unfortunate since the lifestyle of the Dinka herdsmen in the canal zone was to be destroyed by the bucket-wheel. The vast trench it was carving across their pastures would prevent them from taking their cattle on the seasonal migration routes, following the moving edge of the swamps.

In Khartoum there was much talk of development programmes for the Dinka, of schools and health clinics, better drinking water and access to new markets for the sale of livestock. But in the south it seemed as if their traditional independence would be channelled away with the water. In any case, was it sensible, in a country afflicted by spreading deserts and ripped apart by famine, to destroy the livelihoods of large numbers of people who had lived in harmony with their natural environment for thousands of years?

The new road that would run the length of the canal would also open up the area to hunters from the cities with guns to shoot the huge quantities of animals. Most at risk would be the Nile lechwe, a small antelope, and the half-million wild horses, known as tiang, that probably represented the largest population of large wild animals left anywhere in the world. They would be sitting targets as they gathered, queueing at the special ramps, to cross the canal on their migrations twice each year.

By early 1984, the bucket-wheel had carved its way unsteadily along roughly a third of the canal's course, at a cost of $100 million. Egypt and Sudan were talking about using the machine to dig two more canals, taking two more branches of the White Nile on their own by-passes round the Sudd.

But the Sudanese government's poor relations with the people of its own south were about to intervene. Insurrection was in the air. Khartoum appeared able to power its bucket-wheel, but not to provide electricity for Juba. It could dig a canal to fill the taps in Khartoum and Cairo, but not provide villages along its route with clean drinking water. On 10 February 1984, the Sudan People's Liberation Army attacked the bucket-wheel camp, destroying everything except the great machine itself. Government troops returned fire, an Australian pilot was killed and the rebels ran off with hostages who were eventually held for a year before being released unharmed.

The French engineers abandoned the bucket-wheel and

eight years later, at the time of writing, the great machine stands rusting in the wilderness, visible for 20 kilometres in every direction. Behind it, stretching north towards distant Aswan are 267 kilometres of canal and 65 million cubic metres of dumped soil. Ahead of it lies a year's work before it meets the headwaters of the White Nile. To the west, the Sudd, the largest freshwater swamp in the world, remains largely undisturbed.

It was always said of Colonel Nasser in Egypt that he had never heard of the idea of a High Aswan Dam until he grabbed the reins of his country. But John Garang, the founder and leader of the liberation army, was an expert on the Jonglei scheme long before he took up arms against the Sudanese government. In the late 1970s while studying at a university in the US, he had written a thesis on the Jonglei Canal. In it, he argued that the canal would suck southern Sudan dry of its greatest resource – the water in the Sudd.

Three months after the bucket-wheel was halted, the rains failed in Ethiopia, and now it was the north that felt sucked dry by the south. The Blue Nile was little more than a trickle that summer, while the combined flows of the two branches of the Nile were the lowest for a century. It was the first of four drought years which left Lake Nasser more than half empty by the summer of 1988.

Egypt began looking with ever greater anger at the turmoil in Sudan which prevented the conversion of a $100 million investment in the bucket-wheel into water for its fields and hydroelectric turbines. The then foreign minister Boutros Ghali, who has since become Secretary-General of the United Nations, claimed that an extra 400,000 hectares of 'new land' could have been irrigated if the canal had been completed. The rebels in southern Sudan, he said, were receiving assistance from Kenya, Uganda and Ethiopia. These were the three upstream neighbours with their fingers on the pulse of the Nile who had been excluded from the Nile Water Agreement signed between Egypt and Sudan in 1959. Such talk gave unpleasant substance to his earlier, widely quoted, warning that: 'The next war in our region will be over the waters of the Nile.'

In June 1989, on the day before the 1959 Nile Water Agreement expired, there was a coup in Khartoum. The plotters, according to the journal *Africa Analysis*, had enjoyed 'the active encouragement of Egypt'. Egypt's desire to complete the canal, and the belief that the new leaders could bring to an end the turmoil in southern Sudan, may have been a key factor behind its support for the coup.

Despite the coup, Egypt was engaged in secret informal talks to reach peace with its neighbours over the Nile. 'Egypt has quietly come to recognise that the other upstream nations of the Nile must be brought into a new agreement,' said Tony Allan of the School of Oriental and African Studies in London. The arrival of a new government in Ethiopia in mid-1991, with the apparent backing of America, pointed to a new agreement on the Nile based this time not on Pax Britannica but on Pax Americana.

In a speech delivered to an otherwise uneventful Africa Water Summit in Cairo in mid-1990, Ghali warned that: 'If present circumstances continue until the year 2010, Egypt and Sudan will experience a severe deficit in water resources.' Less than a generation after Nasser had announced that the Nile was now in Egypt's hands, Ghali admitted that: 'The national security of Egypt, which is based on the water of the Nile, is in the hands of eight other African countries.' He called for a 'closer working relationship with Ethiopia ... We need more water, and there is no possibility of getting more water unless there is stability in the region.' The nations of the Nile valley, Ghali said, will need access to another 10 cubic kilometres of assured water each year by 2010. Half of that can come from completing the canal scheme. The other half, though he did not say so directly, must presumably come from reducing the 15 cubic kilometres of evaporation losses in Lake Nasser.

That means going back to the old British idea, first proposed by Garstin almost 90 years before, of building dams in the upper reaches of the Blue and White Niles. There, in the steep valleys, as much water can be held as in a full Lake Nasser, but with only a quarter as much water surface exposed to the sun. That, coupled with the cloudier cooler climate, would reduce the evaporation losses by at least 10 cubic kilometres per year. If those dams were built then the High Aswan would become a liability, and in theory it could then be abandoned and Lake Nasser drained.

But that was far from Ghali's mind when he made his offer to deal during his 1990 speech: 'We need water in Egypt and the Sudan, but Uganda and Ethiopia do not need as much water, at least not for the time being. Therefore, Egypt must offer something in exchange for water, and that is energy.' Behind the scenes, the African Development Bank had funded a study into a Nile valley electricity grid. It could link the small Owens Falls hydroelectric plant, built by the British in Uganda in the 1950s, to the High Aswan and new dams in Sudan, Uganda and Zaire. Together, Egypt and its neighbours could turn the Nile into a great electricity generating machine that could supply, said Ghali, 'Jordan, Syria, Turkey and, further, the European Common Market'.

Egypt would be the hub and the mastermind for the scheme. If the upstream states gave Egypt safe passage for its Nile water, Egypt would guarantee safe passage for the electricity from the power plants at the headwaters of the Blue and White Niles towards lucrative markets in the Middle East and Europe.

At this point, delusions of grand megaprojects are taking over. The new technology of superconductors in theory could drastically reduce electricity losses on long-distance power lines, so that: 'Over the next ten years, it will cost relatively little to move electricity from Kampala to Khartoum and Cairo.' In truth, though, there is little prospect of widespread use of superconductors in the next decade or two.

There is hubris, too, in Egypt's desire to mastermind a scheme that will be paid for by loans from development banks and the US government. The hard truth may be that Egypt has very little to offer in return for its hydrological security. After a century of high-handedness by Britain and Egypt alike towards upstream nations, all efforts to secure Egypt's water supplies – through barrages and canals, gunboats and bucket-wheels – have created spiralling demand followed by chronic and growing insecurity. In Cairo the fear remains that, if Egypt was once 'the gift of the Nile', it may now be the gift of sluice-gate operators in Sudan and Addis Ababa.

24

THE WATERS OF ZION

We could decide 'no more orange orchards', give Jordan the
water it needs, and direct our energies towards, say, making
computers.

Arnon Soffer, geographer and adviser to the Israeli
government, 1991

In 1964, Israel hijacked the waters of the River Jordan. The
Jordan valley, which had been irrigated and cultivated longer
than perhaps any other valley on Earth, was deprived of most
of its water. The seizure happened suddenly and without
international agreement. One day, the river poured out of the
Sea of Galilee, a natural holding reservoir within Israel's
borders, and down the Jordan valley through the country of
Jordan to the Dead Sea. The next day, a dam at the outlet of
the Sea of Galilee halted the flow and a huge pumping station
on the opposite shore drained the sea's contents into a
network of pipelines, canals and reservoirs across Israel.

It was as if France had annexed the Rhine as it flowed out
of Switzerland and pumped it over the hills to irrigate the
plains of northern France – leaving a dribble of water to flow
down Germany's main artery. Since then, the lower reaches of
the River Jordan have been a saline trickle, leaving Jordanian
farms along its east bank desperately short of water. The
river's usurper, soon called the National Water Carrier, has
now been extended to create a full-scale national water grid
for Israel that serves Haifa and Tel Aviv along the coast and
continues south to the Negev Desert. It carries more than a
million cubic metres of water every day and, at three metres in
diameter, is wider even then Gadaffi's Great Man-made River.

At the end of the Six Day War, and three years after capturing the waters of the Jordan, Israel occupied the land, known as the West Bank, between its former border and the Jordan valley. It also took the Golan Heights, Syrian territory northeast of the Sea of Galilee that is one of the principal sources of the headwaters of the River Jordan. Thus, a river which prior to 1967 had less than 10 per cent of its basin within Israeli borders, is now almost entirely controlled by Israel.

Israel's determination to make its fields bloom from Galilee deep into the Negev Desert by applying copious amounts of irrigation water has made it as determined to secure its water supplies as its borders. Indeed, through the 1980s, the need to keep its taps running and its irrigation canals full was a publicly expressed reason, some say the main reason, for hanging on to territories gained in the Six Day War. But despite its success in exploiting the River Jordan, by the early 1990s Israel was again running out of water.

Israel today has three main sources of water for its national grid. The diverted River Jordan is the most important. Reliable water statistics are hard to obtain in Israel, but most hydrologists say that it provides around 40 per cent of the national water supply. Next in importance is the mountain aquifer, a large subterranean store of water fed largely by rain falling on to the dolomite hills of the West Bank. While some of its water exits at hill springs, including spring tunnels, most drains underground westwards through the rocks towards the Mediterranean, surfacing on pre-1967 Israeli territory in wells and two large natural springs that feed the Taninim and Yarkon rivers.

The third source is the shallower coastal aquifer, stretching the length of the Israeli coastline. Both the mountain and coastal aquifers are fully used and supply about 20 per cent of the country's water each. Other water comes from locally captured rainfall and from underground reservoirs of ancient salty water beneath the Negev Desert.

The Sea of Galilee is more than 200 metres below sea level. The cost of pumping so much water so far uphill to coastal farms has been prodigious. Water pumping uses a fifth of all

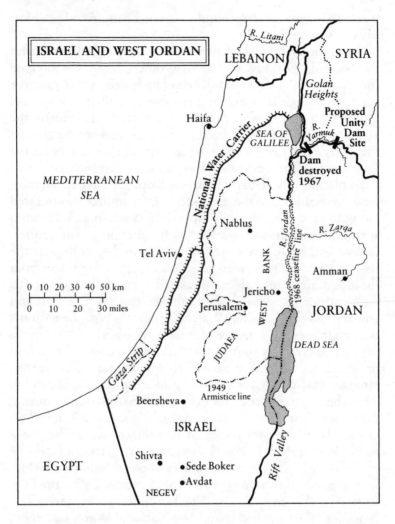

Israel's electricity. Even so, the National Water Carrier has brought huge benefits to Israel. In summer, water from the Sea of Galilee irrigates crops from Haifa in the north to the southern desert city of Beersheva and beyond to the Egyptian border. In winter, surplus water that would otherwise spill into the Jordan is pumped along the Carrier and poured down wells and over sand dunes to artificially 'recharge' the coastal and mountain aquifers. In this way it increases the amount of water that these underground reservoirs can provide the following summer.

From the first years of Israeli settlement of Palestine after the Second World War, the newcomers have overpumped their wells. Ze'ev Golani, now chief hydrologist at Tahal, the state hydrological consulting company, drilled many wells into the coastal aquifer himself. He remembers that by the 1950s so much water had been taken from beneath the ground that salty seawater was flowing in from the sea to replace the fresh water, a process known as saline intrusion.

As plantations of water-guzzling crops such as cotton, tomatoes, avocados and the ubiquitous Jaffa orange proliferated along the coast, the Israelis tapped the Yarkon and Taninim springs, the main western outlets for the mountain aquifer. Golani and his fellow water pioneers also dug wells near the springs. By the early 1960s more water was being taken from the mountain aquifer than was added by rainfall. It was at this moment that the government annexed the River Jordan and constructed the National Water Carrier. At last, the nation's water supplies were secure – or so it appeared.

I visited Israel in 1991 in the middle of a drought that had persisted for several years. With the winter rainy season almost over, there was gloom amidst the endless sunshine. There had been so little rain in the north of the country during the winter that the level of the Sea of Galilee had reached an all-time low. The nation seemed unwilling to accept that there was a water crisis. The parks were still irrigated and citizens of Tel Aviv read newspaper stories about the shortage while sitting beside the cooling waters of the fountain on the Dizengoff in the city centre. The headlines were stark. The *Jerusalem Post* warned that: 'The National Water Carrier is to virtually shut down this year.' But it was worse than that. When the story first appeared, the Carrier had been as good as shut for six months. During the previous winter, the Sea of Galilee had been so empty that there had been virtually no recharge of the coastal and mountain aquifers. They too were in danger of running dry.

Now the crunch had come. The agriculture ministry, after months of dithering, had decided to impose Draconian measures, cutting agricultural use of water by 40 per cent or more. Such a parched-earth policy sounded like the death knell for some of the more heavily subsidised sectors of agribusiness, such as the Jaffa Orange orchards. But then many people thought that was a good thing. The oranges consumed large amounts of water but made little money these days.

What had gone wrong? Hydrologists such as Golani had been predicting the crisis for some years. 'We gave the politicians the figures about their overuse of water,' said Golani, 'but they said we were crying wolf.' Many blamed the national water commissioner, who is in charge of conserving the country's water supplies.

For most of the past ten years, said Golani, the commissioner had been giving out 200 million cubic metres more water than had been going into the aquifers and reservoirs. So over the decade there had been an accumulated overpumping from the aquifers of 2 billion cubic metres – one whole year's supply. A report by the state ombudsman accused the government of '25 years of mismanagement' of the nation's water, irresponsibly subsidising the national dream of a green desert, and pandering to the farmers. The commissioner resigned not long afterwards.

Ronit Nativ, a hydrogeologist at the Rehovot campus of the Hebrew University of Jerusalem, shrugged in exasperation as, in the midst of the drought, she watched gardeners dig up the lawn outside her office to install a new network of irrigation pipes. The water would come from the coastal aquifer which, she said, was being permanently contaminated by salt, sewage and agricultural chemicals because of overpumping.

In its natural state, the water-table in the coastal aquifer is about 3 to 5 metres above sea level, ensuring a continuous flow of fresh water to the sea. This flushes out any contamination. But 30 years of overpumping have left huge areas of the water-table below sea level. 'Pollutants cannot be flushed to the sea because there is no longer any flow of water,' said Nativ. 'Already wells are being shut down because they contain too much salt from the sea, or nitrates from fertilisers or heavy metals from sewage.'

Some damage may be irreversible. As salty seawater penetrates the aquifer, it destroys the matrix of the sandstone
rocks that make up the aquifer, causing fine particles to break
loose and clog the pores in which water is stored. The
capacity of the aquifer is reduced and future flushing, even if
the water-table were restored, is impaired. Already about 10
per cent of water in the coastal aquifer exceeds the national
limit for chloride salts. The figure will double within 20 years,
says Nativ. 'In my view water quality is the major problem
today, not water quantity, and it is being completely over-
looked.'

Hydrologists considering the future of Israel's water
resources fall into two camps: those who want to reduce
demand and those who call for the further development of
resources. Both are optimistic about the potential. Their criticism is of the government for not knuckling down to either
task.

Arnon Soffer, a geographer from the University of Haifa
who also works for the Israeli Foreign Office, wants to reduce
demand. He says: 'Although Israel has difficulties with water
shortages, we have flexibility. We could decide 'no more
orange orchards', give Jordan the water it needs, and direct
our energies towards, say, making computers. Jordan, which
has even greater water problems than us, has no such
options.' In the long run, Soffer believes that all countries in
the Middle East will need to forget their ambitions of agricultural self-sufficiency. Israel, he says, is likely to be the first
nation in the region to decide to cut its water use.

Expansionists, still straining to make their country green,
do not see current rainfall as the ultimate ceiling on water use.
One way to obtain a quart of irrigation water from a pint of
rainfall is to recycle more waste water. A third of Israel's
sewage, 180 million cubic metres a year, is already treated and
distributed on a dedicated pipe network to farmers and parks.
Government policy is to double that figure by the end of the
decade. The danger here is that unless the water-table in the
coastal aquifer is swiftly restored, the recycled sewage will
contaminate wells.

Other optimists look to water imports by tanker from

Turkey, desalination plants to purify seawater, or exploitation of the salty groundwaters that lie under much of the Negev. Others want to revive and develop the techniques of rainfall harvesting by which the Nabateans and later the Bedouin have survived in the desert.

I asked hydrologists what effect the Israeli water crisis might have on negotiations over the West Bank. I had expected to find a state of fervour among Israeli hydrologists – a desire to hang on at all costs to all sources of water and the land beneath which the water lay. Instead, the consensus was rather different.

Arie Issar, professor of water resources at the Desert Research Institute, looked out across a dry wadi of the Negev Desert, towards the mausoleum where David Ben Gurion, the founder of the Israeli nation, is buried. 'The idea that we could make the desert of Palestine bloom was one of the founding pillars of the Zionist movement,' he said. He shared it himself, making a career as a water prospector. But today politicians have perverted this desire in the pursuance of battles with Israel's neighbours. The nation appears to thrive on crises and the sense of being besieged. The water crisis feeds the national identity.

Issar believes that the future of water use in the Middle East lies in cooperation rather than conflict. 'Rivers such as the Jordan, as well as underground water resources, have to be shared.' But 'the agriculture people, such as the minister Rafael Eitan, believe that we can't let the Arabs have control of our water.'

The battle for water is one important element in the battle for land. One reason why Israeli politicians want to hang on to the Golan Heights is that they form part of the catchment for the Sea of Galilee, the largest single element in the Israeli water supply system. The West Bank, too, is seen as vital because it both borders the River Jordan and sits on top of the mountain aquifer. In a classic study, *Water in the Middle East*, published in the mid-1980s, Thomas Naff from the University of Pennsylvania argued that, while the gain of water was not itself a cause of the Six Day War in 1967, it 'seems to be the dominant factor' behind Israel's determination to hang on to the land gained in the war.

Israelis no longer fear losing the waters of the River Jordan. And they know (though politicians often suggest otherwise) that they do not need to control the West Bank in order to tap the water beneath it, which conveniently flows west beneath their own land. What they do fear is that, if Israel handed back the West Bank either to Jordan or to a Palestinian state, then the inhabitants, boosted by returning refugees, would immediately increase their use of the aquifer by sinking new wells.

This, so the argument goes, could threaten Israeli supplies, which account for almost 90 per cent of the water abstracted from the aquifer. But Golani, who was the local water commissioner for the West Bank from 1970 to 1978, dismisses this argument. Arab abstractions from West Bank springs and wells amount to only 1 per cent of total water use in Israel. It would take them 10 years to double that figure. He believes it would be absurd to jeopardise peace for such a trifle. 'We should be able to make arrangements to allow them to pump the water they need,' Golani says. 'Between neighbours, these are normal things.'

But when neighbours are in conflict, the smallest dispute becomes explosive. On the West Bank, access to water remains an emotive issue between Palestinians and Israelis. Since the Israeli forces arrived in 1967, they have prevented Palestinians from sinking more wells, or increasing output from existing wells for agriculture. Golani explains that because the mountain aquifer was already being overpumped, largely by the Israelis, 'I gave no permission for either Jewish or Arab settlements to drill into the aquifer.'

When geologists found a new source of fresh water at a deeper level flowing east into the Dead Sea, again only Israelis benefited. 'We said that if people want to tap this new water they could,' says Golani. 'Because drilling was expensive, only governments could afford it. That is why Israelis did it, whereas the Arabs had nobody to organise it.' Later, during the 1980s, Arab organisations such as the Nablus Municipal Water Authority, which supplies 130,000 people, have been refused permission to tap into the deep aquifer. 'They were refused because the aquifer was by then also being fully utilised,' Golani says.

In places, boreholes dug to this deep aquifer have disrupted shallow wells supplying Palestinian communities. This happened at Jiftlik in the Jordan valley, and at Bardala, where large shallow wells supply water for the town of Nablus. 'We arranged that the affected people got back as much water as they had before,' says Golani. This assurance cuts little ice with Ibrahim Matar, a Palestinian from East Jerusalem who has spent many years organising water resources for his people there. He says, 'When that happens, the Israelis end up controlling the tap.' In 1990, villagers in Jiftlik complained that Israeli soldiers cut off their water for several days in retaliation for an outbreak of stone-throwing at cars on the nearby main road. 'At least 100 villages are without a water supply on the West Bank now,' says Matar.

Meanwhile, the water from spring tunnels on former Palestinian farms trickles away because Israeli farmers will not use it. The unequal politics of water on the West Bank is one reason why Arab villages are emptying, while new Israeli settlements expand.

One more potential flashpoint for dispute over water around the borders of Israel is the River Yarmuk. The river is a tributary of the River Jordan. It flows through Syria and Jordan before crossing into Israeli-occupied territory and entering the Jordan a little south of where it leaves the Sea of Galilee. The river carries floodwaters in winter, but is virtually dry in the summer.

Thirty years ago, the US attempted to underwrite a deal on water in the Middle East under which American engineers would have helped Jordan to build a dam on the Yarmuk to capture the winter floods. In return, Jordan would have ceded to Israel the right to much of the waters of the River Jordan. It was part of an American strategy then of intervening in international water disputes that succeeded, as we saw earlier, in resolving the dispute between India and Pakistan over the tributaries of the Indus. In the Middle East, however, it failed.

Subsequently, Israel unilaterally took the waters of the River Jordan, while Jordan embarked on a plan with Syria to build a larger reservoir on the Yarmuk. The Arab plan was for the reservoir to hold both the Yarmuk's floodwaters and additional water brought by canal from the headwaters of the Jordan above the Sea of Galilee. The canal would have passed through the Golan Heights. In effect, the idea was to capture water from the Jordan above where the Israelis could get at it.

The Six Day War scotched that scheme. Israel's occupation of the Golan Heights ensured control of the Jordan's head-waters. And in the final hours of hostilities, Israeli forces occupied the site of the half-completed dam on the Yarmuk and destroyed it.

By the early 1990s, there was renewed talk of a 164-metre dam on the Yarmuk, quixotically to be called the Unity Dam. The World Bank, at US prompting, again offered to provide loans to help poverty-stricken Jordan build the dam – provided that Israel agreed to the plan. This agreement was necessary because for a few kilometres the Yarmuk flows through Israel, which has seized the opportunity to put some of the river's water into a pipeline and take it to the Sea of Galilee. Israeli ministers refused to allow the Unity Dam to go ahead, threatening to destroy any dam built by Arabs in defiance of their wishes.

That position may change. Soffer decries his government's belligerent tactics over the Yarmuk: 'Jordan is desperately short of water, despite having imported highly efficient irrigation technology. In my view, we could give 20 million cubic metres of water to Jordan without difficulty. It is not worth fighting about.'

Few nations anywhere in the world are as short of water as Jordan. It consumes only a fifth as much water per head of population as Israel. Deprived of the waters of the River Jordan, half its water comes from dams on a collection of short rivers and wadis that drain into the Jordan valley. The rest comes from rain captured on hillsides and from underground supplies, many of which are heavily overused. The water-table beneath the capital Amman, where half the Jordanians live, was falling by three metres per year during the 1980s. And at least one of its precious rivers, the Zarqa, is seriously polluted by sewage and industrial effluent from

Amman. In 1991, polluted water in the Zarqa accumulated behind the King Talal Dam, the main source of water for the East Ghor Canal, which distributes water to farms along the Jordan valley. The dam distributed toxic water to the fields of the Jordan valley, where it damaged vegetable crops worth $100 million – a tragedy for a country at the end of its economic and hydrological tether.

Professor Elias Salameh, a water researcher at the University of Jordan, fears the worst unless the region finds relief from its water crisis. 'Sometime between 1995 and 2005,' he says, 'unless consumption patterns change, there is a high probability that Israel, Jordan and the West Bank will face such progressively worsening water shortages [that there will be] conflict.' War is likely, but not inevitable, he believes. 'The obvious way to avoid conflict would be to restructure the economies of the adversaries so as to alter present patterns of consumption. But deeply entrenched ideological, symbolic and security considerations make the necessary political decisions virtually impossible in both Israel and Jordan at present.' In other words, he feels that fixations with greening the desert and attaining national self-sufficiency in food must be jettisoned.

Among the technocrats – the hydrologists, geographers and engineers – on both sides of this looming conflict, there is a growing consensus that the fundamental problem is not a water shortage so much as a failure of politicians to accept a world of finite water resources and the need to live within their hydrological means. Those at any rate were the hopes of many poised in early 1992 to begin serious negotiations on water at the Middle East peace talks. If these new realists win the argument, then the chances for an outbreak of peace in the region will be that much greater. If Israel cooperates in the construction of the Unity Dam and provides some water to revive the River Jordan, Jordan may accept that some part of that river's flow will continue to enter the National Water Carrier. Equally, a settlement about water would have to be at the heart of any resolution of the 'Palestinian question' on the West Bank.

And Israeli negotiators suggested that within weeks they

could connect 70,000 Palestinians in the Gaza Strip, where local aquifers are so overpumped that they are filling with seawater, to the National Water Carrier.

The one certainty is that Israel will have to concede water as well as the land it occupied in 1967, if it wants to live in peace with its neighbours. 'In the final analysis,' says Salameh, 'without cooperation on water, there will be neither settlement of the Palestinian problem nor peace in the Middle East.'

25

THE WATERS OF BABYLON

O thou river, who didst bring forth all things; when the great
Gods dug thee out, they set prosperity upon thy banks.

Ancient Babylonian text on the Euphrates

If water wars are to be avoided, then nations must both begin
to moderate their water requirements and engage in water
diplomacy. Proposals to ease water crises in the Middle East
through diplomacy have so far been constructed round plans
for large engineering works. In the early 1980s, President
Sadat of Egypt offered to extend a canal already taking Nile
waters to the Sinai on across the border to the Negev and the
Palestinian enclave in Israel, the Gaza strip. In return for a
resolution of the Palestinian issue, he is said to have offered
Israel 400 million cubic metres of water each year from the
canal. Coincidentally, this is the same amount of water as the
annual Israeli 'take' from the River Jordan. Water diplomats
dreamed that, one day, Israel's National Water Carrier could
begin at the Nile, and Jordan could get its river back. But the
talks foundered in acrimony.

During the 1980s, American engineers drew up a $1.5
billion plan to take water from the Euphrates in Iraq and
pump it west to Amman. That plan, too, has trickled into the
sand.

The waters of Lebanon may be the joker in the pack. This
most ravaged of Middle Eastern nations, lying between Israel,
Syria and Jordan, probably has more water than any of them.
Joyce Starr, an American academic who now organises high-
level conferences on water, believes that here, too, lies a key
that could unlock peace in the region:

Compared with its neighbours, Lebanon has plentiful water resources, which could be shared. Its numerous rivers and underground systems are reliably recharged from ample precipitation, especially snow in the mountains. A national water engineering and management system could turn Lebanon into a lucrative Middle East water haven, were there the vision and stability to realise it. Instead the country is crippled by water shortages ... farmlands neglected by lack of irrigation water, and pipelines and aquifers severely damaged by civil war.

Rivers awaiting exploitation, she says, include the River Orontes which rises in the Lebanon, before flowing north through Syria's coastal strip and on into Turkey. The river has watered fields since antiquity. The world's largest waterwheel, the 40-metre Mohammadieh Noria wheel, built in Roman times, is one of a number of creaking wooden wheels that still lift water into aqueducts at the Syrian town of Hama on the Orontes.

The main waterway through Lebanon is the Litani River, which flows south through the hilly heart of the country, reaching the sea near Tyre. Arabs have repeatedly accused Israel of using its occupation of southern Lebanon to capture some of the flow of the Litani River and divert it into the headwaters of the Jordan, though while much of the river is under heavy Israeli guard, there is no hydrological evidence that they have done so.

Projects to harness rivers such as the Litani and the Orontes all require outside investment, probably from bodies such as the World Bank and Western government aid agencies. There is no chance of such cash without a peace agreement in the region. Thus the stakes are raised: without political peace in the region, economies will increasingly be crippled by water shortages. With peace, the scene could be transformed.

Nobody has yet gone to war over water in the Middle East, though it almost happened in April 1975, during a three-way dispute between Iraq, Syria and Turkey over the waters of the Euphrates. For thousands of years, the Euphrates has been manipulated by human civilisations, but nobody had

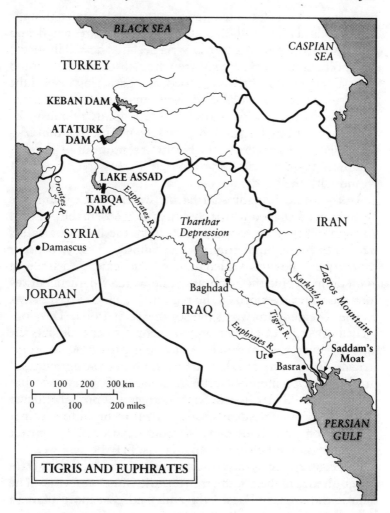

TIGRIS AND EUPHRATES

attempted to halt its flow until 1975, when both Turkey and Syria tried to. As spring snowmelt in the Anatolian hills swelled the river on its journey towards the Iraqi plains, Turkey plugged the flow to fill the reservoir behind its recently completed Keban Dam. And, downstream, Syria captured more of the water to help fill its own giant reservoir on the Euphrates, Lake Assad, at Tabqa.

When the river crossed the Syrian border into Iraq it was

reduced to a fifth of its average flow. Baghdad claimed that the livelihoods of three million of its farmers were threatened, and mobilised troops against Syria. Syria declared herself innocent and pointed to Turkey, but then Iraq threatened to bomb Tabqa dam in order to release the water gathering behind the dam in Lake Assad. Only Saudi Arabian intervention defused the crisis, by persuading Syria to make a 'goodwill' release of water. Afterwards Iraq and Syria agreed unofficially that Iraq is entitled to 60 per cent of the Euphrates' flow out of Turkey, and Syria to 40 per cent. But that left Turkey free to do as it would with the headwaters.

Talks about formally sharing the waters of the Euphrates have dragged on inconclusively since the 1960s. In the political vacuum, Turkey has attempted to take the hydrological, if hardly the moral, high ground. The country where 90 per cent of the river's flow rises has launched a scheme for a series of giant dams to plug the Euphrates, and which will turn Turkey into the water overlord of the region.

The scheme is known as the Southeast Anatolian Development Project, and, apart from any geopolitical ends, has the aim of generating hydroelectricity and providing water to irrigate 16,000 square kilometres and double the agricultural production of remote and rebellious eastern Turkey, which is inhabited largely by Kurds. Such a target will probably never be reached, but President Ozal's target, of providing 50 per cent of Turkey's electricity through hydroelectric power generated on the Euphrates and Tigris, may be achieved.

The centrepiece of the project, putting even the Keban Dam in the shade, is the 184-metre Ataturk Dam near Urfa. The dam is the sixth bulkiest ever built and cost more than $3 billion, making it easily the largest single investment ever made in Turkey. Together with the Keban and Karakaya dams upstream, Ataturk creates a cascade of reservoirs that can hold almost 90 cubic kilometres, three years' flow of the Euphrates. The dams are partly intended to 'solve' the Kurdish problem in the region by bringing prosperity to an undeveloped region. But so far they have had exactly the opposite effect, requiring the 'relocation' of more than 40,000 Kurds to make way for the Ataturk reservoir alone. As dam construction proceeded, archaeologists attempted to rescue relics from some of the earliest buildings ever uncovered, including what may be the world's oldest temple, built 10,000 years ago near Urfa at Nevali Cori, one of the world's earliest towns.

The construction of the Ataturk Dam, like the Keban before it, has also been a source of international tension. In 1986, a decade after the crisis with Iraq, Turkey claimed to have uncovered a Syrian plot to blow up the Ataturk Dam and packed the construction site with soldiers. The following year, in retaliation for alleged Syrian support for Kurdish terrorists, Turkey made veiled threats to use the dam to cut the flow of the Euphrates.

Two years later, five people died when Syrian MIG fighters shot down a Turkish military plane inside Turkish airspace. The incident was widely assumed to be a product of heightened tension over the Ataturk Dam and came just before Turkey halted the Euphrates' flow once more to fill the reservoir. As the river dwindled, there were angry rumbles from the downstream nations, and Turkey restored the flow, which was in any case meagre that year because of drought.

The following year, Turkey resisted the suggestion that it should withhold Euphrates waters as a weapon against Iraq during the Gulf conflict – partly because it would have jeopardised Syria which, thanks to new alliances created by the fighting, had become a friend. After the war, Turkey agreed to guarantee a minimum flow of water over its borders into Syria, in return for undertakings that President Assad end his support for the Kurdish guerrillas.

However, that did not solve Turkey's problem with the dam. After the winter of 1990–1, Lake Ataturk was still only 20 per cent full. The stage appeared set for new arguments in succeeding years between the three nations as Turkey again attempts to fill its giant reservoir. Conflict will only intensify if the drought that has afflicted Turkey and Syria during the late 1980s persists. And it may explode when Damascus, a city without water in its taps most nights and frequently also without electricity in its pylons, starts to fill a new $2.7-billion dam that it is building on the Euphrates, upstream of Tabqa.

If both Turkey and Syria are ever able to complete their irrigation plans, they would reduce by two-thirds the amount of Euphrates water entering Iraq each year. In the summer of 1990, weeks before his invasion of Kuwait, Saddam Hussein ordered a review of a $640-million investment programme to increase Iraq's acreage of irrigated land. He feared that the Euphrates would dwindle too much to allow irrigation channels to fill.

Iraq, as an oil-rich nation, has no special need to feed itself from its own fields. But, like other Middle Eastern nations, the desire for self-sufficiency in food is strong – and the embargoes imposed during and after the Gulf conflict can only have reinforced that desire.

Iraq wants to make greater use of the Tigris, which also rises in Turkey but is much less heavily dammed upstream. It intends to spend $300 million on a scheme to divert Tigris floodwaters into Lake Tharthar. This natural depression was enlarged in ancient times to a capacity of 80 cubic kilometres as an emergency reservoir to take floods, but Saddam wants to fill the depression permanently with Tigris waters, which can then be diverted by canal to top up the Euphrates.

Despite their current antipathy, Turkey and Iraq could eventually do a deal, believes Tony Allan, Middle East water specialist at London's School of Oriental and African Studies. Turkey can offer secure water supplies and hydroelectric power from its dams; in return Iraq has oil, and dollars obtained from the sale of oil. The country with nothing to trade for water, and therefore likely to be isolated in such a deal, would be Syria.

Turkey, despite its high-handed unilateral closure of the Euphrates, talks the language of regional cooperation. 'Turkey will use its plentiful water supplies to bring peace to the region,' declared Kamran Inan, the minister in charge of the Euphrates dams, and President Ozal has enthusiastically promoted the idea of a 'peace pipeline', a vast network of pipes carrying water from Turkey and fanning out across the Middle East. The idea is to tap two lesser Turkish rivers, the Seyhan and Ceyhan, which drain into the Mediterranean, and take their waters by one pipeline to Syria and Jordan, and by a second to Saudi Arabia and the Gulf states, a distance of almost 4,000 kilometres.

The project is similar in size and cost to Libya's Great Man-made River Project. And the blueprints are the work of Brown & Root, the same American consultant engineering company that designed Gadaffi's dream. Ozal's peace pipeline would supply 15 million people – and cost $20 billion. Even so, it is no solution to the region's problems. The pipes could take at the most 2 cubic kilometres a year south, compared to the likely eventual capture by Turkey of 10 cubic kilometres from the Euphrates.

There is an intriguing military postscript to the rising tide of conflict over the management of the Euphrates. Among the ruins of the ancient Sumerian city-states on the Meso-potamian plain, satellite photographs in the mid-1980s began to reveal pictures of an extraordinary new structure. At the height of the Iran-Iraq war, the Iraqis had constructed along the border east of Basra a huge water-filled trench. It was 50 kilometres long and around a kilometre wide, and had a 10-kilometre-wide lake at one end.

The trench filled with water from the Shatt-al-Arab, the waterway to the sea formed where the Tigris and Euphrates join. It was three metres deep – just enough to drown a man or submerge a tank – and appeared to be a giant protective moat for Basra, Iraq's second largest city and the most vulner-able to Iranian attack. But the Iraqis also dug other trenches, leading from the lake north into the Iranian desert and south into marshes near the town of Khorramshahr. It was an extraordinary piece of civil engineering involving, according to one analyst of satellite images, Peter Fend, the excavation of 400 million cubic metres of heavy clay soil. Much of the digging was done under fire from Iranian guns. Could the moat be justified to defend Basra and Khorramshahr? It cer-tainly forced Iranian troops to make the long-predicted 1985 assault on Basra from boats in treacherous marshes, rather than across flat, dry land.

Even so, Fend believes that Saddam Hussein had a larger purpose, to gain control of two ancient rivers along the

border. The two rivers, the Karun and the Karkheh, once
watered the fields of the Sumerian state of Susa. The remains
of ancient irrigation canals today still criss-cross 10,000 square
kilometres of salt-encrusted and abandoned land. The rivers
dissipate into the sand and the old canals are silted up.
Saddam was digging his canals towards those rivers. Once the
rivers were linked to the Shatt-al-Arab, says Fend, Saddam
could have begun to wash salt from the desert badlands and,
perhaps most important, commanded their flows as a weapon
of war. He would have gained the power to control the waters
– to empty channels to allow his troops to pass and refill them
to prevent an advance by Iranian troops.

The works were never completed and Fend's ideas never
demonstrated. So far as is known, the structure was of no use
in Iraq's catastrophic war with the Allied forces in 1991. But
hydrological chaos in the marshes around Basra and Khorramshahr at the end of that war undoubtedly impeded fleeing
Iraqi troops. One press report in late February 1991 spoke of
the Allies 'attacking the few routes that pick their way
through the maze of dykes and ditches, destroying many and
altering the terrain so that maps have become useless. Barriers
have been destroyed, allowing water to flood areas and make
them impassable to mechanised military equipment, much of
which now lies abandoned in the mud.' Once again the Euphrates had the final word.

PART V

Plumbing the Planet

26

PUTTING A PRICE
ON CONSERVATION

We are not running out of water, but we are approaching the
limits of inexpensive water.

Kenneth Frederick, Resources for the Future

If ever a society was based on water it is the desert state of
California. Taken by itself it is the sixth richest economy in
the world, and much of its wealth comes from farming. 'From
one perspective,' says Chelsea Congdon of the Environmental
Defense Fund,

California's is a story of success; of the immense power of
capital, technology and politics, working together. Water
supports a $700 billion urban economy, a population of 30
million people, and one of the largest agricultural industries
in the world, worth $18 billion. California is a prize
example of the heroics of making the desert bloom through
public financing on a massive scale.

The heart of the state is the Central Valley, which extends
from north to south sandwiched between the coastal mountain strip and the higher Sierra Nevada. Here are California's
vineyards, fields of cotton, soya and sugar beet and the
gardens for a quarter of all the US's fruit and vegetables.

The first migrants came in the mid-nineteenth century gold
rush, but soon took up farming, irrigating the valley. As many
of the sparse rivers began to run dry, the farmers switched to
mining the groundwaters. By the 1930s, the wells were dry
too, and the farmers persuaded the federal government to pay
the Bureau of Reclamation to build the Central Valley Project.

This for the first time captured the headwaters of the Sacramento River, the main river in the rainy far north of the state,
behind the Shasta Dam. The dam released water downstream
when required so that it could be removed again from the
delta, and transported south into the San Joaquin valley,
which drained the arid south.

The project was on a scale which put British imperial
efforts in India in the shade, yet in the 1950s it was duplicated
by the State Water Project, which again captured Sacramento
headwaters, this time behind the Oroville Dam. Taken
together, the two projects are the largest man-made water
supply system on the planet. They made pumping water the
biggest single use of electricity in the state. Though the great
majority of the water went to farmers, their charges were
heavily subsided by the sale of electricity generated by turbines set into the dams, and by the high prices charged to the
growing number of urban water consumers.

Today, half the water that once flowed to the sea via the
delta at the head of San Francisco Bay is diverted on to the
state's fields. Most of the delta and the marshes and wetlands
of the Central Valley, which was once home to beaver, elk and
bear, have been drained and turned into prairie. The Shasta
Dam alone destroyed half the Sacramento River's salmon-
spawning grounds. Water diversion pumps in the delta are
now so powerful that sailors miles downstream claim their
boats turn round when the pumps are switched on. Hundreds
of millions of young salmon and striped bass are sucked into
the irrigation canals each year and striped bass numbers have
fallen by 75 per cent since the 1960s. As a result of the
pumping, salt water from the sea penetrates ever further into
the delta, disrupting wildlife.

Growing concern at the fate of the bay, and tightening
pockets, prompted a veto of plans in the mid-1980s to divert
yet more water into a canal that would skirt the delta entirely
and take water from the Sacramento directly south. It would
have greatly increased supply to the dry San Joaquin section
of the Central Valley.

It was in the 1980s, after this unprecedented failure of
a Californian water proposal, that the state got round to

thinking about the demand side of the water equation. Was it using its water wisely? Could farming, which by now accounted for only 3 per cent of the wealth of the state, justify taking 85 per cent of its water? Perhaps farmers should pay the full cost of their water? Perhaps, even, the environment could be protected through the abolition of subsidies and the operation of a free market in water.

On 2 June 1990, a large crowd assembled in the Nevada Desert as the local senator, Harry Reid, turned a tap that switched 30,000 cubic metres of water from the Bureau of Reclamation's 80-year-old Newlands Irrigation Project over the fence and into a neighbouring marsh, the Stillwater Wildlife Refuge.

For old timers it must have seemed as if the world had gone crazy. Newlands, named after Francis Newlands, the man who introduced the bill that established the Bureau of Reclamation, was the federal government's first big effort to make the American desert bloom. Since then, the Bureau had spent trillions of dollars of federal funds trying to reclaim water from nature and give it to farmers. Now another federal agency, the Fish and Wildlife Service, in collaboration with a private body, the Nature Conservancy, was paying good money to pump it back again.

The water, originally from the nearby Truckee River, had been bought as the first few buckets of what was to be a continuing flow to save the wetland. The 1,500-hectare oasis of bullrushes, still a key stopover for migrating bald eagles, peregrine falcons, white pelicans and others on the 'Pacific flyway', is a mere remnant of a glistening wetland that once covered 40,000 hectares of the north Nevada Desert. Drought and salty drainage from the farms killed 7 million fish in 1987.

These days, saving wildlife can attract more cash than farming the Great American Desert. For the five farmers of marginal land on the irrigation project who had agreed to sell, it was a goldmine. Ted beBraga and his colleagues reasoned that at a sale price of $250 per thousand cubic metres, they would make far more from selling the water than applying it to their poor fields to raise cattle and grow alfalfa. For David Yardas of the Environmental Defense Fund it was a 'new regime for western water'. For the first time, water diverted from rivers to irrigate fields would be turned back to nature. Some environmentalists hope it will be a model for future purchases, but others see it as an unhealthy defeat. How come, they ask, that one branch of the federal government was expensively extracting that water, selling it to farmers at a subsidised rate, so that the farmers could sell it back again to another branch of the state?

The Nature Conservancy's first idea, hatched back in the late 1970s, had been to redefine water law to keep water in rivers and natural wetlands, without giving farmers a role as well-heeled brokers. Traditional water law in the West operates according to the 'prior appropriation' principle – or first come first served. All that was required was that a claimant demonstrate that the water was utilised. In practice that has always meant removing the water from the river for some purpose. But for the first time, in 1979, the Nature Conservancy won its argument, in the state of Arizona, that a private body could claim prior appropriation for water kept in the river. Having won its right, nobody can now remove the water from the Ramsey Canyon. It is spoken for. And since then, several donations of water rights have added to the Nature Conservancy's water portfolio. However, in practice most of the water in the Colorado and other western catchments is already appropriated. Hence the Conservancy's strategy of purchasing rights from farmers in order to keep the water in the river. Sometimes the purchase is a one-off. The Conservancy's Idaho office staff once spent the night on the phone arranging the emergency purchase of 350,000 cubic metres of water from the Snake River Irrigation District. The next morning, they freed the water from a dam in order for it to rush downstream and break ice that had formed in freak cold weather. With the ice broken, fish could swim through the river, into the gullets of 500 trumpeter swans wintering on the river that had faced starvation. The Nature Conservancy's mission was accomplished.

Other purchases are for long-term projects, such as saving the Stillwater Reserve. The shake-up involved in allowing a market to develop in water rights should, in theory, ensure that the vested interests behind subsidised irrigation of marginal farms to provide crops in surplus will lose their power. Conservation of water will for the first time get a fair crack of the riparian whip. But water marketing opens up a Pandora's box for environmentalists. Once they have dipped a toe into the water market, others will follow.

There are many other claimants on the water of the Truckee River, for instance. There are two claims from local Indian communities for water. There is another wetland site, Pyramid Lake, which has shrunk drastically since the Newlands project began. Any year, the island in the middle of the lake will be connected to the mainland and its pelicans will wake up one morning to find that the coyotes who prey on them can walk across. Nowadays, nobody would agree with the claim of Congressman Newlands 90 years ago that Pyramid Lake existed 'only to satisfy the thirst of the Sun', but, even so, the thirst of the nearby towns of Reno and Sparks is likely to take precedence in the market place. They are willing and able to pay good prices. Can the market find the right balance between fish and farmer, between pelicans and Reno, between short- and long-term national benefits?

Kenneth Frederick of the Washington organisation, Resources for the Future, says: 'We are not running out of water, but we are approaching the limits of inexpensive water. The nation is approaching the limits of what can be achieved by increased supply and therefore should explore what can be done through managing demand. This means introducing marketing devices.' High prices and a market in water rights will increase efficiency and ensure that water goes to the 'high value' uses. That means, from low- to high-value farm crops and from irrigation to urban uses, he says. But he warns that unless the government is prepared to pay handsomely to preserve fish and wildlife habitats, the new world of high water prices could see conservation squeezed out once more. The 'cheap' purchases of in-stream rights in the 1990s could be relegated to a footnote in history. And the farmers, selling up to the highest bidders, could be laughing all the way to their retirement homes.

One likely conflict will be in the Yampa River valley, a

virgin upland stream that flows into the upper Colorado. These rivers are the last stronghold of several endangered fish, such as the Colorado squawfish and the razorback sucker. Nature Conservancy wants to arrange the purchase of water rights in the Yampa to protect these fish. But there is an even bigger fish in the market – a commercial company that wants to buy the rights, collect the water behind a dam and then pour it downstream for collection and sale to California. Can anybody compete with this water mail service? If the water market is opened up sufficiently in the state of Colorado to allow the sale, what price the razorback sucker?

Scott Hadly, editor of *Bay on Trial*, a newspaper on water issues published in California, asks: 'Have environmentalists created a monster?' The trouble so far as he is concerned is that everybody thought that all water with rights attached to it in the state was in use. Not so, it turns out. And a lot which used to flow unimpeded to the sea, keeping fish and environmentalists alike happy, is now being sold to the highest bidder. Enter the Yuba County Water Agency.

Back in the 1960s, when nobody much cared about such things, Yuba County built the Bullards Bay Dam on the River Yuba. Planning for expansion, it built the dam with a capacity eight times bigger than it needs even today. In the new era of water markets this extravagance has turned into a shrewd investment. During the drought of the late 1980s, the tiny county made $30 million selling its water to downstream cotton farmers. Until the precedents established by the environmentalists, that water had stayed in the river, keeping the Yuba River one of the few surviving flourishing salmon rivers left in a state once awash in salmon.

Other counties are now joining in. 'I don't mind being called a water rancher. Hell, I take pride in it,' said one director of a Sacramento water agency. It may be good economics, but suddenly water markets don't look quite such good ecology. Says Hadly: 'The rivers that these agencies ranch now literally rise and fall with the market for their water, and not because of the season.' And what does the agency want to do with its income? Why, build another dam.

27

OUT OF SIGHT ...

There were plenty of dry summers in my younger days and, do
you know, the pump never dried up, not once.

> Granny Dryden in *Postman Pat's Thirsty Day*
> by John Cunliffe

The well and the spring are two of the earliest and most
universal sources of water. Hundreds of millions of people
still rely on water leaping from rocks or hauled to the surface
in a bucket on the end of a length of rope. There have been a
few embellishments. Many communities use animals driving
treadmills to raise water from deep wells. The people of the
Levant cut holes into the hillsides to increase the flow of
springs. Most spectacularly, by tunnelling deep into the hillsides, the Iranians developed the *qanats* from springs to create
what outsiders called 'chains of wells'.

These systems all relied on gravity and muscle-power
and had their own tight limits on use that prevented over-
exploitation of the resource. Water was simply too heavy
to be mined like coal. All that changed with the adoption this
century of cheap mechanised pumps. Now, even as geologists
are learning for the first time how to map and quantify the
great reservoirs of water beneath the ground, they are being
destroyed.

There are estimated to be some 64 million cubic kilometres
of groundwaters beneath the land masses of the world.
Though most of this is out of reach, an increasing amount can
be tapped by modern pumps. Israelis in the Negev Desert, for
instance, are now extracting water from a kilometre below
the surface. Gadaffi's massive fields of wells in the Sahara will
reach down 450 metres.

Round the world, the failure of large irrigation schemes based on diversions of riverwaters is encouraging farmers to switch to groundwaters. 'Groundwaters offer an incomparably cheaper and a far more efficient and manageable source of irrigation,' says B. B. Vhora, ex-President of the Environmental Planning Committee in India, the most irrigated country in the world. Groundwater exploitation 'demands no investments whatsoever by government for its storage or transport over long distances, requires no big and inevitably corrupt bureaucracies for its management and is available exactly when, and to the extent to which, it is required by the farmer'.

The proportion of India's farmland irrigated from private tube-wells rose from nothing in the late 1950s to 27 per cent by the late 1980s. Tube-wells are cheap, conserve water by eliminating losses from reservoirs and canals, and give power back to the farmer. The problem is that they impose no limits on how much water is taken from the underground reservoir. The only limit is the power of the pump. So people with the deepest boreholes and most powerful pumps will always be able to reach water, while poorer farmers with their shallow wells are left high and dry.

At best, a crazy and increasingly expensive race takes place to keep pace with the falling water-table. At worst, the big pumps that brought the promise of ending drought finish up creating drought for millions of people. This is happening in the northern plains of Iran, where tube-wells are drying up the *qanats*. It is happening in the Thar Desert in India. And around Bombay, in the 'sugar state' of Maharashtra, tube-wells are causing a hydrological crisis.

Sugar is one of the most water-hungry of all crops. Its fields typically need to be spread with three metres of water each year. To keep sugar cane watered in arid countryside, says Jayanta Bandyopadhyay, a former ecological adviser to the Indian government, 'the sugar factories have actively supported farmers in deepening boreholes. As a result, public wells and the shallow wells belonging to small farmers have run dry.' By the end of the 1980s, as sugar production continued to grow, more than 20,000 villagers covering almost half of the state had no source of reliable drinking water and depended on tankers, while the government attempted to revive their wells by supplying stronger pumps. In regions such as this 'water development is having a severe polarising effect on rural society', says Bandyopadhyay.

Ultimately, such exploitation has no winners. The High Plains of the Midwest are part of American history. The first white settlers transformed the plains from buffalo hunting grounds into rough pasture, the land of the cowboy. Then came the plough, and the pasture became dry prairie, until the drought of the 1930s blew the soil away. Since those dust-bowl days, the soil has recovered and been transformed once more, this time into a vastly productive irrigated prairie, with more than a quarter of the nation's irrigated acreage. Most of the water for the new irrigation comes from a giant aquifer beneath the western halves of the states of Nebraska, Kansas, Oklahoma and Texas, and of eastern New Mexico and Colorado. The aquifer is known as the Ogallala, after an old Sioux nation that once hunted buffalo across the High Plains.

In the 1930s, 600 wells tapped this aquifer; half a century later, there were 150,000, watering the fields from long rotating arms. In a good year the High Plains produces three-quarters of the wheat traded on the world market. This is where the grain comes from to feed starving Africans and to restock empty Russian grain stores. But the Ogallala aquifer is fast drying out.

The statistics are brutal. Annual extractions have reached 12 cubic kilometres. Rainfall takes a hundred years to replace that amount of water. At the end of the 1980s, the amount of recoverable water in the aquifer was below 150 cubic kilometres – half the amount in the late 1970s. Wells are already running dry in Texas and Kansas. With government subsidies for farming on the decline and a world glut of grain during the late 1980s, many farmers turned off the pumps and sold up.

A corner of the American dream is dying. The sagebrush and buffalo grass are returning. There is even talk of bringing back the buffalo.

The story of the destruction of the High Plains aquifer is one that Saudi Arabia ought to consider. The Arabian desert is an unlikely place for an agricultural revolution, but during the 1980s the oil-rich desert kingdom indulged in an orgy of agricultural expansion on its own high plains, in the middle of the vast Arabian desert. It irrigated the desert with fossil groundwaters, which were laid down during the last ice age and discovered, like Colonel Gadaffi's water, during oil prospecting.

During the 1980s, the Saudi government spent $40 billion developing its farming, mostly on outrageous price subsidies. Growing wheat in Saudi Arabia, as *The Economist* remarked in mid-decade, 'makes about as much economic sense as planting bananas under glass in Alaska'. But by the end of the decade, Saudi Arabia was a net exporter of wheat.

While the Saudis may have petro-dollars to burn on such projects, they do not have the water. A nation with no permanent lakes or rivers of any kind, Saudi Arabia relies on groundwaters for more than 80 per cent of its water. The much-vaunted desalination works, on which the country has spent $10 billion to make seawater drinkable, provide about 7 per cent. But in the main area of fertile soils northwest of Riyadh in the state of Qassim, groundwaters are the only source.

In a country where outspokenness is not taken kindly, water specialists have voiced their alarm about the state of the nation's water supplies. Abdulla Ali Al-Ibrahim, an economist at the King Fahd University of Petroleum and Minerals at Dahran, says that during the 1980s, the amount of water poured on to Saudi fields increased almost sixfold to more than ten cubic kilometres, 90 per cent of it 'non-renewable'. Half the water went on to the wheat fields of Qassim.

This cannot go on, he says. At the current rate of water use, 'groundwater resources will be exhausted within 77 years'. And with abstractions set to double again inside two decades, the water could run out within 30 years.

Farmers can already see the signs. Beneath the new prairies of central and southern Qassim, the water-table in the Saq aquifer has fallen in places by 45 metres. Almost all the natural springs in the fertile Wadi Fatima have dried up.

Along the country's long Gulf coastline, water is turning
saline as giant irrigation pumps suck fresh water from pores in
the rocks and seawater rushes in to take its place. Near the
Arabian Sea, the hourly yield of some wells ebbs and flows
with the tides.

So far, the authorities have shown a sublime lack of
concern. Virtually no farmer pays a cent for his water. It
either comes free from the government, or from wells on the
farmer's own land. Every farmer 'has unlimited rights to
extract as much water as he wishes without being liable for
the damage', says Al-Ibrahim.

The result is waste and pollution. In theory, a country that
has no long leaking canals, no large reservoirs that evaporate
in the hot sun, and enough money to buy state-of-the-art
irrigation equipment, should be able to make maximum use of
its water. Yet more than two-thirds of the water pumped to
the surface to irrigate fields of alfalfa and wheat or groves of
date palms never reaches plant roots, but is lost to evaporation. Few Saudi farms operate sprinkler or drip irrigation
systems of the kind common in Israel, Jordan and other arid
countries. Most fields are simply flooded and the sun captures
most of the water. Throughout Qassim, waterlogged soils are
turning saline.

If anything, the wastage of water is even worse in the cities.
The gleaming desert capital, Riyadh, is floating on a saline
swamp. A study by the consultants Dames & Moore found
that two out of the three cubic kilometres of water pumped
each year to the city from distant wells goes straight back into
the ground, where it is corroding the foundations of modern
new steel and concrete buildings. It leaks from cracked water
mains, cesspits, irrigation channels, sewers and overloaded
drains. Far from germinating the seedcorn for prosperity after
the oil runs out, the Saudis are destroying one of the few assets
that they may have left by the second half of the twenty-first
century.

Today, right across the Middle East, more and more governments are turning to underground waters to sustain their
ambitions to 'green the desert' and become self-sufficient in

food. Groundwaters are currently where the 'smart money' is in the water business, both in arid regions and elsewhere. The reasons are clear enough. While most of the best sites for large dams have been used up, many abundant groundwaters lie untapped. While it may take a decade or more, and billions of dollars, to bring a large dam on stream, well-fields can be developed in easy stages, with each well yielding income to build the next. So, wherever the need is for water rather than to generate hydroelectricity, groundwaters are in favour.

The 1990s will be a boom decade for water prospectors. Arie Issar is Israel's top water prospector, the former head of hydrogeology at the Geological Survey of Israel. He has charted a series of springs across the Sinai-Negev peninsula. They start at Ayun Musa near Suez, and feed a classic oasis of marsh, reeds and date palms, then continue through Nakhel in central Sinai to springs south of the Dead Sea. Moses drank from these springs during the escape of the tribes of Israel from Egypt. 'A well-guided traveller in ancient times could depend on a reliable supply of water for his party and their pack animals over most of the route from Egypt to the Fertile Crescent,' Issar says.

The springs are where a giant aquifer holding as much as 200 cubic kilometres of water comes up for air. By tapping it, he says, 'Egypt and Israel could develop large areas of the desert into agricultural regions.' It might eventually solve the Jordanian water crisis, too.

This 'fossil water' was laid down when the Negev and Sinai received much more rainfall than today. But Issar has no compunction about using a water source that nature will never replace:

> If nature has been kind enough to fill up reservoirs of water beneath the Negev over tens of thousands of years, why shouldn't we use it? We need a psychological breakthrough to approach water like any other commodity that can be mined – such as coal or oil. By the time it runs out, we will have other sources.'

The problem in exploiting these waters will be cost, especially of pumping. Israel's national water planners believe that, delivered to the farms around Tel Aviv, Issar's Negev groundwaters would be as expensive as desalinated water. But Issar hopes that novel technologies might come to the rescue. One might be a recreation of a high-tech version of the *qanat*. He proposes driving galleries for a kilometre or more into the water-bearing sandstones along the rift valley south of the Dead Sea, so that the water could flow out of the hillsides without expensive pumping.

The latest technique for finding underground water, a kind of space-age version of water divining, is the analysis of aerial photographs from planes and satellites. Remote sensing, say its protagonists, could do for groundwater prospecting what large dams did for the exploitation of rivers. Robert Bisson, an oceanographer before becoming founder and chairman of BCI Geonetics, a high-tech American company specialising in water prospecting, claims that: 'If the world had spent as much money on developing groundwater resources as we have in the past with surface water, the return on investment would be far greater.'

An assessment by BCI of groundwater potential for a large area of northern Somalia, conducted in the late 1980s, relied on old aerial photographs taken by a British RAF plane and found in a decaying heap on the floor of a storage shed in the city of Hargeisa in Somalia. The pictures yielded enough information for Egyptian hydrogeologist and BCI associate Farouk El-Baz to locate potential sites for wells. And when El-Baz took a Somali government drilling team into the field, five wells yielded around 6,000 litres of water a minute – 'reportedly the most water ever discovered in the region, despite decades of searches by teams from around the world'. Then the drilling rig broke down, the drilling team went home, and the region around Hargeisa, where the test drilling took place, became the centre of a violent rebellion by the independence movement of northern Somalia. Refugees fled and within two years were dying in drought refugee camps over the border in Ethiopia. A few more months of peace might, just might, have brought secure supplies of water to a region that is now empty and waterless.

Such tragedies are being played out all over Africa. A

similar plan to exploit the waters of the Red Sea Hills in parched Sudan has also fallen foul of politics and acute cash shortages. Groundwater prospecting, as much as dam-building, requires peace.

The big prize for the 1990s and beyond for men like El-Baz looks like being the fossil waters from beneath the Sahara and the Middle East. Gadaffi's foray into the desert may be only the beginning. Six thousand years ago, the world's largest desert was a savanna grassland filled with wildlife and crossed by great rivers. The landscape has changed as the region's climate has dried out, but much of the rain that fell then is stored in the pores of sandstone rocks that form giant slabs a kilometre or more thick deep underground. The water emerges only at a few coastal springs and at oases.

The Sahara is underlain by seven separate aquifers, from Morocco to the Nile and Algiers to Lake Chad. They contain an estimated 15,000 cubic kilometres of water. The oldest water has been under the Qattara depression in Egypt for 25,000 years, though new water still reaches the aquifer after rainfalls on mountains in the heart of the desert – such as the remote Tibesti mountains in northern Chad.

Libya's giant pipelines will tap two of the smaller aquifers. This has created concern among Libya's neighbours, especially Egypt and Sudan. They read the scientific evidence that the aquifers are linked to each other and note that Gadaffi's hydrological ambitions were raised during the 1980s when his army attempted to capture the remote north of Chad, which contains the Tibesti mountains, source of most of the new water entering the Saharan aquifers.

The Tibesti mountains are more than 3,000 metres high – enough to coax out any moisture left in monsoon rain-clouds after their long trek inland from the West African coast. Many Arab geologists are convinced that rain from the Tibesti mountains may be substantially topping up the Saharan aquifer. Their European and American counterparts disagree. The American hydrogeologist Robert Ambroggi estimated that around four cubic kilometres entered the aquifers each year, but Moid Ahmad, a professor of hydrology at Ohio University in the US whose research is quoted by Gadaffi's staff in defence of their project, puts the figure at 25 cubic kilometres. Unfortunately, the argument cannot be settled yet because there are no rain gauges in the Tibesti mountains.

Ahmad argues that the rainless land of Libya could 'in the near future be an exporter of food'. And if other countries joined in, 'the Sahara can produce 5 million tonnes of wheat each year . . . The need for these kinds of developments is now critical and people throughout Africa cry out to be fed daily.' European hydrologists, by their reluctance to argue for the exploitation of groundwaters, had 'influenced the politics of water from Morocco to Iran. Millions of cubic metres of water are discharging into the sea and evaporating from oases.'

El-Baz has set out to change attitudes through remote sensing. Satellite pictures today are revealing the locations of the ancient Saharan rivers, which could be the best places to find water. In late 1990, Egypt announced the first results of a new campaign of test drilling for water in the Western Desert, with drilling sites chosen by El-Baz after examination of satellite images. A single test-well in the desert west of Aswan, where an ancient Saharan river may have joined the Nile, had discovered enough water to irrigate 800 square kilometres for 200 years. Egypt aims to triple its groundwater abstractions to eight cubic kilometres a year, says Kamal Hefny, director of the Institute of Groundwater Research in Cairo. He hopes eventually to harness the desert winds to turn wind pumps to raise the water.

However much water may be lurking beneath the Sahara, and however much of it is replaceable, matters little while countries waste their water so wantonly. Egypt's wasteful irrigation of its 'new lands' beside the Nile delta has nullified many of the gains from the High Dam, and the country seems set to repeat the same errors in its irrigation projects using underground water round the oases of the Western Desert. El-Baz feels unable to defend his government on this. 'In the Western Desert, I often encounter rice fields,' he says. 'Rice is a crop that should never be grown in such an area, because it needs 6,000 times its own weight in water for a successful harvest.'

Likewise Libya has squandered the aquifers beneath its coastal farms during the past two decades. That is why it is resorting to the desert to provide a new source of irrigation. But there are no signs that it has improved its farming techniques to make better use of the new, expensive water. Says Issar, 'Gadaffi should be building training colleges, not pipelines.'

By separating water resources into two categories, surface and underground, water planners are perpetuating the follies of the old dam-builders who believed that rivers should be treated as if they were simple water conduits. In the real world, rivers interact with the land, through their floodplains, and with underground aquifers. Many rivers start as mountain springs, leaping out of the rocks. And most rivers constantly feed water into aquifers beneath their floodplains. Many engineers now want actively to manage this process. They want to use the aquifers as underground artificial reservoirs to store river-water.

Ancient farmers in the deserts have always done this, building check dams and stone walls that hold flash floods on the land for long enough to soak down, replenishing wells as well as dampening fields. But it is a largely new idea for European and American engineers. In Britain, the high flows of the River Severn are diverted during the winter to fill sandstones in Shropshire. In summer, the water is pumped back out into the river to maintain dry-season flows. Similarly, Israel keeps its National Water Carrier busy in winter, when demand for its irrigation water is low, by applying its water to sand dunes and pouring it down wells in an effort to recharge the country's two main aquifers. The same thing happens on a larger scale still in California, where the canals of the Central Valley spend their winters recharging the valley's aquifers ready for summer irrigation.

Juggling water between the surface and underground could be a realistic solution to a number of major hydrological problems round the world. Aquifers might be used to refill the Aral Sea, for instance. Abduvali Abduazizov, head of the Nature Research Centre in Uzbekistan, says that there is ample water in aquifers within the large Aral Sea basin. Most of the water percolated from the sea when it was much larger. The water was tapped by local villages before Commissar Cotton sealed their wells. But the wells could be reopened and water pumped into canals draining into the sea. Abduazizov's plan would certainly be cheaper than hijacking the rivers of northern Siberia. There are huge amounts of water too beneath that other diminished inland sea basin, the Lake Chad basin, most of it out of reach of traditional wells but within the range of modern pumps.

Roger Revelle, one of the world's leading environmental scientists for several decades, has argued that artificial recharge could be used to even out the flow in the River Ganges, alleviating monsoon floods while increasing dry-season flows. Already during the summer monsoon, as the swollen Ganges pours across its floodplain, it deposits huge amounts of water in aquifers beneath the plain. In so doing the aquifers act like a giant reservoir, moderating the floods that reach Bangladesh. Peasant farmers have for hundreds of years sunk wells to tap this water. Revelle's idea was to make this aquifer work much harder. He proposed building a series of long diversion barrages on the Ganges deliberately to flood fields containing thousands of tube-wells. During the monsoon, the tube-wells would force-feed the aquifer with water from the river, then at the end of each dry season the pumps would be put into reverse to pump water out of the aquifer and keep flow in the Ganges high.

Some hydrologists point out that irrigation projects that divert water from rivers into fields unintentionally recharge aquifers, too. In Pakistan, the intensive irrigation of the Indus valley has produced so much seepage from canals and fields that it deposits 17 cubic kilometres a year into this underground reservoir, double the amount provided from natural sources, such as rainfall and rivers. A century of irrigation has filled the aquifer with 400 cubic kilometres. That is one reason why fields are becoming waterlogged. But far from being dismayed, says Robert Ambroggi, Pakistan should use this resource to the full. All the country has to do is recognise the natural wealth beneath its farmers' feet and start pumping. One calculation suggests that water pumped up from the aquifer costs only a fifth as much to deliver to fields as water collected behind a dam.

Of course, the quality of the water may not be as good as river-water. And somewhere along the line the salt from field drains still has to be removed from the fields. But, says Robert Ambroggi, 'Seepage from irrigation canals is one of the best techniques for artificially recharging groundwater reservoirs on a large scale.'

28

GRAND DESIGNS

Man's first duty is to his species. We should obey the Biblical command to go forth and subdue the Earth.

Professor Otto Hittmaier, in keynote address to International Commission on Large Dams, Vienna, 1991

The River Colorado in the US is the world's most heavily used river. Every drop of water is allocated, and anything left behind by the upstream states is snapped up by thirsty Californians. It provides around 17 cubic kilometres of water each year to the American West. But within 50 years, the annual flow of the artery of the American West could be cut in half by the greenhouse effect.

At the beginning of the 1990s, the world's governments seem unsure whether to continue with ever larger water engineering projects, or to turn back, daunted by their cost, their long gestation periods, their growing unpopularity and their unpredictable environmental side-effects. There have been ever stronger calls for them to invest instead in groundwater development, in small-scale 'greener' projects with faster completion times, and in measures to make more efficient use of both water and electricity. But there are also calls to restart the planning of megaprojects. And first among the reasons given is the fear of permanent drought raised by the looming spectre of the greenhouse effect.

Many climate researchers predict that the consequences of the greenhouse effect for water supply will in many places far outweigh any impact from warming itself. There appears to be an amplifier effect ready to operate in every stage of the water cycle that will convert modest temperature changes into massive alterations in river flows.

Current computer simulations suggest that, with the burning of fossil fuels on a continuing rise, there will be an average global warming of maybe 2 degrees Celsius by around the middle of the next century. This extra heat will intensify the water cycle in all its facets. More water will evaporate from the oceans and form more turbulent storm clouds. Average rainfall round the world will be as much as 10 per cent higher. But the increased rainfall will be concentrated in coastal regions – and especially in the monsoon lands of Asia.

Away from the coastal regions, there will often be less rain. This is because the air systems that create the large deserts in the centres of land masses such as the Sahara, Kalahari and Great American, will enlarge. The deserts themselves will grow, invading higher latitudes. What's more, a hotter world will evaporate water from the surface of the Earth more quickly than at present, and increased evaporation will be greatest where rainfall decreases and the parched soils are exposed to unremitting sunlight. The combined impact could be immense, causing desertification in middle latitudes right round the world.

So the Sahara Desert seems likely to spread: maybe it already has. The greenhouse effect could be the reason for the Sahel drought, which has now lasted almost uninterrupted for more than two decades. The arid lands of former Soviet central Asia may also dry out, adding to the distress of the Aral Sea. And so will the American Midwest.

In 1986, Syukuro Manabe and Richard Wetherald of Princeton University, New Jersey, home of one of the top five computer models of world climate, startled their colleagues when they warned of possible drastic reductions in the amount of moisture in soils in many regions. They calculated that soil moisture in the greenhouse world 'would be reduced in summer over extensive regions of the middle and high latitudes, such as the American Great Plains, western Europe, northern Canada and Siberia'. A predicted reduction in rainfall in these places of 15–20 per cent could translate into a 50 per cent reduction in soil moisture over wide areas. Drier, sunnier summers would leave soils to bake. More than that, in many cooler areas winter snows would melt much earlier than now. While the snow is on the ground, there is no loss of moisture to evaporation, but if the snow disappears even a few weeks earlier, soil would dry out early in the growing season and never recover. In most temperate regions, including Europe, drought conditions could become semi-permanent. Headlines about rivers reduced to a trickle, reservoirs empty and water-tables dropping, which we now see at the end of a hot summer, could be on the front pages in mid-June most years.

Other American researchers have reached similar conclusions. Peter Gleick of the University of California at Berkeley looked at the likely consequences for the Sacramento River basin in northern California. The river provides more than a quarter of the state's water, including most of the flow in the aqueducts that distribute more than 120 cubic kilometres of water a year to Central Valley, the world's largest and most expensive irrigation system. Gleick predicts that within 50 years the amount of moisture contained in soils in the Sacramento basin may fall by more than 40 per cent. Combine this with similar losses in the River Colorado, the second great river supplying California, and the future for the vineyards and orange orchards, corn fields and tomato groves of California and much of the American West does not look good. Californians may soon be looking back with affection to the droughts of the late 1980s as a time of hydrological plenty.

These predictions remain controversial. Some researchers believe that there will be more rain and snow in winter and that this will recharge aquifers and reservoirs, compensating for summer losses. By and large, the climate modellers are pessimists, while the agricultural researchers, who believe they know more about the soil than the weathermen, are optimists. But even they agree that crops will need extra irrigation. They don't say where the extra water to fill the irrigation canals will come from. The answer is likely to be a new generation of massive water-transfer projects.

Few governments have come to grips with such analyses. One that has got furthest is Australia, where the hydrological impact of the greenhouse effect has become a serious domestic political issue. Leading politicians have opened conferences and attended seminars on the likely impact of changing climate on Australian life – on coral reefs and ski resorts, bush fires and kangaroo migrations, but especially on irrigated agriculture.

Top of the agenda is the southern half of the Australian continent, which is currently still buffeted by friendly rain systems. But one predicted result of the greenhouse effect is to divert those storms south away from the continent. It has been happening periodically over the past decade, making farmers nervous and causing the Water Authority of Western Australia to predict a decline in rainfall of 20 per cent in the southern half of its domain by the year 2040. That will translate into a 45 per cent cut in river flows, the Authority says. Reservoirs would empty, wells and boreholes would run dry. The state's expenditure on building dams and operating its water supply system would have to treble to keep up.

In 1988, engineers published plans to continue irrigating the state's fields by laying a $8 billion pipeline all the way from Perth to Lake Argyle in the Kimberley mountains of the north, a distance of 2,000 kilometres. Western Australia's Minister for Water Resources, Ernie Bridge, suggested that Adelaide in South Australia might like to share the cost and build its own extension. Meanwhile, on the other side of the country in New South Wales, another state afflicted by recent drought, the authorities predict that the amount of land under irrigation in the state might have to be slashed by three-quarters unless new sources of water can be found.

On these kinds of calculations, dozens of superdams and several entire national economies would appear to be under threat. The uncertainties in future water supply created by the greenhouse effect may soon lead many nations to consider a new generation of superdams, canals and pipelines to bring water to cities and parched fields.

Nobody knows if the Sahel drought of the 1980s was a direct consequence of the greenhouse effect. But the emptying of Lake Nasser behind the High Dam at Aswan on the Nile during that decade, which brought Egypt within a few weeks of having to shut down its hydroelectricity turbines, points to the dangers. The reservoir emptied because flows fell in the Blue Nile, a change predicted by several climatic models.

Likewise, the state of European water supplies is beginning to cause concern. In 1990, French farmers sabotaged pumps delivering water to cities, the Italian olive crop failed, water only reached taps in Istanbul for four hours a day, and the Greek authorities raised water prices by 300 per cent in an effort to reduce demand. Water tables fell to record lows in England. There was a growing realisation that such scenes, too, may be part of the greenhouse effect.

Fear of climate change is also worrying California and Israel, which have both experienced damaging droughts. Suddenly, nobody trusts the rain to come any more, and already engineers with big projects in mind are reaching for climate change as another argument in favour of their projects. The British consultants Mott Macdonald in a report to the World Bank and UN Development Programme, *Sub-Saharan Africa: A Hydrological Assessment*, warned: 'Global warming is predicted to increase aridity over most of the African continent.'

The impact will not be uniform. Some climate modellers suggest that in northern Africa the average flows of the Niger, the Chari, the Senegal and the Volta and the Blue Nile might all *increase* because of their more monsoon-type rainfall. On the other hand, flows in the upper and middle reaches of all these rivers, being in the continental interior, might diminish. Flow in the Zambezi is among the most likely to decrease, as the Kalahari Desert spreads north. A study by the International Institute for Applied Systems Analysis predicts a 20-per-cent reduction in inflow to the Kariba reservoir. This could happen just as competition for the river's ill-used waters hots up.

Elsewhere in the world, modellers predict reduced river flows for the Yangtze and Yellow rivers in China, raising particular problems in the already water-short northern Chinese plain. There is bad news too for the rivers flowing into the Aral Sea, and for the Tigris, Euphrates and Danube. But the modellers expect increases in other great rivers: the Mekong, for instance, and the Ganges and Brahmaputra. Rise or fall, the changes will be used as evidence for large man-made structures, though many such interventions could well make matters worse.

Engineers will insist that predicted increases in flow along both the Ganges and Brahmaputra make more urgent the building of flood embankments in Bangladesh. But equally, it can be argued that the chances of embankments successfully taming these mighty rivers is reduced, and that money should be spent on protecting people in ways that would be more effective.

Many existing dams will be undermined both physically and economically by flood or drought. But new ones will fare little better, since the one thing that climatologists are certain about is that the local impacts of global climate change are beyond their capacity to predict with any accuracy. Almost every prediction ever made about the risks of flooding and dam failures and drought – all the claims about droughts that can only happen every thousand years, and once-in-a-million-years floods – should be thrown away. They have no meaning any more.

The case for dams on the Mekong will be strengthened in engineers' eyes. The river will offer more hydroelectric potential, they will say. There will be higher monsoon flows to be held back for winter harvests, and greater flood risks that can be abated. But, in practice, the uncertainties involved in the predictions make it foolhardy to build large inflexible structures.

The proponents of the Three Gorges Dam will say that the perils of a wilder and wider Yangtze mean their dam must be built. They will be silent on the greater risks that such a river poses to the structure of their dam. Designed to withstand a once-in-a-thousand-years flood in the 1990s, it may be unable to cope with a once-in-a-hundred-years flood by 2040. Certainly, nobody will have a way of calculating what those risks are.

The threat of conflict over rivers and dams will also grow. Turkey may tell itself that if flow in the Euphrates is to diminish, more dams are needed to ensure the success of its irrigation plans in Anatolia. But that would give another turn to the ratchet that may yet lead to a water war between Turkey and its downstream neighbours, Syria and Iraq, over the river.

One of the central lessons of this book has been that where men try to harness rivers with dams and other giant structures, they create conflict. The uncertainties of the greenhouse effect can only worsen those conflicts. Low flows in the Nile make Egypt's sabres rattle, a sound heard all across East Africa. But a thirsty South Africa will also be a more dangerous neighbour. Lesotho knows that well already. So do Israel's neighbours.

One of the craziest schemes mooted during the era of European imperial expansion in the nineteenth century was to flood part of the basin of the River Zaire, the world's second largest river, to form a Congo Sea. The idea was that the sea would eventually spill over into the Chad basin of the Sahara to the north, providing unlimited water to irrigate the desert. Suddenly, a century later, a revised version is being promoted by the nations around Lake Chad.

The lake is today a pathetic remnant of its former self, a victim of more than two decades of drought in the Sahel, accentuated by ill-starred dams and irrigation schemes. There is a growing concern that the drought may be part of the shifting climatic patterns caused by the greenhouse effect – and therefore could prove permanent.

Now, rather as the Soviet Union's engineers proposed to refill the Aral Sea by diverting Siberian rivers, so Nigerians have a similar vision for Lake Chad. They are proposing a capture of part of the flow of the great River Zaire in order to divert water north, across the Central African Republic and into the headwaters of the River Chari, which drains into Lake Chad. It would, claims J. Umolu of Nigeria's National Electric Power Authority, provide 'a final solution to the problem of drought in west central Africa'.

It sounds preposterous. One can only guess at the ecological havoc that might be caused by the transfer into the Saharan fringes of the plants, fish, insects and diseases of a rainforest river. But the distances involved are not great. The entire route from the River Zaire to Lake Chad is about 1,300 kilometres, the length of the Soviet Union's Karakum Canal. And the River Fafa, one of the tributaries of the Chari, rises only 150 kilometres from Elephant Falls on the Ubangi, one of the main tributaries of the River Zaire. Linking these two rivers, says Umolu, could form the first phase of the project, with extra water transferred later from the upper reaches of the Zaire itself into the Ubangi. Eventually, says Umolu, pumps could divert a third of the flow of the Zaire at Bumba into the Chad basin.

The proposal remains a gleam in relatively few eyes. No detailed feasibility studies have been done. But it has backing among officials in both the electricity and agricultural bureaucracies in Nigeria, as well as from the Lake Chad Basin Commission, an inter-governmental body overseeing the lake at its 1988 conference. In 1989, President Mobutu of Zaire added his backing. Zaire sees the project as a way of attracting funds to finance hydroelectric projects, which could be generated at holding reservoirs along the route of the water transfer. The scheme is the kind of project that could attract wider support if the lake continues to empty and Sahelians once more begin to starve as they did in the early 1970s and early 1980s. The Japanese, for instance, might see it as one of a portfolio of 'megaprojects' for economic development in the Third World that they want to promote in the early years of the next century.

The scheme currently exists in two forms: the Nigerian proposal described above, and a yet more ambitious plan drawn up by an Italian consulting firm, Bonifica, and known as Transaqua. 'We must not be afraid of thinking big,' says the company's prospectus for the project.

The Zaire basin is a vast saucer-shaped area, around which the River Zaire and its main tributaries circle anti-clockwise, before tumbling down into the Atlantic from the saucer's most westerly point. The Nigerian scheme would pump the waters of one tributary, the Ubangi, up and over the northern rim of the saucer. The Transaqua plan would construct a giant navigable canal travelling round the rim of the saucer for 2,400 kilometres, starting in the east near Burundi, barely a stone's throw from the headwaters of the Nile. On its way round the fringes of the rainforest, the Transaqua canal would intercept numerous tributaries of the River Zaire, before heading across the sparsely populated bush of the Central African Republic and pouring into the Chari at the point where that river becomes navigable.

Bonifica claims that the Transaqua canal could carry 100 cubic kilometres of water a year – more than the Nile. It could irrigate up to 70,000 square kilometres of fields and pastures in the Sahel, a quarter of the world's current irrigated acreage. And hydroelectric plants at strategic points along its route could generate more than 30 million megawatt-hours of electricity a year – the equivalent of two-thirds of Italy's electricity output. Bonifica promises that Transaqua would be 'a decisive propulsive element for the practical start-up . . . of the African post-colonial dream of the international economic and productive integration of the continent'. There would be 'a massive influx of international capital to Zaire, unprecedented in African territory'. Transaqua's electricity could be sold throughout central Africa and would power two giant industrial parks drawn on the map by Bonifica in the backwoods of the Central African Republic and Zaire.

Until now, almost all large water management schemes have taken place within river basins, mostly with the aim of evening out seasonal flows or retaining water for use in drought years. The largest exceptions have been the watering of southern California with flows from the north of the state and the River Colorado, and the Soviet Union's disastrous diversion of water out of the Aral Sea basin. Now there is also Colonel Gadaffi's Great Man-made River and Turkey's talk of a 'peace pipeline'.

For some, such projects for inter-basin transfers seem relics from another era. Several schemes, including the Soviet Siberian rivers diversion to revive the Aral Sea basin, were dropped in the more cautious financial and environmental climate of the 1970s and 1980s. But they could stage a come-back in the greenhouse world. One such scheme, first proposed in the 1960s, would refill the Ogallala aquifer beneath the High

Plains of the USA by pumping massive amounts of water from the great Mississippi on to the plains. The plan for the Trans-Texas canal was published in 1968. One of its architects was George Brown of the engineering firm Brown & Root. Now water engineers in chief to Colonel Gadaffi, the company was best known at that time as patron to Lyndon Johnson, who was then the free-spending occupant of the White House.

The scheme was big even for Texas. The canal would have lifted 120 cubic kilometres of water each year to a height of 820 metres on to the High Plains. It was a bigger job than pumping the Nile back upstream from the Mediterranean to Lake Albert in Uganda, and would have required a third of the entire electricity generating capacity of Texas. Ecological effects were barely considered, though some farmers were worried that the poisonous water moccasin snake might make it up the canal on to their fields.

Even Texan voters, more and more of whom now live in cities and make their money out of oil rather than the soil, vetoed the idea as too costly. And by the time the key decisions were taken, President Johnson had decided not to run for a second term, and the plan foundered. In the early 1980s the Corps of Engineers reviewed the proposals for Congress. It concluded that construction costs alone would probably run into tens of billions of dollars and farmers would have to pay at least ten times more for their water than they could afford.

If farmers may have to accept that such projects are too costly, cities may not. They can afford to pay far more for water. California, drought victim of the late 1980s, is the biggest player. It has the cash, the clout and the desire for more water – and it has the ideas. It was in the engineering offices of the Los Angeles Department of Water and Power that one Donald McCord Baker conceived the biggest of all water transfer schemes. It is called NAWAPA, an acronym for the North American Water and Power Alliance, and has been promoted ever since by the Ralph M. Parsons engineering company in nearby Pasadena.

The idea is simple and explosive: America wants Canada's water. The execution is equally devastating: a remaking of the

surface water distribution system of much of the continent of
North America. The plan is to capture the great rushing rivers
of the northwest: the Columbia in the US, and then, going
northwards, the Fraser, Liard, Skeena and finally the mighty
Yukon. The names of some of these rivers are barely known
outside Canada, but they are among the largest rivers in the
world. When the spring snowmelt is on in British Columbia,
around 10 per cent of all the water in all the rivers of the
world is flowing through this single province. Yet only a few
hundred kilometres south, as the greenhouse effect bites, the
High Plains will be parched, the Colorado reduced to a trickle
and California permanently drought stricken.

So if James Bay is Quebec's project of the twentieth
century, why not make NAWAPA the continent's project of the
twenty-first century? The waters of British Columbia's rivers
would be caught in their canyons behind dams up to 540
metres high. Canals would funnel this water into the Rocky
Mountain Trench, a 1,800-kilometre-long natural depression
in the Rockies, that would be turned into a reservoir holding
700 cubic kilometres of water, almost three times the capacity
of all the major dams in the US today.

From there, some water would go east along a great waterway into Alberta and Saskatchewan, which also face desiccation in the global greenhouse, and on to the Great Lakes,
and even, via Lake Michigan, into the upper reaches of the
Mississippi. But most water would flow south into the Colorado headwaters, before transferring again to California, the
Rio Grande and, if the Americans were feeling generous,
Mexico. NAWAPA would involve 240 large dams and 17 major
aqueducts to transfer each year 140 cubic kilometres of water,
ten times the natural flow of the Colorado. It could be
expanded to carry double that amount. This is a lot of water,
but only a little more than is tapped by the irrigation schemes
of the Aral basin. NAWAPA, it is claimed, could irrigate 220,000
square kilometres of farmland, an area the size of the state of
Colorado or twice that of England. It would generate 70,000
megawatts of power or six-and-a-half Grand Coulees, mostly
in Canada.

Even in the mid-1970s, the bill was put at $120 billion. Now it would be $350 billion plus – and could be funded with a cut in the Pentagon's budget of maybe 5 per cent for each of the next 30 years – although it would take 30 years to build. Put like that it doesn't sound quite so crazy, after all – even if Prince George, a town with a population of 150,000, would disappear beneath one reservoir, and most of the greatest salmon rivers in the world would be dammed out of existence.

The USA could build it – and could fund it, if necessary in easy stages. Dismissed through the 1980s as impractical lunacy, NAWAPA reemerged in 1992 when both Canadian and US negotiators for a North American Free Trade Agreement backed it. Quebec's premier, Robert Bourassa, gave it his approval. Former US health education and welfare secretary Robert Finch called it the 'next major priority' after the signing of the free trade agreement. The carrot for Canadian trading in its 'sinfully wasted' water was an estimated 40,000 megawatts of hydroelectricity.

The single most potent signpost pointing towards NAWAPA's eventual execution is the predictions of climatologists that Canada and the Midwest prairie states of Canada and the USA are destined to dry out drastically as the greenhouse effect gathers pace. If climatologists are right that the Colorado and Sacramento rivers will lose half their flows, then, so the argument goes, either farming will have to shut down across many states and provinces, or NAWAPA or something like it will have to be built. Certainly the Canadians as much as their cousins across the border will be eyeing Canada's great rivers. Sixty per cent of Canada's waters flow north to the Arctic, far away from the country's centres of population and industry. They could, in President Johnson's phrase when proposing dams on the Mekong to Ho Chi Minh, 'cut a deal'.

Canadian engineers already have their own pet mega-transfer project, known as GRAND, for Great Recycling and Northern Development project, which like NAWAPA would bring Canadian Arctic water south. First proposed in 1959 by a Newfoundland engineer, Thomas Kierans, the idea is to divert south water currently flowing north through the rivers of Quebec to Hudson Bay. A 270-kilometre-long cascade of reservoirs would take the water to Lake Huron, one of the Great Lakes. With this extra flow into the lakes, excess water could be taken from the westernmost lake, Lake Superior, into the Canadian and American Midwest, and from Lake Michigan into the headwaters of the Mississippi.

GRAND has influential friends. The Quebec government of prime minister Robert Bourassa supported it, and a consortium called Grandco established to promote it includes Bechtel, the US construction firm, which does big business in Canada.

Canada's GRAND canal would be no larger than China's thousand-year-old Grand Canal. And the $100 billion bill works out, with interest, at $50 for each of 160 million anticipated beneficiaries each year for 50 years.

Donald Gamble, top Canadian water analyst, lambasted the project in the *Journal of Great Lakes Research* in 1989. Kierans, he said, was seeking 'a patina of respectability for an engineering venture that ... is scientifically unsupportable, technically questionable, economically unjustifiable, socially harmful and politically unacceptable'. But might it be built? 'On pure, hard economic analysis, the project is nuts. It just doesn't make sense. But,' admits Gamble, 'if global warming turns out to be what we think it is, by the beginning of the next century no price will be too high for water.' And those who can pay will.

The greenhouse effect changes many things and that is why hydroelectric power, even more than nuclear power, will be offered as a way to head off the rising sea levels and climatic shifts. So it should, but growing concern about the social and ecological impacts of hydroelectric dams and a shortage of good dam sites will drive hydroelectric generation further from the populated areas and towards the great untamed rivers of the north – of Alaska and northern Canada, of Siberia, Iceland and Greenland. Will James Bay be the first of such projects? The Cree or Inuit may be noisy, but, it will be asked, what price their future compared to clean power for New York?

Electricity, even more than water, may travel long distances. At the opening of the 1990s, researchers proposed

laying a deep-sea power cable from Iceland to Britain to allow
it to benefit from the hydro-potential in the mountains of
Iceland. Tasmania wanted to send sparse hydro-power to the
mainland of Australia. There was growing enthusiasm for the
potential of new super-conducting materials that could send
electricity for thousands of miles without losing power. That
would allow the Russians to take yet more power from
north-flowing Siberian rivers, just as much as it could allow
Nile power to reach Europe and the Zaire to generate for
Zululand.

Hydroelectric power from the remote north could become
the key to development of a new global energy source long
dreamed about by futurologists. And hydrogen may be the
missing link in the chain. Hydrogen could be the fuel of the
future – a cheap, clean greenhouse-friendly substitute for oil
and gas that can burn in cars and home-heating systems as
well as in power stations. When it burns, it produces mainly
water vapour – no carbon dioxide.

The key to its development is its large-scale manufacture,
which requires passing electricity through water. What better
job for a hydroelectric dam, where the water and power are
on tap? The European Community is spending $4 million on a
study of how feasible it would be to harness Quebec's spare
generating capacity at James Bay to manufacture hydrogen
that would be brought across the Atlantic in supertankers.
Tapping massive amounts of electricity in giant wilderness
dams and shipping it to where the customers are may be the
ultimate solution. Dream or nightmare, it could be the future.

There is an additional, and potentially important, advantage in hydrogen at hydroelectric plants, however. If the water
in the river were converted on site into hydrogen, then there
would be no need to store water for conversion into power
when it is needed. The storage function would be performed
by the hydrogen rather than the reservoir. A run-of-river
hydropower plant, with a small reservoir to provide the raw
material, could manufacture hydrogen as and when the river
flood regime dictated. Besides saving land, this would also get
round the problem of the silting up of reservoirs. This would
allow massive power generation *without* destroying the flood

cycles of great rivers, *without* drowning fertile valleys and forcing the evacuation of millions of people and *without* destroying the resource itself beneath a mountain of silt. Suddenly, hydroelectric power might become genuinely renewable and the bad old days of impoundment dams be put behind us.

CONCLUSION

Running to Waste

It is the growing chasm between the intended purpose and the actual consequences of technology that promotes the fear that technology may be running amok.

Daniel Headrick, technology historian

Despite the increasing body of evidence about the folly of many large water engineering projects, the schemes keep on coming. The World Bank, after forty years' experience of irrigation projects that have, by its own assessments, failed to live up to expectations, and of funding dams that destroy more lives than they enhance, remains happy to put more money into all but the worst-conceived schemes. And there are other banks and governments waiting in the wings. The Japanese government wants to build as big as possible, all over world. It wants to construct the Three Gorges Dam, help Nepal tame the headwaters of the Ganges and may next offer great projects to water the Sahel. Arab money has poured into projects such as the Manantali Dam on the River Senegal. While experience has made the aid agencies of the British and US governments more cautious, in France, President Mitterand still talks of 'mobilising the world's energies' with megaprojects to aid development.

There remains a certain terrifying logic behind megaprojects. Big problems, it is said, need big solutions. How else are we to feed and sustain the hundreds of millions of inhabitants of the new megacities of the Third World? How else are we to respond to the huge hydrological changes that the greenhouse effect will create? Somehow, the news does not get through that investments in energy conservation and water saving can bring down demand for water and hydroelectric power faster and more cheaply. The urge to play God with the natural resources of the planet – to draw up blueprints that could industrialise Zaire or irrigate the Sahel or forever prevent flooding in Bangladesh, or seal off the American West from the consequences of climate change – is still strong in many hearts. Engineers and politicians are remembered for building dams and canals, not for lowering demand.

This book is full of examples of how unexpected or ignored consequences of large hydrological projects have overwhelmed the benefits. And with most superdams only completed in the past 20 years, we can be sure that the tally of impacts will grow. As the technology historian Daniel Headrick says: 'It is the growing chasm between the intended purpose and the actual consequences of technology that promotes the fear that technology may be running amok.'

In tropical Africa most large water projects do more harm than good, rewarding a few to the detriment of many and the long-term destruction of natural wealth. Irrigation projects in many arid regions grow fewer crops than the farms they replace, while fisheries, floodplains and groundwaters die. Zambia has gained little from flooding the most fertile and heavily populated river valleys in central Africa to provide power for copper mines. Ghana lost far more than it gained from the Akosombo Dam. Many of the dams on these rivers should simply be dismantled.

The High Aswan is a more complicated case, but its water has mostly been used to perpetuate Egypt's role as a source of water-guzzling export crops, such as cotton and now rice and sugar cane. It also drives turbines that power Cairo, allowing it to become a megacity of more than 10 million people expanding across the fertile fields of the Nile.

Headrick argues that such problems are a failure of rational analysis and problem solving. 'A linear view of production and consumption apparently has dominated industrial technology, solving the immediate problem without necessarily assessing the wider impacts,' he says. This leaves him hopeful.

In the post-industrial era, when computers and advanced information systems will allow us to assess those wider impacts, we may be able to manage our natural environment rather better. 'Industrial technology, which is powerful enough to break the self-renewing cycles of nature, is also capable of protecting the biosphere from its own excesses,' he says.

But this is to underestimate the nature of the dams, the irrigation projects and the rest as products of a political and economic malaise. We can see this malaise today in the basin of the Aral Sea. As Communist power subsides, so the folly of Commisar Cotton is exposed. But the same is true in Africa, where many projects have been built as symbols of nation-hood, intended by their leaders to bind the nation together. Today, as the despots begin to tumble, the uselessness of their dams becomes clear. Likewise Brazil's dams in the Amazon are symbols of the failure of that country's efforts to advance through exploitation of the rainforest.

Everywhere large water projects are both the consequence of and the justification for authoritarian government. From India to Turkey to Paraguay, soldiers stand guard over dam construction sites and herd refugees to their new homes. It is no surprise that one of the USA's great dam-building organi-sations is the US Army's Corps of Engineers. Or that Stalin's secret police supervised construction of his dams and canals. Or that soldiers such as Nasser and Gadaffi and the military commanders of South America have been so prominent in the promotion of large dams. The urge, and frequently the lan-guage, of domination and rule runs through their world. It is a long way from the dreams of the pioneers of the 1930s who believed that dams could help bring peace, prosperity and social justice.

Large water projects have become symbols, too, of corrup-tion. Are Kolawole in Nigeria says that the 'project fever' in his country is fuelled less by the naive application of tech-nology than by the politics of graft and patronage. The great irrigation projects of the green revolution may have as their declared aim the elimination of famine. But the idealism is warped through a prism of economic and political interests that can result in the most famine-prone people being placed in a state of growing dependency and, until the arrival of the water tankers and shipments of grain, still more vulnerable to famine.

Likewise, since the development of the first 'cash register' dams in the American West in the 1930s and 1940s, the hydroelectric dream of cheap power for all has been perverted by the desire to serve, and then actively entice, energy-intensive industries such as aluminium smelting. Much power has been generated along the way. But the road from the early ideals of the Tennessee Valley Authority and the New Dealers has led to Tucurui and Balbinas, Lake Pedder and James Bay. The roadside is littered with millions of refugees who never did find their promised new homes. The world's rivers are being consumed to make frozen-food trays and beer cans.

Maybe the customers of these products are entitled to flood their own lands in such a cause. But should the former residents of the Volta valley have paid such a price? The undoubted financial success of many hydroelectric dams in the rich world has for a generation fatally distorted efforts at the sensible use of rivers.

None of the examples of national and international river basins examined here provide evidence of rational management. Witness the chaos of the Zambezi and the Senegal; the stand-offs on the Danube and the Ganges; the hijacking of the Jordan; the upstream tyranny of Turkey on the Euphrates, of the US over the Colorado; even the downstream tyranny that still seems to operate on the Nile. For management, read control. Domination over rivers produces domination over people, too.

Some environmentalists believe that making customers pay the real cost of water will bring a semblance of rationality. This might work to reduce the power of the irrigators in the American West and to restrain the worst demands of green revolution fat-cats. But in most places it will only increase the hold of the hydroelectric dam over the world's rivers. American conservationists may be rich enough to buy water rights and preserve their favourite streams, but how will water markets ensure the livelihood of the farmers on the *fadama* in Nigeria or the preservation of the Mekong's fisheries or the Ganges silt? Is a beer can today really worth more than a shoal of fish a generation hence? The cash register suggests that it is.

In most places, at most times, even acute water shortages have failed to concentrate minds on water conservation. The US High Plains are being abandoned because nobody considered it worth investing in water conservation measures on farms. Right to the bitter end of farming in the Aral Sea basin, they are building new superdams in the mountains of former Soviet Central Asia. Drought in the Sahel has intensified the appropriation of scarce water by the rich and the well-connected. Indeed, from Riyadh to Tripoli to Phoenix, nobody seems better able to squander water than modern societies living in the desert. Even Israel, which for a long time took pride in its record of efficient water use, now stands exposed by its own ombudsman as a water wastrel.

The contrast between modern methods of water management and the remains of traditional systems in Africa, Asia and the Americas is stark. From the Thar to the Valley of Mexico we can see how the new drives out the old, but also how the old often shows the greater hydrological virtue, the greater prospect of providing sustenance in an increasingly water-hungry world. It is ancient, not modern technologies, that allow the Thar to be the most heavily populated desert in the world.

Modern engineers, in their hubris, have become the anti-rationalists, the mystics and ideologues. Their view of a river as a piece of plumbing does not fit reality. It makes them as brutal towards the environment as any Stalinist hack towards the inhabitants of a people's republic. No wonder these two groups, both perhaps destined to be dinosaurs from the fading age of modernism, have often got on so well together. They talk the same language of rationality and order, while creating disorder and tyranny.

But the true rationalists are those who attempt to see the whole picture, to view a river as part of a wider world, rather than as a piece of hydraulic engineering. As Phil Williams pointed out to the ICOLD conference, large dams are an experimental technology, and he believes that the experiment has largely failed.

The physical form of a natural river and the ecosystem that depends on it have evolved together over thousands of years, created by the natural flows and sediment moved from the river's watershed. The construction of a large dam destroys this balance, setting in motion deleterious changes that may take decades to become apparent, but which ultimately negate the economic benefits of the dam and bequeath financial and environmental costs for future generations.

In India, where Nehru's dams and canals have gathered up half this great nation's waters, they can see clearly the difference between exploitation and conservation of water. Says Vandana Shiva, the Indian ecologist:

Rivers are drying up because their catchments have been mined, deforested or over-cultivated to generate revenue or profits. Groundwater is drying up because it has been over-exploited to feed cash crops. Village after village is being robbed of its lifeline, its sources of drinking water, and the number of villages facing water famine is in direct proportion to the number of 'schemes' implemented by government agencies to 'develop' water.

Anil Agarwal heads the Centre for Science and the Environment in India. He began his career as an engineer, but says now: 'As we move closer to the limits of water resource utilisation, our water management system is not becoming more disciplined or efficient. If it does not, the resulting social and ecological imbalances will destroy the very fabric that we are building.'

What goes for India, goes for the planet. The creed of exploitation has squandered resources. What matters most is drastically to increase the efficiency with which water is used, to ensure fairer allocations and to conserve the resource. In economists' jargon, more dams can only provide a supply-side solution to a demand-side problem.

There are plenty of demand-side solutions. The half-

forgotten world of traditional water systems is full of them. So
are the laboratories of modern science. Even the sale rooms
contain the drips and sprinklers that can cut water use on
farms by 50 per cent or more, and the energy-saving devices
for factories, homes and offices that can reduce energy bills by
as much. What is missing is the willingness of customers to
use them and the desire of governments to abandon their
megaprojects in favour of investment in conservation and
efficiency.

This does not mean looking always for small solutions to
problems. It means looking for genuinely effective solutions.
And it means taking the long view. Large-scale transformation
of the landscape is not a phenomenon of the modern world.
The systems of terraces, floating gardens and raised fields in
the Americas were vast feats of engineering. So in their way
were the stone walls that once captured rainfall across deserts
from the Negev to Libya and the American West. What
groundwater engineer has thought bigger than the *qanat*
diggers of Iran? The Bengalis didn't think small either, when
they redesigned the Ganges River delta simultaneously to
prevent floods and fertilise crops, but they thought effectively,
and they built to last.

For all the modern talk about planning and river-basin
management, few engineers think ahead for longer than a
generation. You cannot manage a river basin in such a way,
and the ancients never did. Their great canals and dams and
raised fields and terraces lasted for many hundreds, sometimes
several thousand, years. As David Gilbertson, an anthropologist at the University of Sheffield, put it: 'The wisdom of the
ancients in managing these harsh landscapes is more substantive than our own.'

Modern analysis as much as ancient wisdom can, however,
help show the way, if properly applied. Thus the Germans are
learning to think afresh about the Rhine, coming to understand the value of the natural services once provided by a
floodplain that engineers have drained and paved. So has
Howard Odum on the Mississippi. Yes, he says, overall
economic development on the floodplain, once a source of
vast natural wealth and 'environmental services', has been

beneficial to the region and to the nation – largely because they found oil there. But the gains 'were much lower than those possible with a better use of the river'. Odum's analytical tools, if applied to other natural systems under threat from human economic activity, could yield some interesting results of as much relevance in the third as the first world.

The path of megaprojects and the increasingly intensive management of the water cycle leads to both the destruction of natural resources and conflicts, both within and between nations. But it may be that the corner has already been turned. Perhaps we are already beginning on a path towards the more efficient use of the world's resources, to an understanding that untrammelled engineering of our environment can do more harm than good. The victories of the dam protesters suggest that it is happening. The engineers at ICOLD appear suddenly to be genuinely out of touch with the attitudes of the outside world, still believing that what they are doing is for the good of the world, but uncomfortably aware that they are no longer loved.

If we can learn the language of conservation and restraint, understand Francis Bacon's words that 'we cannot command nature without obeying her'; if we can persuade engineers and politicians to think of conserving resources that they now exploit, and to cease believing that any water left in a river is somehow wasted; then with six, eight, ten billion or even more people on this planet, we shall still be able to live decent and happy lives.

NOTES ON SOME SOURCES

Material for this book was gained during trips to India, Bangladesh, the USA, Israel, Jordan, France, Germany, Austria, Czechoslovakia, Hungary, Nigeria and Canada.

The references below are not a complete record of written sources, but identify the key texts used, with a bias towards those more easily available journals. References are to page numbers.

Introduction

1 GMRP opening: BBC Radio news broadcasts, September 1991.
2 *The Great Man-made River Project* (1989), from GMRP Authority, Hampton Wick, London; UNESCO Libyan Valleys Civilistion Project, *Libyan Studies*, various issues (1979–89).

1: Hydraulic Civilisations

10 G. Garbrecht, 'Ancient Water Works – Lessons from History', *Impact of Science on Society*, no. 1 (UNESCO, Paris, 1983), p. 10; K. Wittfogel, *Oriental Despotism* (New Haven, Conn., 1957).
11 T. Jacobsen and R. Adams, 'Salt and Silt in Ancient Mesopotamian Agriculture', *Science*, vol. 128 (1958), p. 1252; Sir L. Woolley, *Ur of the Chaldees* (London, 1936).
12 Sir W. Willcocks, *Restoration of the Ancient Irrigation Works of the Tigris* (London, 1903).
13 Wittfogel, *Oriental Despotism*.
14 E. Goldsmith and N. Hildyard, *The Social and Environmental Impact of Large Dams* (Sierra Club, San Francisco, 1984).
15 P. M. Chesworth, 'The History of Water Use, in Sudan and

Egypt', in *The Nile*, ed. P. Howell and J. Allan, proceedings of conference held at SOAS (London, May 1990).

16 K. Butzer, *Early Hydraulic Civilisations in Egypt* (University of Chicago Press, 1976).

18 L. Changming et al, 'Water Transfer in China: the East Route Project, in *Large-scale Water Transfers*, ed. A. K. Biswas (Tycooly, Dublin, 1983); 'Yangtze Diversion Goes under Yellow', *World Water* (August 1988), p. 5; R. L. Brohier, *Ancient Irrigation Works in Ceylon* (London, 1908); E. Leach, 'Hydraulic Society in Ceylon', *Past and Present*, no. 15 (April 1959), p. 21; J. Madeley, 'Leaks and Landslides Loom in Sri Lanka', *New Scientist* (7 April 1983), p. 8.

2: Figs, Vines and Olives

21 K. M. Kenyon, *Digging up Jericho* (London, 1957).

23 K. Butzer et al, 'Irrigation Agrosystems in Eastern Spain', *Annals of Assoc. Am. Geogs*, vol. 75 (1985), p. 479.

24 Author's visit to Israel, March 1991; Z. Ron, Development and Management of Irrigation Systems in Mountain Regions of the Holy Land, trans. Inst. Br. Geog, vol. 10 (1985), p. 149.

26 G. Garbrecht, 'Ancient Water Works – Lessons from History', *Impact of Science on Society*, no. 1 (UNESCO, Paris, 1983).

27 D. Cosgrove, 'An Elemental Division', in D. Cosgrove and G. Petts, *Water, Engineering and Landscape* (Belhaven, London, 1990).

3: Renaissance and Reason

29 S. Schama, *The Embarrassment of Riches* (London, 1987).

30 H. C. Darby, *The Changing Fenland* (Cambridge, 1983); R. Butlin, 'Drainage and Land Use in the Fenlands in the 17th and 18th Centuries', in D. Cosgrove and G. Petts, *Water, Engineering and Landscape* (Belhaven, 1990).

31 J. Purseglove, *Taming the Flood* (Oxford, 1988).

32 C. V. Wedgwood, *The King's Peace* (London, 1955), p. 47.

34 Darby, *Changing Fenland*.

35 D. Ingle Smith, 'A Dam Disaster Waiting to Break', *New Scientist* (11 November 1989), p. 42.

36 J. Berber, *Rivers in International Law* (London, 1959).

37 E. Dister et al, 'Water Management and Ecological Perspectives of the Upper Rhine Floodplains', *Regulated Rivers: Research*

and Management, vol. 5 (1990); G. Petts, 'Forested River Corridors: A Lost Resource', in Cosgrove and Petts, *Water, Engineering and Landscape*.

4: The Louisiana Purchase

41 J. McPhee, *The Control of Nature* (London, 1990); D. Pierce, 'The Mississippi: That Old Dammed River', *Not Man Apart* (Friends of the Earth, Washington D.C., September 1986), p. 6.
44 M. Robinson and J. Tuttle, 'US Drought: Crisis Management', *World Water* (June 1990), p. 60.
45 J. Hecht, 'The Incredible Shrinking Mississippi Delta', *New Scientist* (14 April 1990), p. 36.
46 Sir W. Willcocks, *60 Years in the East* (London, 1935), on 'how the ancients would have controlled the Mississippi' with natural inundation.
47 H. T. Odum et al, *Energy Systems Overview of the Mississippi River Basin* (Centre for Wetlands, University of Florida, Gainesville, 1987).

5: The Alternative Tradition

50 G. P. Nabhan, 'Papago Indian Desert Agriculture', *Applied Geography* theme volume on runoff farming in rural arid lands (1986).
51 M. Reisner, *Cadillac Desert* (New York, 1986); 'Comprehensive guide to Mesa Verde, Canyon de Chelly and Hovenweep', *National Parkways* (Washington DC, 1988).
52 D. D. Gilbertson, *Applied Geography*, theme volume on runoff farming in rural arid lands (1986).
53 Visit by author to Avdat and Shivta run off farms, March 1991, interviews with Berliner, Issar and others; M. Evenari, *Runoff Agriculture in Arid and Semi-arid Lands* (Jacob Blaustein Institute for Desert Research, Ben Gurion University of the Negev, 1986); A. Pacey and A. Cullis, *Rainwater Harvesting* (Intermediate Technology, London, 1986).
55 G. Garbrecht, 'Ancient Water Works – Lessons from History', *Impact of Science on Society*, no. 1 (UNESCO, Paris, 1983).
56 H. E. Wulff, 'Qanats of Iran', *Scientific American* (April 1968), p. 100; P. Beaumont, 'Qanats of Veramin Plain, Iran', Trans of Institute of British Geography, vol. 45 (1968), p. 169.
57 A. Issar, *Water Shall Flow from the Rock*, (Springer-Verlag, Berlin, 1990), p. 158.

58 W. Qinghua, 'Still Growing After all These Years', *World Water*, (September 1991), p. 43, on revived Chinese *karez*.
59 M.D. Coe, 'The Chinampas of Mexico', *Scientific American* (July 1964).
62 C. Erickson, 'Prehistoric Landscape Management in the Andean Highlands, paper to 1990 annual meeting, American Association for the Advancement of Science; C. Erickson, 'Raised Field Rehabilitation Projects in the Northern Lake Titicaca Basin', unpublished manuscript, 1991; W. M. Denevan, 'Aboriginal Drained-field Cultivation in the Americas', *Science*, v. 169 (1970), p. 647; J. J. Parsons and W. M. Denevan, 'Pre-Columbian Ridged Fields', *Scientific American* (July 1987).

6: Irrigating India

67 N. Sengupta, 'Irrigation: Traditional Versus Modern', *Economic and Political Weekly* (November 1985), citing Cotton's lecture 'Irrigation Works in India', 1874.
70 M. A. Chitale, 'Indian Experiences of Irrigation and Power Projects', *Water Resources Development*, vol. 4, no. 2 (1988). D. R. Headrick, *The Tentacles of Progress: Technology Transfer in the Age of Imperialism* (Oxford, 1988).
71 J. Colvin, *The Ganges Canal: A Simple Presentation for the Natives*, among Indian papers at School of Oriental and African Studies, London University; D. Worster, *The Ends of the Earth* (Cambridge, 1988), p. 15.
72 I. Stone, *Canal Irrigation in British India* (Cambridge, 1984); E. Whitcombe, *Agrarian Conditions in Northern India* (California, 1972).
74 J. Morris, *Pax Britannica* (London, 1968).
75 J. Farmer, *Agricultural Colonisation in India* (Oxford University Press, Delhi, 1974); A. Michel, *The Indus Rivers* (Oxford, 1967).

7: The Gift of the Nile

77 M. Strage, *Cape to Cairo* (London, 1973) on Ali.
80 Overseas Development Institute Network Paper 1/80/3, *Irrigation in Egypt, Past and Present* (1980) on Willcocks.
81 Sir W. Willcocks, *60 Years in the East* (London, 1935).
83 R. O. Collins, *The Waters of the Nile* (Oxford, 1990); A. Moorehead, *The White Nile* (London, 1962).
84 Willcocks, *60 Years*.
85 T. Barnett, *The Gezira Scheme: An Illusion of Development*

(London, 1977); N. Pollard, 'Sudan's Gezira Scheme', in
E. Goldsmith and N. Hildyard, *The Social and Environmental
Impact of Large Dams*, vol. 2 (Sierra Club, 1984).

8: How Water Won the West

87 C. R. Koppes, 'Efficiency, Equity, Esthetics: Shifting Themes in
American Conservation', in *The Ends of the Earth*, ed.
D. Worster (Cambridge, 1988); D. Worster, 'The Hoover Dam,
a Study in Domination', in E. Goldsmith and N. Hildyard, *The
Social and Environmental Impact of Large Dams*, vol. 2 (Sierra
Club , 1984).
88 M. Reisner, *Cadillac Desert* (New York, 1986).
89 N. Hundley, 'The Great American Desert', in *Water and Arid
Lands of the Western US*, ed. M. El-Ashry and D. Gibbons
(Cambridge, 1989).
91 Worster, 'The Hoover Dam'.
92 Reisner, *Cadillac Desert*.
93 Koppes, 'Efficiency, Equity, Esthetics'.
95 Author's visit to Phoenix and Central Arizona Project, 1987.
97 B. Blackwelder et al, 'Alternatives to Traditional Water Development in the US', *Ambio*, vol. 16 (1987), p. 32.
98 R. Shaefer and F. Gregg, interviews with author, 1987;
R. Repetto, *Skimming the Water* (World Resources Institute,
Washington D.C., 1986); Worster, 'The Hoover Dam'.

9: Commissar Cotton

100 C. E. Ziegler, *Environmental Policy in the USSR* (London,
1987).
101 B. Komarov, *The Destruction of Nature in the Soviet Union*
(London, 1978).
104 D. Wilson, *Soviet Energy to 2000* (*Economist* Intelligence Unit,
1986).
105 V. M. Desyatov, 'Soviets Challenge Amur Hydro Projects',
World Rivers Review (International Rivers Network, San Francisco, March 1991).
106 G. V. Voropacv and A. L. Velikanov, 'Partial Southward Diversion of Northern and Siberian Rivers', *Large-scale Water
Transfers*, ed. A. K. Biswas (Tycooly, Dublin, 1983).
108 N. Precoda, 'Requiem for the Aral Sea', *Ambio*, vol. 20 (May
1991), p. 109.

110 K. D. Frederick, 'The Disappearing Aral Sea', *Resources* (Resources for the Future, Washington DC, Winter 1991).

111 'I belong to those scientists', quote taken from Precoda, 'Requiem for the Aral Sea'.

112 V. M. Kotlyakov, 'The Aral Sea Basin', *Environment*, vol. 33 (January 1991), p. 4.

113 P. P. Micklin, 'Desiccation of the Aral Sea', *Science*, vol. 241 (1988), p. 1170; 'Canal May Save Aral Sea', *Enginering News Record* (8 October 1987), p. 16.

114 P. Rogers, *Environment*, vol. 33 (January 1991), p. 2.

10: A Source of Everlasting Prosperity

116 R. O. Collins, *The Waters of the Nile* (Oxford, 1990).

118 'Egypt Earns High Rate of Return on Aswan High Dam Investment', *Engineering News Record* (6 May 1982), p. 28; M. Lavergne, *The Seven Deadly Signs of Egypt's Aswan High Dam*, in E. Goldsmith and N. Hildyard, *The Social and Environmental Impact of Large Dams*, vol. 2 (Sierra Club, 1984); G. F. White, 'The Environmental Effects of the High Dam at Aswan', *Environment*, vol. 30, no. 7 (September 1988); M. Abu Zeid, 'Environmental Impacts of the High Aswan Dam', in *Environmentally-Sound Water Management*, ed. N. C. Thanh and A. K. Biswas (Oxford University Press, Delhi, 1990).

119 D. MacKenzie, 'Egypt's Great Brick Crisis', *New Scientist* (30 May 1985), p. 10.

120 I. Murray, 'Struggle to Make the Desert Fertile', *The Times* (16 November 1987); A. Charnock, 'The Greening of Egypt', *New Scientist* (22 January 1986), p. 44; A. Bishay, *Land Reclamation for Sustainable Desert Development*, paper to African Water Summit, Cairo, organised by Ministry of Foreign Affairs of Egypt (June 1990).

121 J. A. Allan, 'Natural Resources as National Fantasies', *Geoforum*, vol. 14, no. 3 (1983), p. 243.

123 D. Hart, *The Volta River Project* (Edinburgh, 1980); G. Lanning and M. Mueller, *Africa Undermined* (Harmondsworth, 1979), p. 429.

124 B. Lapping, *End of Empire* (London, 1985).

125 R. Graham, 'Ghana's Volta Resettlement Scheme', in Goldsmith and Hildyard, *Large Dams*, vol. 2.

126 R. Chambers (ed.), *The Volta Resettlement* (Symposium papers, Kumasi, 1963).

127 M. Collins and G. Evans, 'The Influence of Fluvial Sediment on Coastal Erosion in West and Central Africa', *Journal of Shoreline Management*, vol. 2 (1986), p. 5.

128 C. K. Annan, 'Was Ghana's Akosombo Dam the Best Option?', *World Water* (September 1989), p. 35.

11: To Subdue the Earth

134 Data on global dam statistics: E. T. Haws, *Environmental Issues in Dam Projects*, presentation to ICOLD conference 1991 as head of its environment committee.

135 M. Reisner, *Cadillac Desert* (New York, 1986).

136 D. Deudney, *Rivers of Energy*, Worldwatch Paper 44, Worldwatch Institute, Washington D.C. (1981).

137 T. Scudder, 'The African Experience with River Basin Development', unpublished manuscript prepared for US Agency for International Development, 1988.

138 T. W. Mermel, 'The World's Major Dams and Hydro Plants', *Water Power and Dam Construction* (June 1991); 'Yacyreta: The Longest Dam in the World', *Travaux* (May 1991).

12: A Rumble in the Hills

146 Author's visit and interviews in Tehri, December 1990; *The Tehri Dam, a Prescription for Disaster*, Indian Trust for Art and Cultural Heritage (INTACH) environment series no. 6 (New Delhi, 1987).

148 Judgment of Supreme Court of India, given 7 November 1990.

151 V. Gaur, in INTACH no. 6; J. N. Brune, correspondence to V. Gaur, 1990; J. N. Brune, *Seismic Hazards at Tehri Dam*, memorandum, 1990, and telephone interview with author; S. K. Roy in INTACH, no. 6.

153 P. Hurst, *Rainforest Politics* (Zed Books, London, 1990), p. 197.

156 Kedung Ombo farmers protest to World Bank, *Down to Earth*, newsletter of Campaign for Ecological Justice in Indonesia, c/o Survival International (London, May 1991).

157 *The Narmada Valley Project: A Critique* (Kalpavriksh, New Delhi, 1988); O. Sattaur, 'India's Troubled Waters', *New Scientist* (27 May 1989), p. 46; V. Paranjpye, *High Dams on the Narmada*, INTACH Studies in Ecology and Sustainable Development 3 (1990).

13: A Trickle in the Sand

159 Visit to Jhanwar by author, December 1990; A. Agarwal and
    S. Narain, 'Fighting the Big Thirst', *Illustrated Weekly of India*
    (9 July 1989); N. S. Vangani et al, *Tanka – A Reliable System of
    Rainwater Harvesting in the Indian Desert* (CAZRI, Jodhpur,
    1988).
160 A. S. Kolarkar et al, 'Khadin', *Journal of Arid Environments*,
    vol. 6 (1983), p. 59.
161 Interview with Goyal, December 1990; A. Agarwal and
    S. Narain, *Towards Green Villages* (Centre for Science and the
    Environment, New Delhi, 1989).
163 S. P. Malhotra and L. P. Bharara, *Role of Human Factor in
    Desert Development* (CAZRI, 1988).
164 L. P. Bharara and S. P. Malhotra, *Social Impact of Irrigation
    Development in the Arid Zone of Rajasthan*, report for USAID
    (1985); P. C. Chatterji, *Water Resources in Arid Rajasthan*
    (CAZRI, date unknown).
165 S. M. Mohnot and L. S. Rajpurohit, *The Old Water System of
    Jodhpur* (INTACH, 1990).

14: African Harvest

167 P. Warshall et al, *The Lake Chad Diagnostic Basin*, report for
    Lake Chad Basin Commission and UNEP (Nairobi, 1990).
170 *IUCN Sahel Studies 1989* (IUCN, Gland).
171 B. Beckman, *Bakolori: Peasants Versus State*, in E. Goldsmith
    and N. Hildyard, *The Social and Environmental Impact of
    Large Dams*, vol. 2 (Sierra Club, 1984).
172 Visit by author to Hadejia-Nguru Wetlands Conservation
    Project, February 1992; W. M. Adams and M. R. Hughes,
    'Irrigation Development in Desert Environments', in *Tech-
    niques for Desert Reclamation*, ed. A. S. Goudie (Chichester,
    1990).
173 W. M. Adams and E. Hollis, *Hydrology and Sustainable
    Resource Development of a Sahelian Floodplain Wetland*
    (Hadejia-Nguru Wetlands Conservation Project, London,
    1989); K. Kimmage and W. M. Adams, 'Wetland Agricultural
    Production in the Hadejia-Jama'are Valley, Nigeria', *Geo-
    graphical Journal*, vol. 158, no. 1 (1992).
174 S. Barghouti and G. LeMoigne, *Irrigation in Sub-Saharan
    Africa*, World Bank Technical paper No. 123 (1990).

175 A. Kolawole, 'Environmental Change and the SCIP', *Journal of Arid Environments*, vol. 13 (1987), p. 169.
176 Warshall, *Lake Chad*.
177 A. Kolawole, 'Cultivation of Floor of Lake Chad', *Geographical Journal*, vol. 154 (1988), p. 243; A. Kolawole, 'Underperformance of Nigerian Irrigation Systems', *Water Resources Development*, vol. 5, no. 2 (1989).
178 Adams interviewed by author, Cambridge, January 1992; Adams and Hughes, 'Irrigation Development' (on Bura); C. Harrison, 'East Africa Has a New Lake', *Courier*, UNDP (May 1982).
179 D. D. Gilbertson, in *Applied Geography*, theme volume on runoff farming in rural arid lands (1986).
180 P. Harrison, 'The Magic Stones', *Fragile Future*, Oxfam supplement in *Observer* (1988).
181 Gilbertson, *Applied Geography*.

15: Feed the World

182 R. Repetto, *Skimming the Water* (World Resources Institute, Washington D.C., 1986).
183 'Irrigation's heavy environmental toll', *World Water* (October 1991).
184 Repetto, *Skimming the Water*.
186 V. Shiva, 'The Green Revolution in the Punjab', *Ecologist*, vol. 21, no. 2 (March 1991).
187 *World Agriculture: Toward 2000* (London, 1988).
188 M. Falkenmark, 'The Massive Water Scarcity Now Threatening Africa', *Ambio*, vol. 18 (1989), p. 112.
190 R. M. Humphreys, *Vesical Schistosomiasis in the Gezira*, trans. Royal Soc. of Tropical Med. (London, 1932); M. Amin, 'Schistosomiasis' in Sudan, in *Arid Land Irrigation in Developing Countries*, ed. E. B. Worthington (Pergamon, Oxford, 1977); ODU Bulletin, 'Hydraulics Research' (Wallingford, Oxon, July 1987).
191 R. Wade, 'Irrigation Reform in Conditions of Populist Anarchy, *Journal of Development Economics*, vol. 14 (1984), p. 285.
192 *Global Freshwater Quality, a First Assessment*, ed. M. Meybeck et al (UNEP and WHO, Blackwell, Oxford, 1989); A. F. Pillsbury, 'The Salinity of Rivers', *Scientific American* (July 1981), p. 32.

193 J. van Schilfgaarde, 'The Wellton-Mohawk Dilemma', *Water Supply and Management*, vol. 6 (1982), p. 115.
194 F. Pearce, 'Banishing the Salt of the Earth', *New Scientist* (11 June 1987); J. D. Rhoades, 'Principles and Practice of Salinity Control in North America', *Water and Water Policy in World Food Supplies*, ed. W. R. Jordan (Texas A&M University Press, 1987).

16: The Unhappy Valley

196 R. Stoner, 'Engineering a Solution to the Problem of Salt-laden Soils', *New Scientist* (3 December 1988), p. 44; H. Olivier, *Dam It* (Cape Town, 1975).
197 A. Bingham, 'Pakistan Contests a Bitter Legacy', *South* (February 1987), p. 11.
198 G. R. Sandhu, 'Avoiding an Ecological Catastrophe', *Earthwatch*, no. 40 (1990), p. 12; Stoner, 'Engineering a Solution'; A. Michel, *The Indus Rivers* (Oxford, 1967).
199 *River Indus Right Bank Master Plan* (Mott MacDonald, 1991).
200 A. Kazi, interview with author, June 1991.
201 M. N. Gazdar, *An Assessment of the Kalabagh Dam Project* (Environmental Management Society, Karachi, 1990).
202 R. Chambers et al, *To the Hands of the Poor* (Intermediate Technology, London, 1989); Bingham, 'Pakistan Contests a Bitter Legacy'.

17: The Pull of the Periphery

203 G. M. Binnie, *Early Dam Builders in Britain* (Thomas Telford, London, 1987).
205 N. Smith, 'The Origins of the Water Turbine', *Scientific American* (undated).
207 W. Churchill, *My African Journey* (Leo Cooper, London, 1989); H. Olivier, *Dam It* (Cape Town, 1975).
208 P. Thompson, *Power in Tasmania* (Australian Conservation Foundation, 1981); P. Thompson, *Saving Tasmania's Franklin and Gordon Wild Rivers* in E. Goldsmith and N. Hildyard, *The Social and Environmental Impact of Large Dams*, vol. 2 (Sierra Club, 1984).
210 M. Reisner, *Cadillac Desert* (New York, 1986); G. Petts, *Water, Engineering and Landscape: Development, Protection and*

Restoration, in D. Cosgrove and G. Petts, *Water, Engineering and Landscape* (Belhaven, London, 1990); 'Guri's 10 000 Mw ready to roll', *Engineering News Record* (17 July 1986), p. 36.

211 *Down to Earth*, newsletter of Campaign for Ecological Justice in Indonesia, c/o Survival International, London; P. Hurst, *Rainforest Politics* (Zed Books, London, 1990), p. 112.

212 E. Monosowskiy, *Brazil's Tucurui Dam*, in Goldsmith and Hildyard, *Large Dams*, vol. 2; C. Caufield, 'Brazil, Energy and the Amazon', *New Scientist* (28 October 1982), p. 240.

213 S. Hecht and A. Cockburn, *The Fate of the Forest* (London, 1989); L. A. de O. Santos and L. M. M. de Andrade, *Hydroelectric Dams on Brazil's Xingu River* (Cambridge, Massachusetts, 1990).

214 P. M. Fearnside, 'Brazil's Balbina Dam', *Environment Management*, vol. 13 (1989), p. 401, plus interview with Fearnside, Vienna 1991.

216 C. Caufield, *In the Rainforest* (London, 1985), p. 17, on Brokopondo; 'Le barrage de Petit-Saut', *Travaux* (May 1991).

18: Hewers of Ingots and Drawers of Water

218 Public lecture and interview by Matthew Coon-Come in Vienna, June 1991.

220 P. Gorrie, 'The James Bay Power Project', *Canadian Geographic* (February 1990), p. 21; W. Hamley, *Hydrotechnology, Wilderness and Culture in Quebec*, in D. Cosgrove and G. Petts, *Water, Engineering and Landscape* (Belhaven, 1990).

221 J. Linton, 'The Geese Have Lost Their Way', *Nature Canada* (Spring 1991), p. 27.

222 J.-F. Rougerie, James Bay development project, *Canadian Water*, vol. 3 (July 1990), p. 560.

223 Letter from the major of the Municipality of Sanikiluaq to the mayor of New York City, 19 December 1990; 'Subsidising Electricity for Smelters to Cost Quebec Billions', *Montreal Gazette* (11 October 1990); 'Norsk Hydro Reveals Contracts', *Toronto Globe and Mail* (30 April 1991).

224 Nick Auf der Maur, 'Hydro-Quebec's Secret Deals Hide the Export of Good Jobs', *Montreal Gazette* (11 April 1991); *Why James Bay II Imported Hydropower is Bad for New York City*, James Bay Defense Coalition, New York Chapter (1991).

225 H. S. Geller, J. Goldemberg et al, 'Electricity Conservation in Brazil: Potential and Progress', *Energy*, vol. 13 (1988), p. 469.

19: The Myth of Renewable Energy

226 'Hydroelectric Power on the Yellow River', *Water Power and Dam Construction* (June 1987); E. B. Vermeer, *Water Conservancy and Irrigation in China* (Leiden, 1977); D. Harland, 'Once More Unto the Breach', *New Scientist* (21 July 1988), p. 31.

227 D. Qing, *Yangtze, Yangtze* (Earthscan, London, forthcoming); *Water Power and Dam Construction* (June 1987).

228 B. Bowonder et al, 'Sedimentation of Reservoirs: Management Issues', *International Journal of Water Resources Development* (date unknown); D. N. Bhargava, *Water Power and Dam Construction* (January 1987), p. 30.

229 K. Mahmood, *Reservoir Sedimentation*, World Bank technical paper no. 71 (Washington D.C., 1987).

230 S. P. Nautiyal, in *The Tehri Dam*, INTACH Environment Series, no. 6 (1987), p. 15.

231 H. J. Leonard, 'Managing Central America's Renewable Resources', *International Environmental Affairs* (date unknown).

232 T. W. Mermel, 'The World's Major Dams and Hydro Plants', *Water Power and Dam Construction* (June 1991).

20: China's Sword of Damocles

235 G. Ryder, *Damming the Three Gorges: What Dambuilders Don't Want You to Know* (Toronto, 1990).

236 J. Gittings, 'China's Rising Tide of Chaos', *Guardian* (30 August 1991), p. 30; D. Qing, *Yangtze, Yangtze* (Earthscan, London, forthcoming).

237 C. Xuemin, 'The Environmental Factor', *World Water* (January 1991), p. 36; Ryder, *Damming the Three Gorges*.

238 Firms' work on Chinese dam study condemned by environmental group, *Montreal Gazette* (24 September 1990). Group is Probe International, Toronto.

239 Qing, *Yangtze, Yangtze*; Ryder, *Damming the Three Gorges*.

21: Banking on a Flood-free Future

242 Visit to Bangladesh in December 1990; *Bangladesh Action Plan for Flood Control* (World Bank restricted document, December 1989).

243 Jamuna erosion renders 5,000 families homeless, *Bangladesh*

Observer (24 November 1990); Ainan Nishat in interview with author.

244 Sir W. Willcocks, *Overflow Irrigation of Bengal* (London, 1930).

245 B. Dalal-Clayton, *Environmental Aspects of the Bangladesh Flood Action Plan* (International Institute for Environment and Development, London, 1990).

246 M. Michel et al, 'A Gigantic Scheme: Flood Control in Bangladesh', *Travaux* (May 1991).

247 P. Rogers et al, *Eastern Waters Study: Strategies to Manage Flood and Drought in the Ganges-Brahmaputra Basin* (US Agency for International Development, 1989).

248 M. Naser et al, *In Quest of a Golden Dream: Study of the Meghna-Dhanagoda Irrigation Project* (Lokejan, Dhaka, 1989); interview with van Ellen by the author, Dhaka, December 1990.

250 H. Brammer, 'Floods in Bangladesh: Flood Mitigation and Environmental Aspects', *Geographic Journal*, vol. 156 (July 1990), p. 158.

22: Tales from the River Bank

252 T. Scudder, 'The African Experience with River Basin Development', unpublished manuscript prepared for US Agency for International Development, 1988; F. Mounier, *The Senegal River Scheme: Development for Whom?*, in E. Goldsmith and N. Hildyard, *The Social and Environmental Impact of Large Dams*, vol. 2 (Sierra Club, 1984).

253 A. Beye, 'Dams on the Senegal River', *Ecoforum* (Environmental Liaison Centre, Nairobi, 1990).

254 Interview with Hollis by the author, London, 1991.

256 Interview with Wagner by the author, Vienna, 1991.

257 K. Perczel and G. Libik, 'Environmental Effects of the Dam System on the Danube at Bos-Nagymaros', *Ambio*, vol. 18 (1989), p. 247.

260 Visits to Hungary in 1989 and Slovakia in 1991; F. Pearce, *Green Warriors* (London, 1991); P. Pomichal, 'On the Slovak Side of the Dam', *Panos Feeback* (London, September 1990); K. Boucher, *Landscapes and Technology: the Gabcikovo-Nagymaros Scheme*, in D. Cosgrove and G. Petts (ed.) *Water, Engineering and Landscape* (Belhaven, 1990).

261 Interviews by author, June and December 1991.

262 J. E. Bardoch on Lower Mekong in *Careless Technology*, ed. T. Farvar and J. Milton (London, 1973).

265 W. Shawcross, *Sideshow* (London, 1979), p. 42; J. V. Dennis, *Kampuchea's Ecology and Resource Base* (UNDP, 1988).
266 L. Lohmann, 'Engineers move in on the Mekong', *New Scientist* (13 July 1991), p. 44.
267 C. K. Sharma, 'Nepal's Hydro Schemes: Progress and Plans', *Water Power and Dam Construction* (March 1989), p. 22; *Karnali (Chisapani) Multipurpose Project, executive summary* (Himalayan Power Consultants for Nepal Ministry of Water Resources, December 1989).
268 C. K. Sharma, 'Energy and Environment in Nepal', *Ambio*, vol. 20 (1991), p. 120.
269 'Power: Seeking Radical Solutions', *India Today* (January 1989); P. Rogers et al, *Eastern Waters Study: Strategies to Manage Flood and Drought in the Ganges-Brahmaputra Basin* (US Agency for International Development, 1989).
270 M. G. Rahman, 'Reducing the Flow of the Ganges', in Goldsmith and Hildyard, *Large Dams*, vol. 2; B. Crow, 'Why are the Ganges and Brahmaputra Undeveloped?' (c. 1982).

23: Pylons for Peace – or War

272 G. Lanning and M. Mueller, *Africa Undermined* (Harmondsworth, 1979), p. 180; H. Olivier, *Dam It* (Cape Town, 1975).
273 T. Scudder, 'The African Experience with River Basin Development', unpublished manuscript prepared for US Agency for International Development, 1988; L. Ramber et al, 'Development and Biological Status of Lake Kariba', *Ambio*, vol. 16 (1987), p. 314.
274 G. Pinay, *Hydrobiological Assessment of the Zambezi River System* (International Institute for Applied Systems Analysis working paper, Laxenburg, Austria, September 1988).
276 C. Gandolfi, *Multiobjective Operation of Zambezi River Reservoirs*, IIASA working paper (July 1990); B. R. Davies and K. F. Walker, *The Ecology of River Systems* (Junk, Dordrecht, 1986).
277 Pinay, *Zambezi River System*.
278 Lesotho Highlands Water Project, Lesotho Highlands Development Authority, Maseru, 1991; D. Dodwell, 'Project that Posed a Real Banking Challenge', *Financial Times* (6 January 1992); P. Smith, 'Water Project in the Pipeline', *South* (December 1990), p. 66.
279 *Sub Saharan Africa Hydrological Assessment, ASDCC countries*, Sir M. MacDonald, Cambridge and Hidroprojecto Con-

sultores, Lisbon, for World Bank and UNDP, draft, September 1990; 'Zambezi Up for Grabs', *World Rivers Review* (November 1987), p. 3.

280 H. Olivier, *Hydroelectric Potential in Southern Africa*, Proceedings of Institution of Civil Engineers (London, 1990), p. 115.

281 A. Charnock, 'A New Course for the Nile', *New Scientist* (27 October 1983), p. 285.

283 R. O. Collins, *The Waters of the Nile* (Oxford, 1990).

285 Egyptian water fears 'prompted Sudan coup', *World Water* (September 1989), p. 7; B. B. Ghali, *Water Management in the Nile Valley*, paper to African Water Summit, Cairo, organised by Ministry of Foreign Affairs of Egypt, June 1990; J. R. Starr, 'Water Wars', *Foreign Policy*, no. 82 (Spring 1991).

24: The Waters of Zion

287 Visit to Israel by author and sundry interviews, March 1991.

289 J. R. Starr, 'Water Wars', *Foreign Policy*, no. 82 (Spring 1991).

290 Interview with Ze'ev Golani, Tel Aviv, March 1991.

290 Headlines in successive days' copies of *Jerusalem Post*, 'Water Crisis to Drain National Carrier'; 'Not a Drop, Nor a Moment, to Spare'; 'The Parched Earth Policy'.

291 R. Nativ, 'Problems of an Over-developed Water System – the Israeli Case', *Water Quality Bulletin*, vol. 13 (October 1988); interview with Ronit Nativ, March 1991.

292 Interview with Arnon Soffer, London, 1991; H. I. Shuval, 'The Development of Water Reuse in Israel', *Ambio*, vol. 16 (1987), p. 186.

293 Interview with Arie Issar in Sede Boker, March 1991; T. Naff, *Water in the Middle East* (Westview, 1984).

295 Starr, 'Water Wars'.

296 Jordanians dispute dam contamination, *World Water* (June 1991), p. 8.

287 E. Salameh, *Water Resources of the Jordan River System and the Surrounding Countries*, paper to World Conference on Water Law and Administration (Alicante, December 1989).

25: The Waters of Babylon

299 'Jordan Water Plans Hatching', *Engineering News Record* (c. 1985); J. R. Starr, 'Water Wars', *Foreign Policy*, no. 82 (Spring 1991).

301 T. Naff, *Water in the Middle East* (Westview, 1984).
302 'Bridging the Gap', *World Water* (April 1992), p. 21.
305 P. Fend and I. Gunther, 'Iraq's Secret Weapon: Water', *New Scientist* (17 January 1985), p. 10.

26: Putting a Price on Conservation

310 C. V. Moore and R. E. Howitt, 'The Central Valley of California', in *Water and Arid Lands of the Western US*, ed. M. T. El-Ashry and D. C. Gibbons (Cambridge, 1989); F. H. Nichols et al, 'The Modification of an Estuary', *Science*, vol. 231 (1986), p. 567.
311 J. Lancaster, 'Buying Peace in Western Water War, *Washington Post* (16 June 1990); P. Steinhart, 'Trouble at the End of a River', *Pacific Discovery* (January 1990).
312 K. Wiley, 'Untying the Western Water Knot', *Nature Conservancy Magazine* (March 1990), p. 5.
313 K. Frederick, 'The Legacy of Cheap Water', *Resources*, Resources for the Future, Washington DC (Spring 1986).
314 'Colorado Water Stirs Debate', *Engineering News Record* (22 November 1984), p. 13; S. Hadly, 'Water Marketing: Have Environmentalists Created a Monster?', *Bay on Trial* (Bay Institute of San Francisco, Summer 1990), p. 17.

27: Out of Sight ...

316 B. B. Vhora, *Managing India's Water Resources*, INTACH Environment Series No 11 (1990).
316 J. Bandyopadhyay, 'Riskful Confusion of Drought and Man-induced Water Scarcity', *Ambio*, vol. 18 (1989), p. 284.
317 R. D. Lacewell and J. G. Lee, 'Land and Water Management Issues: Texas High Plains', in *Water and Arid Lands of the Western US*, ed. M. T. El-Ashry and D. C. Gibbons (Cambridge, 1989); 'What Do We Do When the Well Runs Dry', *Science*, vol. 210 (1980), p. 754.
318 A. A. Al-Ibrahim, 'Excessive Use of Groundwater Resources in Saudi Arabia', *Ambio*, vol. 20 (1991), p. 34; 'Green Grow the Deserts O', *The Economist* (6 April 1985), p. 74; *Proceedings of Institution of Civil Engineers* (1984), p. 753, discussions of paper 8662.
319 Saudi faces rising groundwater crisis, *World Water* (September 1990), p. 7.
320 A. Issar, 'Fossil Water under the Sinai-Negev Peninsula',

Scientific American (July 1985); interview with Arie Issar at Sede Boker, March 1991.

321 R. A. Bisson and P. D. Hoffman, 'Ground Water – the Paradoxical Economic Mineral', *Water Resources Journal*, UN (September 1989).

322 A. Issar and R. Nativ, 'Water Beneath Deserts: Keys to the Past, a Resource for the Present', *Episodes*, vol. 11 (December 1988), p. 256; R. Ambroggi, 'Water Under the Desert', *Scientific American* (May 1966); M. U. Ahmad, 'A Quantitative Model to Predict a Safe Yield for Well Fields in Kufra and Sarir Basins, Libya', *Ground Water*, vol. 22 (1983), p. 58; M. U. Ahmad, 'The Role of the Sahara in Food Production', *Water International*, vol. 6 (1981), p. 126.

323 'Water Running from Desert Stone Is No Mirage', *Guardian* (29 June 1990) quoted Kamal Hefny; F. El-Baz, 'Do People Make Deserts? *New Scientist* (13 October 1990), p. 41.

325 R. Revelle, 'The Ganges Water Machine', *Science*, vol. 188 (1975), p. 611; R. Ambroggi, 'Underground Reservoirs to Control the Water Cycle', *Scientific American* (May 1977), p. 21.

28: Grand Designs

328 S. Manabe and R. T. Wetherald, 'Reduction in Summer Soil Wetness Induced by an Increase in Atmospheric Carbon Dioxide', *Science*, vol. 232 (1986), p. 626.

329 P. H. Gleick, 'Regional Hydrologic Consequences of Increases in Atmospheric Carbon Dioxide and Other Trace Gases', *Climatic Change*, vol. 10 (1987), p. 137; R. M. Adams et al, 'Global Climate Change and US Agriculture', *Nature*, vol. 345 (1990), p. 219; P. E. Waggoner (ed.), *Climate Change and US Water Resources* (Chichester, 1990).

330 C. Ayris, 'Pipe Dreams', *The West Australian* (2 March 1991).

331 *Sub Saharan Africa Hydrological Assessment, ASDCC countries*, Sir M. MacDonald, Cambridge and Hidroprojecto Consultores, Lisbon, for World Bank and UNDP, draft, September 1990; Z. Kaczmarek, *Impact of Climatic Variations on Storage Reservoir Systems*, IIASA working paper (April 1990); Z. Zhao and W. Kellogg, 'Sensitivity of Soil Moisture to Doubling of Carbon Dioxide in Climate Model Experiments', *Journal of Climate* (April 1988), p. 348.

333 J. Umolu, *Zaire-Chad-Niger Interbasin Water Transfer Scheme*, paper presented to 1986 International Water Resources

Needs and Planning in Drought-prone Areas organised by UNDP; *Transagua*, Bonifica, paper to Lake Chad Basin Commission 1988; G. Baker, 'Optimising Water Supplies on a Grand Scale', *World Water* (July 1989), p. 35.

336 C. Greer, 'The Texas Water System', in *Large-scale Water Transfers*, ed. A. K. Biswas (Tycooly, Dublin, 1983); P. Micklin, 'Inter-basin Water Transfers in the US', in *Large-scale Water Transfers*, ed. Biswas; K. MacQueen, 'It's the Biggest Pipe Dream of Them All', *Montreal Gazette* (22 December 1990).

339 D. J. Gamble, 'Commentary: the GRAND Canal Scheme', *Journal of Great Lakes Research*, vol. 15 (1989), p. 531; T. Kiernans, *Recycled Run-off from James Bay*, submission to National Association of Regulatory Utility Commissions (November 1989).

340 L. Bolkow, *Energy in the Next Century*, paper to Hamburg conference on greenhouse effect (July 1989).

Conclusion

350 H. T. Odum et al, *Energy Systems Overview of the Mississippi River Basin* (Centre for Wetlands, University of Florida, Gainesville, 1987).

351 G. Petts, *Water, Engineering and Landscape: Development, Protection and Restoration*, in D. Cosgrove and G. Petts (ed.), *Water, Engineering and Landscape* (Belhaven, 1990).

INDEX